WATERMILLS

(Kent and the Borders of Sussex)

Monograph Series
of the
Kent Archaeological Society

(General Editor: A.P. Detsicas, B.A., M.A., D.Litt., F.S.A.)

No. II

WATERMILLS

(Kent and the Borders of Sussex)

By

M.J. Fuller and R.J. Spain

Published by the
Kent Archaeological Society
Maidstone
1986

Produced in England and distributed by
Alan Sutton Publishing Ltd.,
30 Brunswick Road, Gloucester GL1 1JJ

CONTENTS

		PAGE
Illustrations	. . . .	vii
Bibliography	. . . .	x
Introduction	. . . .	1
I.	Watermills:	
	Addington Mill	13
	Ashbourne Mill	13
	Basted Mill	20
	Bayton Mill	21
	Bockingford Mill	22
	Bowley Mill	23
	Branbridge Mill	25
	Burnt Mill	27
	Chart Mill	33
	Chartham Mill	35
	Chegworth Mill	38
	Chilham Mill	44
	Christian's Mill	53
	Church Mills	53
	The Comb	54
	Darenth Mill	54
	Dunster's Mill	55
	Eyhorne Mill	58
	Field Mill	59
	Ford Mill	61
	Groombridge Mill	61
	Gurney's Mill	64
	Hammer Mill	66
	Hartridge Manor Mill	72
	Hawley Mill	73
	Hayle Mill	73
	Hope Mill	75
	Horton Kirby Mill	77
	Hothfield Mill	77
	Hythe Mill (Spring Grove Mill)	81

Leeds Castle Mill 89
Leg-o-Mutton 90
Le Nethertoune Mill 91
Loose Village Mill 92
Lovehurst Manor Mill 92
Lower Mill 95
Maplehurst Mill 95
Mereworth Mill 103
Middle Mill 103
Mill Hall Mill 103
Moat Mill 104
Newbridge Mill 107
Old Mill, Borough Green 108
Old Mill, Hollingbourne/Leeds 108
Paley Mill 109
Park Mill (Bateman's) 110
Pole Mill 116
Slip Mill 116
South Darenth Mill 119
Swanton Mill 120
Wandle Mill 128
Warden Mill 134
White Mill 134
Winfield Mill 138

II.   The Wells Collection 140

III. Millwrights' memories
      Alf Spain 141
      Philip Hancock 149
      Gordon Clementson 157
      Dr. W. Urry 163
      Wally Nye 165
      Ted Uren 171

IV.   Glossary 179

V.   General Index 201

ILLUSTRATIONS

PAGE

FIG. 1. Map of watermills 12
2. Addington Mill (Site) 13
3. Ashbourne Mill, Tenterden (Site) 14
4. Ashbourne Mill, Tenterden (Plan) 15
5. Ashbourne Mill, Tenterden (Bin floor) 16
6. Ashbourne Mill, Tenterden (External view) 19
7. Basted Mill (Site) 20
8. Bayton Mill (Site) 21
9. Bowley Mill (Site) 24
10. Branbridge Mill (Site) 25
11. Branbridge Mill (View) 26
12. Burnt Mill, Lenham (Site) 28
13. Burnt Mill, Lenham (Plan) 30
14. Burnt Mill, Lenham (Governors) 31
15. Burnt Mill, Lenham (Tun case) 33
16. Chart Mill (Site) 34
17. Chart Mill (View) 35
18. Chartham Corn Mill (Site) 36
19. Chartham Corn Mill (View) 37
20. Chegworth Mill (Site) 38
21. Chegworth Mill (View across pond) 39
22. Chegworth Mill (Floor plan) 40
23. Chegworth Mill (The mill-stone floor) 42
24. Chegworth Mill (The mill-stone floor) 43
25. Chilham Mill (Site) 45
26. Chilham Mill (Plan) 47
27. Chilham Mill (Plan) 50
28. Chilham Mill (View) 51
29. Church Mill and Christian's Mill (Sites) 53
30. The Comb, alias Lower Milgate Mill (Site) 54

31. Sutton Mill and Darenth Paper Mill (Sites) 54
32. Dunster's Mill (Site) 55
33. Dunster's Mill (Plan) 56
34. Dunster's Mill (View) 57
35. Eyhorne Mill, Grove Mill and Park Mill (Sites) 58
36. Field Mill (Site) 59
37. Ford Mill and Groombridge Mill (Sites) 61
38. Ford Mill (View – *based on a sketch by A. Wells, 1933*) 62
39. Groombridge Mill (Plan) 63
40. Gurney's Mill and Wilson's Mill (Sites) 65
41. Hammer Mill, Sissinghurst (Site) 65
42. Hammer Mill, Sissinghurst (Plan) 67
43. Hammer Mill, Sissinghurst (View) 70
44. Hartridge Manor Mill (Site) 72
45. Hawley Mill (Site) 73
46. Upper Crisbrook Mill, Hayle Mill and Bockingford Mill (Sites) ... 74
47. Hayle Mill (The vat house) 74
48. Hope Mill, Goudhurst (Site) 75
49. Hope Mill, Goudhurst (Detail of water-wheel shaft) 76
50. Horton Kirby Paper Mill (Site) 77
51. Hothfield Mill (Site) 78
52. Hothfield Mill (Plan) 79
53. Hythe Mill (Site) 82
54. Hythe Mill 83
55. Hythe (Spring Grove) Mill 85
56. Hythe Mill (The mill-stone floor) 87
57. Hythe Mill (Friction drive) 88
58. Leeds Castle Mill (Site) 89
59. Le Nethertoune Mill (Site) 91
60. Loose Village Mill (Site) 92
61. Lovehurst Manor Mill (Site) 93
62. Lovehurst Manor Mill (View) 94
63. Lower Mill, East Malling (Site) 95
64. Lower Mill, East Malling (View) 96
65. Maplehurst Mill, Frittenden (Site) 97
66. Maplehurst Mill, Frittenden (Plan) 98
67. Maplehurst Mill, Frittenden (Water-wheel) 102
68. Mereworth Mill (Site) 103
69. Mill Hall Mill (Site) 104

70. Moat Mill (Site) 105
71. Newbridge Mill (Site) 107
72. Old Mill, (Borough Green) and Paley Mill (Sites) 108
73. Old Mill (Hollingbourne/Leeds) (View) 109
74. Old Mill, Hollingbourne (View) 110
75. Park Mill (Bateman's), Burwash (Site) 111
76. Park Mill (Bateman's), Burwash (Plan) 112
77. Pole Mill (Site) 116
78. Slip Mill, Hawkhurst (Site) 117
79. Slip Mill, Hawkhurst (Plan) 118
80. Swanton Mill, Mersham (Site) 120
81. Swanton Mill, Mersham (Plan) 121
82. Swanton Mill, Mersham (Flow) 124
83. Swanton Mill, Mersham (View) 126
84. Swanton Mill, Mersham (Weathercock) 127
85. Wandle Mill, Benenden (Site) 129
86. Wandle Mill, Benenden (Plan) 130
87. Warden Mill and Winfield Mill (Sites) 135
88. White Mill and Black Mill, Sturry (Sites) 135
89. White Mill, Sturry (Site) 137
90. White Mill, Sturry (Detail of the water-wheel) 138

PLATE   I.   Alf Spain 141
PLATE   II. Philip Hancock 149
PLATE   III. Wally Nye 165
PLATE   IV. Ted Uren 171

BIBLIOGRAPHY

C.E. Bennett, 'The Watermills of Kent, East of the Medway', *Industrial Archaeology Review*.

W. Coles Finch, *'Watermills and Windmills'*, (1933).

C. Connell, *'Crabble Mill'*, 1972.

M.J. Fuller, *'The Watermills of the East Malling and Wateringbury Streams'*, (1980).

M.J. Fuller, *'The Watermills of the Leybourne Stream'*, (in preparation).

R.H. Goodsall, *'The Kentish Stour'*, (1953).

R.H. Goodsall, 'Watermills on the River Len', *Arch. Cant.*, lxxi (1968), 106–129.

Kentish Register, 'Description of the Capital Flour Mills at Canterbury called Abbot's Mill', (1794).

P.W. Lewis, 'Changing Factors of Location in the Papermaking Industry as illustrated by the Maidstone area', *Geography*, July, 1967.

S.G. McRae and C.P. Burnham, *'The Rural Landscape of Kent'*, (1973), 197–200.

G.M. Meyer, 'Early Water-mills in Relation to Changes in the Rainfall of East Kent', *Quart. Journal, Royal Met. Soc.*, liii (1927), 224.

A. Percival, *'The Faversham Gunpowder Industry'*, (1967).

K.C. Reid, 'The Watermills of Kent', *Kent County Journal*, (1939).

A.H. Shorter, 'Early Paper Mills in Kent', *Paper-Maker and British Paper Trade Journal*, (October 1951).

A.H. Shorter, *'Paper Mills and Paper Makers in England 1495–1800'*, (1957).

A.H. Shorter, 'Paper Mills in the Maidstone District, I – IV', *Paper-Maker and British Paper Trade Journal*, (1960).

R.J. Spain, 'An eighteenth-century Corn Watermill', *Arch. Cant.*, lxxxv (1970), 113–22.

R.J. Spain, 'The Len Water-mills', *Arch. Cant.*, lxxxii (1967), 32–104.

R.J. Spain, 'The Loose Watermills, Part I', *Arch. Cant.*, lxxxvii (1972), 43–79.

R.J. Spain, 'The Loose Watermills, Part II', *Arch. Cant.*, lxxxviii (1973), 159–86.

R.J. Spain, 'Romano-British Watermills', *Arch. Cant.*, c (1985), 101–28.

R.J. Spain, 'The second-century Romano-British Watermill at Ickham, Kent', *History of Technology*, ix (1984), 143–80.

R.J. Spain, 'An Analysis of the Millstone and Quern Fragments from Ickham, (1980), unpublished report.

A.J. and D. Stoyel, 'Watermills of the Upper Darent', *Kentish Historical Newsletter*, no.2, October 1957.

B.D. and A.J. Stoyel, 'The Old Mill, Bexley', *Arch. Cant.*, lxxxiii (1968), 105–10.

C.J. Young, 'The late-Roman Mill at Ickham and the Saxon Shore', in (Ed.) Alec Detsicas, *Collectanea Historica, Essays in Memory of Stuart Rigold* (1981), 32–40.

INTRODUCTION

It is a lamentable fact that watermills have not received the attention that they deserve. This is due partly to their wind-powered brothers stealing the limelight. For obvious reasons, windmills have long attracted the public eye, particularly the attention of artists, writers and historians, with the inevitable result that some of them have become protected buildings. Such public interest is commendable and the preservation justly deserved, but it is a great pity that watermills do not enjoy the same attention.

For many centuries, watermills had the singular distinction of providing power for all industries requiring something greater than animal or manpower. Windmills were very limited in their application to many industries and being subject to the vicissitudes of the wind became devoted, with very few exceptions, in these islands, to the corn-milling industry. Thus, watermills were of far greater significance in our industrial development; their history is synonymous with our industrial history up to the advent of steam power.

Of course, watermills, by their very nature, are often out of sight of the public eye, either unobtrusive, among the village buildings, or tucked away in quiet valleys. During the last two centuries many maps have appeared showing where watermills once stood, but such records are historical and often bear little relation to what exists now. Their greatest value lies in helping us to find the original site and to determine what changes have since occurred to the local topography. It is surprising how fast the English landscape can change under social and economic pressures, so that at times it is very difficult to determine where a watermill once stood. Questions such as how many there were, what industries they served, why they ceased to work, remain to be answered.

However, this study is not concerned with their history. That is a task for the future. Of much greater importance is the need to record the extant physical evidence, and this is the primary aim of this work. Because this study occurs long after the demise of watermills, it must inevitably convey a feeling of despondency, for the process of natural deterioration and decay is well advanced at nearly all sites. This survey is too late – probably by at least two generations.

In our villages and towns very few building sites are pre-medieval. There are only two buildings which we can point to with confidence and claim them to be very old sites. One is the church, and the other is the watermill. Generally speaking, both have been in continuous use through the centuries. Admittedly, the waterpower was probably used for different purposes, but the mill is easily the oldest industrial site in the landscape. Indeed, on the basis that the position of many villages seems to have been determined by geographical or physical factors, as were watermills, one is tempted to suggest that the generation of water-power may have been a prime influence on settlement.

Recently, the remains of two Roman watermills were discovered at Ickham near Canterbury. These rare structures – only six other confirmed sites exist in Britain – prove that watermills existed long before the Saxons came to farm our lands. Hitherto, it had always been assumed that the Saxons had introduced the watermill to these islands, but now we must review our historical interpretation of the evidence. How many more Roman watermills remain to be discovered? We should not let the paucity of the evidence cloud our view of this matter. After all, not one of the hundreds of Domesday watermills that existed in Kent has yet been found by archaeologists. The point is made: archaeologists have much to discover and learn from; our history will need to be re-written.

For the moment we should assume that most watermill sites were founded by the time of the Domesday Survey. As in churches, any Saxon structures have long since been swept away or lost among later building fabric. Very few mill buildings are older than the sixteenth century. Like all buildings of great age, they have been continuously modified, adapted, extended and rebuilt to meet the changing requirements of the occupiers.

There is currently a greater interest in vernacular architecture. Our old buildings are important to us, particularly those which were a common feature in our forefathers' day. We should permanently preserve an adequate number of examples to illustrate the different regional architectural styles which occur in domestic, agricultural and industrial buildings. Watermills fall into that rare category of buildings in which the design of the fabric, both external and internal, is greatly affected by the function of the building. Few buildings can claim this; maltings and oasts are examples and, of course, windmills. But watermills are important for another reason. No other type of building has had such great effect on our landscape. The appearance and development of mill-ponds and water-courses, the tracks and roads associated with the mills and industries which flourished, all affected the changing face of the land. Only agriculture itself can claim greater influence on our landscape.

In this volume, hopefully the first of a series, the authors have tried to maintain a balance in the material, to intersperse good examples, the more complete, with details of those sites where evidence is scant. It has not been possible to survey the area in a logical order; we have examined the sites as and when the opportunity presented itself.

Whilst this study is not primarily concerned with history, it is not possible to examine and discuss the remains of watermills without paying some regard to the events leading up to their demise.

The brief historic notes that follow are not intended as a summary or even an introduction to the history of Kent watermills; they are submitted rather by way of a prelude to what is discussed later, to put the survey findings into some sort of perspective.

There is a popular image of the English village which holds that in each there was a church, a mill and an inn. Centuries ago not every village would have had an inn or tavern, but almost certainly would have had a church or chapel and not far away, the village mill. In most villages, especially those having a river or stream passing through or near, there was a watermill. The number of watermills in existence at any one time has always been greater than the number of windmills and, besides, they were well established long before windmills appeared. William of Normandy recorded approximately 350 mills in his inquisition of Kent in 1086. A few of these may have been animal-powered, but their coincidence with manors and parishes having water-courses is strong. Most of the Weald, then covered by the great Forest of Anderida, was unsettled at the time of the survey.

Properly managed, watermills provided a good income, a fact confirmed by the survey. Nearly all early medieval corn mills were held by the landlords, both lay and ecclesiastical. The people were obliged to use these mills and the use of quern stones was discouraged. The usual arrangement was for the landlord to maintain the machinery while the tenant who 'farmed' the mill would render money or payment in kind (grain usually, sometimes eels, and, rarely, salt or honey) while taking a 'multure' or toll from the grist or flour. In addition to the toll, the miller by custom, always retained the offal, mostly bran and pollards.

The reference to eels in the Domesday Survey reminds us that a great number of millers must have regularly fished the rivers and streams. Later, when mill-ponds became widespread, they provided a valuable food store, not only to the monastic and church estates with their stew-ponds, but to the common folk as well.

Windmills first appeared in the late twelfth century and were almost wholly employed in corn-milling. In Kent at least 404 windmill sites are known, though the maximum number standing at any one time was probably close to 240. But it was to the better developed, more powerful and reliable water-power that numerous industries turned in the centuries following the appearance of the windmill. During the medieval period the Weald, with its natural resources of iron ore and wood, became an industrial centre of England. Here the iron-masters used water-power, for their blast furnaces and forges, from the thirteenth to the eighteenth centuries. A far greater number of mills were devoted to the fulling and scouring of cloths which were being produced by the Kent clothiers and, later, generally after 1650, water-powered paper-making mills spread to other areas in Kent.

Long before steam power became available (c. 1800) almost every possible site for water-power was exploited. The power in industry was rurally based. Existing sites were continually improved while different industries came and went. There were river mills which adversely affected the navigation, mills on winter-bournes and on streams so insignificant that they stood idle for want of water for much of the year – such was the demand for power.

The number of watermills reached a maximum during the eighteenth and early nineteenth centuries and thereafter reduced, slowly at first but by the turn of the century a rapid decline in their numbers had set in. A good indication of the abandonment of water-power and the disappearance of millers is given by the following extract from Kelly's *Directories of Kent*:

Date of Directory		1874	1895	1907	1913	1922	1930	1933
% of mill sites powered by	WIND	not given	$44\frac{1}{2}$	37	$31\frac{1}{2}$	$26\frac{1}{2}$	22	26
	WATER		$32\frac{1}{2}$	$33\frac{1}{2}$	37	$35\frac{1}{2}$	$45\frac{1}{2}$	42
	STEAM		23	$29\frac{1}{2}$	$31\frac{1}{2}$	39	$32\frac{1}{2}$	32
No. of millers		295	230	155	127	121	76	66

During the interpretation of this table the following points should be kept in mind: (a) at some mills two types of power were used, often steam with either wind or water; (b) gas and oil engines and electricity were present in some mills, especially after the turn of the century, but these do not appear to have been categorised by Kelly.

It is interesting to note that the percentage of operating watermills increased relative to windmills throughout the period although the actual numbers diminished. The appearance of alternative power sources working alongside the traditional methods is a reflection of the millers' efforts to maximise their production in an attempt to achieve the same economies of scale enjoyed by the huge steam-powered mills. The success of these large mills, especially those situated at ports, was due to (i) their ability to purchase in bulk the cheap grain coming from the developing corn lands of North America, (ii) they were more favourably positioned, geographically, to develop and expand their sites, and (iii) their appearance and growth coincided with the public demand for ever-whiter bread, which stimulated the development of roller milling and associated refining process machinery. This invariably meant that more energy per unit of product was required, which made it harder for the small milling concern to compete. The larger mills were also more able, financially, to take advantage of these developments.

In addition to these factors, the spread of a railway network, metalled roads and the appearance of motor transport tended to work against the smaller mill. Within this rapidly-expanding market for flour, bread, other foodstuffs and animal feeds, it was the more aggressive opportunity-seeking manufacturers that eventually dominated the scene. New technology and the caprice of public demand won the day. Little wonder that wind and watermills faded away, to take their place in the more romantic chapters of national and local history.

Coincident with the exploitation of other primary sources of energy came improved water-power generators. Various turbines appeared which, having greater efficiency than water-wheels, were installed in a number of mills. At some sites, generally those in the industrialised quarters of towns, water-power was abandoned in favour of other power sources. Water-wheels could no longer serve the needs of expanding manufactories; steam and electricity gave engineers convenient and unlimited power, no longer tied to river banks or water courses. With the demise of water-power, many mills, especially rural corn mills, were abandoned. The redundant machinery was removed and sold for scrap or sometimes left to decay through the ravages of nature and time.

Of the total number of watermill sites which existed at one time or another in the area covered by this survey – an exact number is difficult to ascertain but it is probably well in excess of 500 –, perhaps only half a dozen have been preserved or renovated close to their original condition and are now capable of water-power work. A similar number, with a questionable amount of repair work, might be brought back into working order. At all other sites the incidence of incompleteness and decay – both of building and machinery fabric – is high. At 80% of these sites so little remains that there is no need for a plan of the building; often only the waterways can be seen.

By any standard, we have all but lost this part of our inheritance.

All of the remaining watermills last worked two generations or more ago, so it is not surprising that the state of decay we discover is invariably well advanced and often structural in nature. Time overtakes us all, but in a disused or un-maintained mill, so full of friable fabric, the rate of decay is very fast.

Cast-iron work withstands the ravages of time well, but sheet iron and steel, so often found in the water-wheels, does not. All too often the only evidence to be found of wheels is skeletal remains and ugly oxide encrustations where bolts once existed. Most of the machinery inside watermills is made of wood which has its own array of enemies, including damp, beetle and rot; these also attack the wooden fabric of the building, often weakening the load-supporting elements. Whilst the decay of the machinery is disheartening, it is the decay of the building frame and floors which is the potential danger to the visitor. When the frame becomes unsafe, it sometimes prompts the owner to remove the machinery or even demolish the mill. The rates at which weather gains entry and damp rises from below are the prime determinants of the rate of decay. Most abandoned watermills have the weather gaining entry through the roof, broken windows and decayed weatherboards. A smaller number have suffered from damp rising from the ground floor, usually caused by the ingress of water from the tail-race.

On many of the sites where the mill is long gone we are left only with a scarred landscape of old waterways and unattended sluices. Mill-ponds with their shallow waters are soon reduced by the encroaching sedges and rushes, especially when sluices, mill-dam and the banks are no longer tended. Long gone are the days when the miller could boast of a well-stocked pond.

When a mill ceases to use water-power one other important function is usually lost – the customary water rights associated with the property. Such rights, hitherto enjoyed probably for centuries and passed from miller to miller, were essential to each watermill. The ability to control and use the rivers and streams through the winter rains and the dryness of summer, year after year; the manipulation of the various water-gates to ensure adequate water for his working day and to facilitate the most economic water consumption consistent with his power demands hour by hour – all this was part of the miller's craft. With the cessation of water-power and the absence or death of the miller and his assistants such knowledge is lost. Unless these water rights are preserved in title deeds or are covered by statutory powers, it is virtually impossible to reinstate them. This appears to be an injustice, especially in view of the undeniable fact that a watermill in use, until recently, must have enjoyed water rights. Presumably, the lengthy and costly process of re-establishing such rights is intended to protect the legal position of other riparian owners.

Another injustice to watermill owners is the licensing which water authorities apply to water-wheels, even wheels which do not consume water in the true sense of the word and which, more importantly, save other more expensive types of energy when used for work.

Many owners have good intentions and high regard for their mill but their pocket cannot follow their heart. The costs of maintenance are prohibitive. Aside from the repairs necessary to the building, which is the first line of defence, the internal fabric is usually of such an age and in a state of disrepair as to require immediate attention. But the costs associated with such work are on a scale much higher than domestic work. Often people buy watermills with the intention of refurbishing them and working them once again; unfortunately, the majority enter into the scheme without having much of an idea of the labour and though their hearts are in the right place, they unwittingly contribute to the inexorable decay of the mill by their inactivity. Such people have arrived on the scene far too late – they have missed the optimum period for such work by at least 50 years.

It is an undeniable fact that many owners of historic buildings worthy of preservation are unable to maintain them in satisfactory condition. This is especially true of watermills where preservation of the building fabric must go hand in hand with the machinery fabric. The machinery should be preserved in a *working* condition. So often the machinery and power transmission elements in watermills are disregarded by owners; they understandably fail to appreciate the need to keep such critical parts – those which carry loads (e.g. bearings, pivots) or transmit power (e.g. cogs, gears, pulleys) – in working condition.

With the building fabric, the peeling coat of paint or the sign of weather gaining admittance acts as the trigger for action. But with machinery, decay is far less obvious, and the point is soon reached where, without regular attention, it becomes unworkable. One way to avoid this condition is for the mill to be regularly worked, and the wheel, shafts, gears and pulleys rotated, although it is doubtful if one owner in a hundred does this. Water-wheels can last a long time if they are turned a little, regularly, but when idle they deteriorate very fast. In many respects owning and maintaining a watermill is no different to having a vintage car. To preserve all its mechanical functions it should be regularly worked – there is no better way. In fact, the cost of maintaining a watermill, one that has been regularly worked, is not beyond the pocket of most owners, no more than having a second car in the garage. However, very few existing mills have been regularly worked all their life. Once such attention lapses, even briefly, the costs of recovering the *status quo* escalate and quickly become prohibitive.   This then is the state of our watermill stock, much depleted and in a state of advanced decay.

The decay and disappearance of watermills has taken place at different rates throughout Britain due largely to varying local geographic and economic influences. Kent has suffered badly in this respect, the total remains in comparison with other counties being rather poor. Consequently, those wishing to own an old watermill, and there is an increasing number these days, must accept a poor representation of what once existed or, alternatively, search richer areas of Britain to realise their dreams. All the more reason why recording must come before preservation. Such a survey does identify where and what remains exist, which should be helpful for those attempting to refurbish a watermill. This is one of the intentions of this survey: to provide a record of extant corn-milling machinery and equipment.

The study of watermills can offer much more than a passing satisfaction to a mechanical or romantic mind. Mills can provide a great deal for an enquiring mind, especially for the purposes of education. Each watermill is, in essence, a concentration of potential educational material; a micro-environment of the sciences and arts which concerns all teachers.

This survey material can itself be analysed. The buildings themselves offer the most obvious material for analysis; what are the constant and variable elements of building design; how are they influenced by the environment or the geology of the area; what is their effect on the landscape or the flora and fauna? What part did watermills play in the development of the intricate English landscape?

The engineering aspects are numerous and embrace such areas as *hydraulics* (analysis of streams; flow through channels and sluices; power of falling water; potential power and efficiency of various water-wheels and turbines, etc.), *mechanics* (mechanical advantages of levers; mechanical ratios in the transmission of power between the water-wheel, mill-stones and ancillary machines, etc.), *engineering design* (water-wheel, gears, pulleys, shafts, castings, etc.), *power transmission* methods of driving; power losses in transmission with belts, chains, ropes, gears; power needed by mill-stones, ancillary machinery etc., and the different uses of metals, (cast-iron, wrought iron, steel, brass, bronze, white metal, etc.). Mathematics can find expression in the calculations associated with all of the above engineering work.

Those students interested in wood and its uses will find a watermill a fascinating place. In some ways the skills associated with wood-working reached a higher state of achievement in mills than that associated with metal-working. The carpenter struggled for centuries with problems of construction and power transmission long before wood was supplanted by metal. We shall probably never have full knowledge of how the carpenter, working with the miller, improved and developed the application of water-power to many industries during the medieval period. When metals became more widely used in millwork, the millwright initially copied the carpenter's designs – he had no craft traditions to call on. In modern parlance, the millwright was at the beginning of his learning curve whereas the carpenter, in comparison, was well advanced. These skills, as applied to many different woods, can be found in water-wheels, shafts, gears and cogs, pulleys and in many fittings and fixtures throughout the mill. We are in great danger of losing our inheritance of these skills, not simply because they are historically older but because the skills of metal-working continue in numerous other branches of industry, permanently replacing much of the carpenter's work. Moreover, the carpenter's materials are more susceptible to the ravages of time and nature.

A knowledge of the various grains, their uses, processing and derivatives, might interest the agricultural student, just as an analysis of purchase and sales ledgers would provide material for social and nutritional studies. Add to this the ergonomics of corn-milling; the number of floors and their layouts; the process flow lines and the physical relationships between process machinery, grain, its derivatives and human labour, the contra-flow of power transmission (upwards) and product flow (downwards).

The botanists and zoologists may find most of their rewards in the environs of the mill and in its effect on the landscape. The ecological balance of ponds and their surroundings is well known, but mill-ponds have a distinctive life-cycle of their own determined by deposition. How and why does the zoological spectrum change throughout the life-cycle, how are the pond-cycles influenced by river regimes? How is the plant and animal life affected by pond life, local geology, etc.? The inside of an abandoned or unused mill holds considerable life. Apart from rats and mice, birds, spiders, etc., the woodwork plays host to quite a few living organisms.

And so a watermill can become an educational aid, but its preservation is necessary for other reasons. The history of watermills confirms that the industry of corn milling, together with all of the local supporting skills, has been in the community for many centuries. So, it is proper that selected specimens should be preserved so as to represent this once common element of rural life.

As with other archaeological work, we are learning about people. In this case, it is the builders, millers and millwrights who modified the landscape to produce water-power, and applied it to the reduction and processing of grains and pulses. In essence, the builder provided a rather special timber frame which in the South-East took a post and truss form. Such a frame, usually of heavy scantling, was ideal for supporting heavy loads and for absorbing the vibration of the water-wheel, mill-stones and machinery. The foundation problems brought about by building beside or over existing streams were often reduced by taking a new water-course to the mill site. This advantage was recognised centuries ago. Although evidence is rather scant, it is probable that in earlier times the supporting structure for the mill-stones and primary gearing was integrated, wholly or in part, with the main building frame. Later, when the number of mill-stones driven by one water-wheel increased, as did the size of the stones and the associated gearing, the timber supporting the structure (hursting) became more massive and tended to be separate from the building frame. Certainly, in the later centuries, the hursting, main footstep bearing and usually the mill-side water-wheel bearing were supported on mass brick or stone foundations, separated from the building foundations by the gear-pit.

The history of the English millwright, his appearance and development in our history, has yet to be defined. We know that in many mills it was the village carpenter and blacksmith who maintained the fabric. In earlier times they, together with other building tradesmen, must have been co-ordinated by the owner or miller to provide and maintain what was required. Such skills were also applied and developed in windmills, but it should be remembered that it was the application of water-power to numerous, ever-developing industries that was the essential feature of this work during the medieval period. Slowly, the engineering skills of this work developed and became the responsibility of the millwright – hence the origin of the word. This development was later accelerated by the adoption of more scientific principles in the design of water-wheels and gearing, together with the use of cast-iron in mill work. In time, as the millwright's function grew, they acquired their own carpenters and foundrymen who worked alongside their fitters.

With the decline of water- and wind-powered corn mills, the number of millwrights dwindled. Larger mills had their own millwrights, but many of the smaller mills, especially those in the more remote areas, employed the local carpenter and blacksmith once again.

What the church did for masons, the watermill (and to a lesser extent the windmill) did for the millwright. Their work embodied the best of traditional skills in different woods and metals and this can still be seen in many watermills. Much of the machinery that remains inside watermills was made and installed after 1850. Understandably, the foundation and the frame are usually the oldest parts of the mill, often dating back to its erection. But, just as in churches, the building and its contents have been modified, added to, and developed to meet the ever-changing demands of the user. The physical evidence that we find is the result of the workings of an endless succession of millers and millwrights.

The archaeology of watermills can be said to stem from three main sources: (i) printed and manuscript, (ii) physical, and (iii) the memory of man. The printed and manuscript sources might well be called the paper sources for they cover such things as books, directories, maps and archive material. The physical source is, of course, all material evidence on, or originating from the site, above or below ground, including all related landscape changes. The 'memory of man' includes the oral traditions and extant memories which are uncommitted to paper or tape. When oral evidence is included in a survey such as this, regardless of whether or not it is published, it becomes a 'paper' source for any subsequent researcher. Oral evidence is, therefore, in one sense, transitory. Because watermills generally are in a constant state of decay the physical evidence is slowly and irrevocably being lost. As time passes, it follows that parts of this survey may become the sole record of what once existed; it then becomes a primary source for future industrial archaeologists.

Prior to embarking on this study, the authors had both made studies of watermills in the valleys of mid-Kent. All of the aforementioned sources were included with special concentration on history. The amount of time necessary to undertake such historical research was considerable, and it became obvious that if such a study were extended to cover the whole county it would take probably two decades. Clearly we must concentrate on those sources which are damaged or reduced with the passing of time; in other words, the physical and oral evidence must be recorded first, the historical researches can follow later.

Of all the watermill sites that have at one time existed, only a very small percentage, probably much less than 10%, still have a reasonable amount of water-power machinery. It is inevitable, therefore, that a survey such as this must have a high proportion of mill sites where the fabric (both building and machinery) is incomplete and decayed, or absent altogether. No excavation work has been undertaken in this survey; it is entirely a product of field observation and enquiry.

The prime concern of the industrial archaeologist is with the mechanical engineering fabric, i.e. that which is associated with the generation and transmission of power and its application to the industry concerned. He must also pay regard to the building fabric, its structure and design and note how it was influenced by and adapted to the industry within. In one sense, he is seeking to define how different skills and ingenuity have been applied for a particular purpose, and the craftsmen concerned are millers, builders, carpenters, blacksmiths and millwrights.

What to cover in this study, and in what detail, were the major questions initially facing us. Luckily, our earlier experience of watermill surveys proved helpful and gave us confidence in the decisions we have made.

In extending our survey to cover the county we have decided to adopt hydrological rather than administrative boundaries. So our search area includes the whole of the drainage area of the Medway and Rother river systems, which take us deep into Surrey and Sussex.

Styles of mill architecture and machinery have little relationship to administrative or hydrological areas. The larger the area the more valuable the survey, but not just simply because of its scale. Clearly, for any regional variation to be defined, it is necessary to encompass several geological areas and to include upland, lowland, rural and urban elements. It seems likely that the area chosen covers a range of building styles and, more important, it was served by several millwrights.

In deciding what limitations to place on surveying, and what terms of reference to adopt, a balance has to be struck between time, labour and reward. To consider a full survey with measured drawings and a thorough interpretation at each site was out of the question. The labour involved at the sites would have resulted in either only a few being recorded or a considerable delay in publication. The majority of our readers would not want such detail. As time is of the essence, it is far better to have a limited knowledge of a number of mills rather than risk losing some forever from history; the very least that occurs with time delay is that the evidence is degraded and its interpretation becomes more difficult.

It is possible to visit a mill again and again and learn something new on each occasion. The marginal value of the additional information diminishes as the visits continue, and it quickly raises the question as to whether or not the time would be better spent at another mill. In practice, it is usually a matter of ensuring that when a basic machinery survey is completed any spare time is then put into the most promising area of the mill, including the building itself. A typical rural watermill with a near-full complement of machinery can take a single surveyor most of the day to cover in a basic manner. This entails a schematic layout of each floor, measurements of all shafts, pulleys, mill-stones and descriptions of gears, machines, etc. A short break to consume sandwiches with grubby hands will allow one to ponder over the notes taken and, perhaps, spot something that has been missed. Very few mills have electric lighting systems and so a torch is required to examine name-plates, construction and arrangement details and explore gloomy cog-pits, cupboards and corners. On winter days a storm lantern is of great benefit allowing a wider appraisal of spaces in addition to the solace afforded by its heat and the gentle hiss of its incandescent mantle. But a torch is still necessary for probing. With two people surveying there is an additional advantage, one can measure and observe while the other sketches and makes notes. Moreover, two minds are better than one when trying to resolve problems of interpretation.

Entering a strange mill is always a moment of anticipation and some excitement, for you never know what you will find. It is a unique feeling that few archaeologists experience. Imagine a historian entering a church in his locality which has never been recorded or surveyed before. What a moment! And so it is with the industrial archaeologist. The exploration of a mill is definitely more enjoyable when it is undertaken in solitude or with a colleague who shares the same interests and values. As much as we respect the knowledge of an owner or tenant acting as a guide, their presence always precludes the pleasure of pure discovery. Needless to say, they are usually able to make important contributions to the history of the mill and invariably have fascinating tales to tell which must go on record.

All too often the industrial archaeologist, like other archaeologists, is left with much reduced evidence to ponder over and interpret. Mechanical and process development was rife during the heyday of water-power milling and a decade or so later peculiar things happened when the millers found they were fighting for their livelihood. They reacted, as any other craftsmen would do with dwindling trade and reduced circumstances, by adapting and experimenting. And so the surveyor of mills should always be asking himself questions such as has the mill been extended? Have any mill-stones been added or removed? Is the shaft older than the water-wheel or pit-gear, or vice versa? The oil stain on the beam where a plummer block once stood – what was the drive arrangement and what did it power?

A surveyor must not simply survey; he must interpret, deduce and recognise where skills have been exercised in wood and iron. He should watch for interesting cast-iron work which is intricate or involved. Unusual carvings or fabrication in wood should be noted such as the segmented and laminated pulley wheels, unusual timber joints, the elements in a large wood gear (felloes, cants, arms, rib, hub), etc. The work of a particular millwright is often distinctive. Quite apart from recording the millwright's name from sole plates, wheel frames or trough panels, his castings can often be readily identified by their design. Foundries tended to re-use patterns again and again.

Somebody will retort 'but they're all the same – well, on one theme'. It is true that all watermills have common identifiable physical features; the course which the power takes is always from the lower levels to the higher; the main gearing is always at the lowest floor, the mill-stones next above and the bin floor always at the top of the mill. Even the gearing follows a theme, pit-wheel – wallower – great spur – stone nuts. All this becomes very clear from the following pages but are these the ingredients of boredom? The railway steam-engine enthusiast always finds the smoke comes out of the funnel and that the wheels are at the bottom. Have not steam engines normally gone in the same direction that you throw the coal onto the fire box? Back to the parish church – the sanctuary, choir, nave and tower are usually in the same relative position; pulpit and lectern are always between the pews and choir; you always know where to look for scratch dials and squints. But we are not surprised that such spaces and objects have a physical order about them. The arrangement of a church, steam engine or watermill has been determined by the development of human and mechanical functions. And yet they have all been influenced by two factors which make each specimen quite different from the next, and their study so interesting to the historian. The two factors are:

(a) the variations in the skill and expressions of craftsmen to meet
(b) the ever-changing fashions and technical developments of man.

These influences manifest themselves as differences and variations in fabric and its design; they also affect the landscape. No two watermills are alike, for the changes that man has made with mill-dam and water-courses in the natural landscape to gain and control a head and flow of water are unique to each site. So, too, is the orientation, shape and layout of the mill itself.

Sometimes it has not been possible to approach some machinery or areas because of dangerous floors, or because the decay of beams has been such that collapse was likely. On such occasions it has always been possible to complete the schematic plans although some gears and shafts have had to be viewed from afar. This has usually occurred in gear chambers where entry would have been at the risk of life and limb with mill-stones and gears overhead. There is one paramount rule when surveying a mill; there must be a *continuous* assessment of the safety of the surroundings. Before treading on a floor, look carefully for signs of decay; test it and, if in doubt, proceed with great caution. Before climbing any stairs check previously from below the main floor beams and floorboards above and dispel all doubts as to their safety. Never get below large shafts and gears on vertical shafts, especially the great spur gears which are often wedged on to the main rising shaft. Avoid getting under mill-stones even when the hursting looks in reasonable condition; the decay in these massive frames is not always discernible.

A knowledge of watermills does not depend solely on the survey of remaining evidence and its interpretation; it must also spring from the living memory. The memories of those who operated the watermills or who witnessed them working are perhaps the most valuable part of this study. Unfortunately, people age just as buildings do. It is a lamentable fact that the working of the last few watermills in the early part of this century is within the memory of so few men. They, the surviving millers, millwrights and others, hold the last remnants of experience; operating procedures and the knowledge of milling as a craft, especially the oral traditions. Once the memories have gone they are lost forever; no amount of reconstruction or speculation can replace the prime knowledge, won by experience, of what took place and what it was like to be there.

Let the following extract, taken from a conversation with the miller at Chegworth some 50 years ago, speak for itself . . .

"It was Good Friday, and the mill pond was full to the brim. As I approached the mill I heard the familiar thud! thud! of the revolving wheel and the deep rumble of the mill-stones . . .
. . . He (the miller) said he had no English wheat to grind and told me the reason why. He recalled how that, 70 years ago, when as a lad he first came to the mill, teams of horses were continually there, chafing, stamping and neighing impatiently, while the music of their jingling latten bells was sweet to hear, for they were bringing the English wheat from the adjacent farms to be stored in the capacious granary at the mill, to be ground into flour as required . . . He remarked with a sigh, that once the country around the mill was a vast corn-producing area, but was now hop, fruit and pasture land . . ."
(William Coles Finch, *Watermills and Windmills* (1933) 114.)

Such memories as these, reaching back 120 years, are priceless to us; remember that historians and archaeologists are concerned with people and the human experience.

ACKNOWLEDGEMENTS

The authors gratefully acknowledge the invaluable help given by the many people they met during the preparation and production of this work. Sadly, they are too numerous to mention individually but, without their generous assistance, this book would have lost nearly all its value.

Particular thanks are owed to the Council of the Kent Archaeological Society for accepting the work for publication, and to Dr A.P. Detsicas for his labours in bringing this work up to the high standard for which he is so renowned.

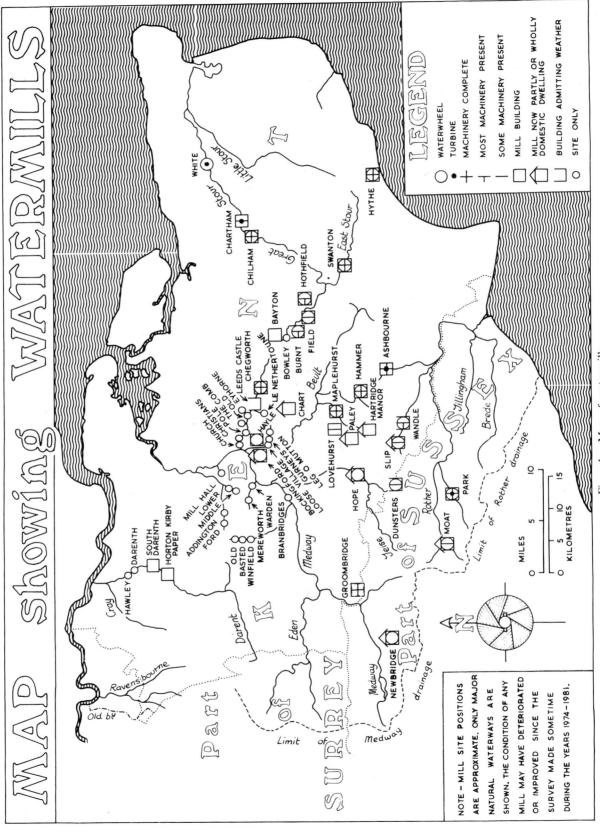

Fig. 1. Map of watermills

I. WATERMILLS

ADDINGTON MILL, Addington. TQ 656 587

Surveyed 1980.

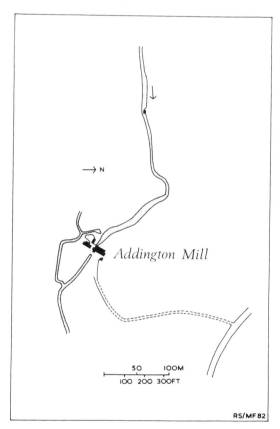

Fig. 2. Addington Mill

No remains of this mill, or its pond, could be found. In recent years, the site had been absorbed into the grounds of the West Malling Golf and Country Club, but this had not resulted in the loss of any archaeological evidence. The waterways appeared to have changed somewhat and the site was a little distance away from the stream. Documentary evidence suggested that the mill was demolished, or at least was derelict, by the end of the nineteenth century.

ASHBOURNE MILL, Tenterden. TQ 864 328

Surveyed November 1974.

To the east of Tenterden lay a broad but shallow valley, through which the Newmill Channel ran from north to south. Close to where the Tenterden—Rolvenden road and the old railway crossed the stream was Ashbourne Mill. Although the mill and mill-house were joined together, they had been constructed differently; the house had brick walls and elevations, whilst the mill had the traditional weather-board-clad timber-frame body supported on brick foundations and walls at ground-floor level. That portion of the mill which lay against the house had external walls of brick up to the first floor and this, together with its plan, suggested that it may at one time have been part of the house. Moreover, all other machinery in the mill was confined to the basement and the floors immediately above. An interesting feature of the mill was that the floor above the ground floor had a headroom of only 5 ft., and it was decided to identify this floor as a mezzanine, being devoid of machinery and used only for the storage of grain and meal.

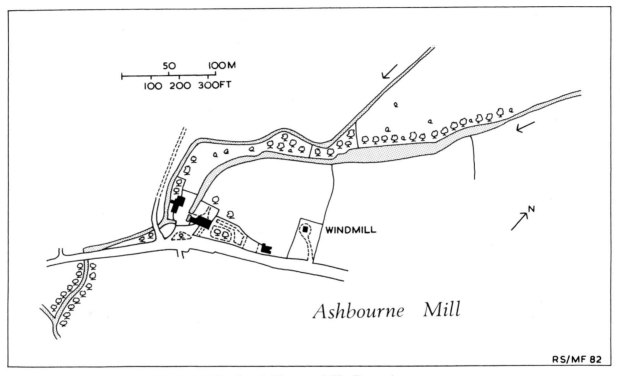

Fig. 3. Ashbourne Mill, Tenterden

We began our survey at the top of the mill on the first floor (Fig. 4), which nestled under a clay-tile mansard roof having bitumenised felt under the battens. The absence of division walls suggested that the east end of the floor had been used for the storage of sacks of grain, and it was served by the nearby lucam overhanging the access road outside. Near the lucam was a set of platform scales (see F on the plan), which had a circular cast-iron column with a cantilever weight shelf supported by a scroll. The platform had a backrail. Cast on a plate at the top of this column was 'Fennemor & Son Cranbrook' whilst on the platform surface were the words 'Warranted London Make'. Clearly the scales had been provided by Fennemore acting as agents for the manufacturer. Presumably, they sold a reasonable number in the area – enough to warrant having a special cast-iron name-plate made.

The hoist chain was still in position, suspended on a large iron pulley within the roof of the lucam and supported on stout planks on either side of the large wooden sheave which changed the direction of the chain. A pulley wheel was also positioned over the internal sack hoist, though whether served by a separate chain or not was unclear. The portion of the shaft (j) which

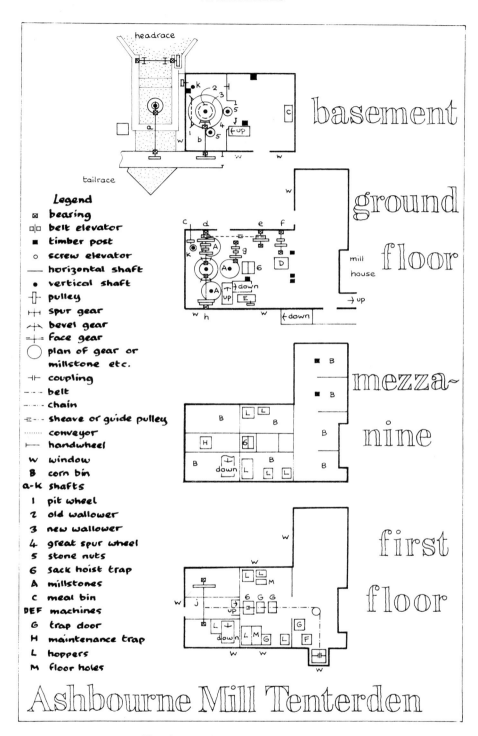

Fig. 4.   Ashbourne Mill, Tenterden

served as the bollard was wrapped with sacking to increase the friction. The ends of the wooden shaft had iron journals and were bound with a single iron hoop that suggested the use of cross-wing gudgeons, but it was not possible to see them.

Shaft (*j*) was driven from below by a canvas belt which was boxed in where it passed through the grain bin. The slack side of the belt had a wooden guide roller on the floor and, close against the edge of the pulley, there were three planks whose faces acted as a belt guide. The pulley was built entirely of wood and was 42 in. in diameter with an open-box section rim, 9 in. wide. It was carried on eight flat arms arranged in the clasp-arm manner around the 8½ in. square-section shaft (*j*). These arms were cross-halved, having been split and dowelled together in order to present a flat face on each side of the pulley. Adjustment of the pulley was by a compound lever arrangement which 'failed-safe', i.e. when relaxed, it automatically gave a slack pulley and thus broke the drive. There were several floor traps leading to the bins below, and the opening nearest to the lucam was presumably the entrance to the mezzanine below, because it was the only one with a fixed ladder.

The ground floor of the mill contained three pairs of stones, a vertical shaft and five high-level lay shafts; this equipment, together with steps, horses and two ancillary machines presented a congested atmosphere in the confines of the mill. Such an arrangement was not unusual in watermills and windmills as these invariably had very high utilisation of space.

Fig. 5.   Ashbourne Mill, Tenterden

The primary drive into this floor was, of course, the main vertical shaft from the basement which passed up to, but not through, the floor above. Above the top bearing of this shaft was a trap-door (h) giving access for maintenance and lifting of the shaft for replacing gears, etc. The wooden vertical shaft was sixteen-sided where it pierced the floor collar but, at higher level, where it carried the crown wheel, it was square, and was 14 in. across the flats. At the top of the shaft, just below the floor above, was a single-flanged wooden pulley which drove the high-level governor on the vertical spindle (k). The central spindle of the centrifugal governor was supported by a beam which was cantilevered off the wall. As the two 4½ in. diameter lead weights lifted the sliding collar, a yoke straddling the beam lifted the ¾ in. spindle (k) which passed down through the floor and transmitted movement, by link rods, to the tentering gear of the two Peak stones. The 54 in. diameter crown wheel, which drove high-level shafts (d) and (h), was made entirely of wood and carried sixty morticed cogs. The rim was in segments, apparently not laminated, and carried four straight cants on top, dowelled at the joints down into the rim. The wheel was supported by four radial arms which were morticed into each face and bolted to the rim and cants. Dowels held the cogs, which were morticed through the rim and additionally secured by little tapered wooden pegs on the underside. Very little wear was exhibited by the cogs, and the wheel was in good condition for its age. Shafts (d) and (h) were driven from the crown wheel by cast-iron bevel gears with four flat arms and sixteen teeth. Shaft (h) was a 2 in. square iron shaft supported close to the external wall by a bearing in the top of a 6 ft. high, pivoted, wooden lever. The pivot point was high in the lever, and manual adjustment was made at the lower end by means of a peg which could be moved in a series of holes in a horizontal board. This movement adjusted the belts carried by the stepped pulley on the end of shaft (h). This wooden pulley had two diameters measuring 35 × 5½ in. and 40 × 5½ in., respectively. The rims were segmented and laminated and each face was boarded and carried by a morticed cast-iron cross. This combination pulley drove machine (E) which was a corn and seed crusher made by Hammond & Co. of Croydon. It had a cast-iron frame and a cast-iron drive pulley measuring 9 × 3½ in. This drove the heavy crushing roll, which measured 18 × 4 in., and had a ⅝ in. thick rim carried by six curved arms of heavy square section. An 8 in. pulley on the other end of the drive shaft drove a 6 in. pulley for the hopper feed.

Shaft (d) was also a 2 in. square iron shaft and carried five pulleys. Taking them in order from the bevel gear, the first had an 18 × 4 in. wooden, segmented and laminated rim carried on four, tapered + section, radial, cast-iron arms which were morticed into the rim; the second was a 14 × 9 in. solid wooden pulley having a segmented rim; the third, an 11½ × 4 in. single-flanged, solid, wooden pulley, was in rather poor condition; the fourth, a 34 × 5½ in., solid beech pulley had an interesting construction. It had a relatively small bore, and the heavy solid rim was carried on an iron centre-piece having four straight arms, ⊥ section, each morticed and screwed into the rim. The fifth and last pulley measured 12 × 4 in. and was made from solid wood, and carried a leather belt which drove shaft (e). This shaft was of 1¾ in. square iron and, at each end, a plummer block was carried in a vertical cast-iron bracket, bolted to the floor beams above, and incorporated horizontal adjustment of the bearing. Of the two pulleys mounted on this shaft one was of solid wood, 14 × 9 in., with a segmented rim, and the other, a 24 × 4½ in. cast-iron single-piece pulley having six, straight, radial, oval-section arms mounted on a round hub which was packed off the shaft with steel packing pieces.

Shaft (f), a 1¼ in. diameter steel shaft, carried a 12 × 6 in., single-piece, cast-iron pulley together with a 15 × 6 in., single-piece, cast-iron pulley with six curved arms. Mounted next to this pulley on a short separate spindle, was a small, wrought-iron, 8 × 1½ in., single-piece, four-armed pulley which was friction-driven from inside the rim of the larger pulley. The purpose of this was not clear, but it was probably connected with machine (*D*). The 2 in. diameter, high-level, steel lay-shaft (*g*) carried three pulleys. The one nearest the stairs was the largest, being a 24 × 5 in., single-piece, cast-iron pulley with six tapered + section arms. In the middle of the shaft was a 5 × 5 in., barrel-shaped, solid, wooden pulley and at the other end of the shaft was a 12 × 6 in. single-piece cast-iron pulley with four flat arms.

Spindle (*C*) was 1¼ in. square and carried a solid, wooden pulley measuring 8 × 3¼ in. The spindle passed through the mill wall and, outside, the end bearing was supported on a steel frame. This probably controlled the penstock spindle.

There were three pairs of millstones (*A*) in the mill. The two nearest the stairs were hooped Peak stones, each complete with an octagonal tun, horse and hopper. The pair of stones furthest from the pond measured about 44 in. in diameter, and those in the middle measured 46 in. The third pair, nearest the pond, were French burrs, but their vat and top gear were missing. This pair was 46 in. in diameter, the runner stone was 11½ in. thick and carried weight boxes in the rim, with the name COOMBE & CO, COMARK LANE, LONDON, cast on them.

Machine (*D*) on the floor in the middle of the mill carried the inscription 'Horizontal separating and special close scarring m/c'. It was made in the U.S.A. by S. Howes of Silver Creek, New York State, and, apparently, was sold through the agency of an office at 64 Mark Lane, London. According to a further inscription, its capacity was twenty to thirty bushels per hour.

On the floor nearby was the circular frame of a wire machine, some 20½ in. in diameter and 46 in. long. It had sixteen, circular, wooden frames and the whole thing was split in half and bolted together. A similar dressing frame, 28 in. in diameter and 65 in. long, and made entirely of metal, was also on the floor. Its cylinder had solid ends, supporting longitudinal bars which in turn supported a ½ × ⅛ in. continuous steel bar which was twisted round the outside of the frame like a helix. At one end, the rim held annular teeth which were driven by chain, confirming that the frame could be rotated independently of the central shaft. The shaft still had bearings at each end and these were bolted to pedestal brackets, and at one end was a solid iron pulley measuring 12 × 4 in. Inside the frame, mounted on the shaft, was a smaller circular frame whose outer surface consisted of spaced 1 × ¼ in. bars. These bars were not quite parallel to the axis, but were slightly inclined to impart motion to the meal. The cloth, or wire, that at one time surrounded the outer frame was not present.

Steep, well-worn steps led down into the basement which had a different atmosphere to the rest of the mill. The floor was partly rotted and the air was damp, not surprising perhaps since two of the walls were underground. It was dark down in the basement, even though there were two dusty windows admitting light, but no doubt the top half of the external door would have been swung open for much of the time. The working area in the basement was partitioned off from the machinery by an internal, wooden-framed and panelled wall pierced by numerous opening panels and doors. Against one wall was a wooden meal bin (*c*), which used to stand under one of the meal spouts projecting through the division wall. There were several wooden rubbing strakes around the walls at waist height, against which the full sacks were leant.

Surveying the gearing by a hand-torch through the access doors was not easy, but it would have been foolhardy to have entered the chamber with six millstones overhead without a detailed structural survey having been made first. The gearing and bridges were supported by several substantial timbers sprung off brick and timber foundations, and the earth floor fell away at different levels towards the back of the chamber. A relic of bygone days was the old pit-wheel (*l*), once mounted on the end of the water-wheel shaft, but now defunct since the wheel had been replaced by a water-turbine. Both halves of the gear were embedded in the ground, or perhaps they were left in the old cog-pit which was subsequently filled. A visual appraisal of the pit-wheel suggested that it was cast-iron, with a morticed bevel rim, having a square bore, and that it was some 9–10 ft. in diameter with perhaps a 12 in. deep casting at the bore. When the turbine drove the mill, the wallower (2) also became defunct, but it was still in position, slung underneath the great spur wheel by drop-rods which were suspended by each of the six arms. The wallower was a single-piece cast-iron bevel carrying approximately twenty-nine teeth, and was not much larger than the hexagonal vertical shaft. Its bore was hexagonal and there were vertical cast webs radiating from the corners and mid-faces of the hub. Each face of the bore was packed with wood off the vertical shaft.

ASHBOURNE MILL.

Fig. 6. Ashbourne Mill, Tenterden

The great spur wheel (4) was made entirely of wood, and had six radial arms morticed and wedged into the faces of the wooden, hexagonal, vertical shaft. The cants were straight, and were bolted on top of the rim, giving a total depth of 8 in., and the cogs, approximately 102, were morticed through the rims and the cants. Resting on the arms of the great spur gear was another all-wood bevel gear (3) carrying some sixty-six cogs which were nailed at the back, outside. This 'ring-gear' – for it had no arms – was rebated and bolted into the arms of the great spur wheel.

Only two cast-iron stone nuts (5) remained in place, the third was missing, together with its shaft. Both of the existing nuts had four radial webs and approximately eighteen teeth, and were carried on 2 in. square iron vertical shafts. These in turn were supported by wooden bridge trees and brayers, which were automatically adjusted via long iron rods from the vertical spindle of the governor (k). The nut furthest from the pond was taken out of gear by a forked lever which held the nut by two chains.

The drive into the mill came from a 3 in. diameter shaft (b) which drove ring gear (3) via a single-piece cast-iron bevel, with four arms and twenty-four teeth. This shaft was supported by a stauffer-fed bearing on top of a cast-iron tapered beam, + section, and pivoted so that the bevel could be lifted out of gear. The other end of this shaft was supported by a bearing where it passed through the mill wall, and outside was an overhung cast-iron pulley 66 in. in diameter and 7 in. wide having six radial arms. The pulley was not split and had a round hub keyed on to the end of the shaft. It was belt-driven from the 30 × 6 in. cast-iron, single-piece pulley carried on six, radial, + section arms on shaft (a). The bevel which had been mounted on the other end of shaft (a) was missing, but it was probably identical with the cast-iron one, carrying twenty-six teeth, mounted on top of the 3 in. diameter turbine shaft.

The turbine, which was still in position at the bottom of its square concrete pit, was some 3½ ft. in diameter, and was of the inward flow/downward discharge type. Apparently, it operated in a flooded state, under some 9 ft. of water. Access was not possible at the time of the survey to establish the maker's name; a summer inspection would be favourable when the silt and deposit in the bottom of the pit should be dry. Operation of the peripheral parts was by a quadrant ring-gear turned by a small pinion mounted on the bottom of a vertical control spindle, which was missing.

It is probable that, when the turbine replaced the water-wheel, a new penstock was made at the entrance to the new concrete apron – its vertical side timbers were still in place though the gate had disappeared. The gate was controlled by a 2 in. diameter spindle, with pinions and end bearings, and, at the mill end, it had an overhung, single-piece, cast-iron pulley measuring 30 × 4 in. In the narrow gap between the wall of the turbine pit and the gable wall of the mill was a small, solid, double-flanged, cast-iron pulley 8 × 5 in. wide which was carried on the end of a spindle projecting through the mill wall. As this was not aligned with the remaining penstock pulley, it probably served the earlier water-wheel.

BASTED MILL (Lower Mill), Basted, TQ 605 554   Surveyed 1980.

The only evidence we have for this possible mill site was the recording of the names of two fields in the schedule accompanying the Wrotham tithe map of 1840. The fields were identified as
'Mill meadow orchard' (628)
and   'Mill meadow and old road' (611)

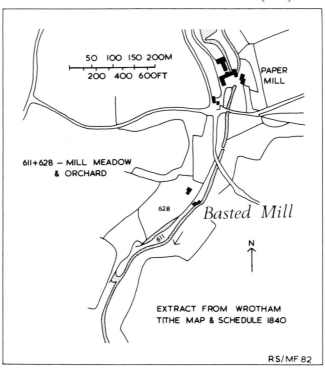

Fig. 7.   Basted Mill

Their positions were sufficiently distant from the nearby Basted paper mill to have made it unlikely that they had been named after the paper mill. No traces of any buildings that could have been the remains of Lower Basted mill were shown on the tithe map.

An examination of the area in the vicinity of a bridle path that followed the River Bourne as it wound its way through a small wood at this point revealed, as expected, not the slightest trace of the mill, its site, or its waterways.

There is, however, a good possibility that this is one of Kent's 'lost watermills'.

BAYTON MILL, Lenham. TQ 903 503   Surveyed March 1975.

This mill had been converted into a residence and, but for the presence of four millstones in the garden, it would never have occurred to the observer that this had been, at one time, a watermill. The mill-pond had disappeared, apparently filled in, for its surface was level with the surrounding ground. On the north-west side of the 'old mill pond', flowed the Great Stour, a considerable distance away from the mill-house. At the west end of the house, the gable wall, the water-wheel was positioned, open to the weather. The position of the wheel-shaft, where it passed through the brick mill wall, could still be seen, for it had been filled in with weather-boarding. Judging by its level in comparison with the surrounding ground, a breast wheel had existed here. The wheel-pit was filled in, and so were the first 100 ft. or so of the tail race, lost below the concrete road of the farm. Further away, the tail-race still existed.

All of the wheel and machinery had gone; nothing remained except the local memory of the mill, and its four millstones. One of the millstones was embedded in a concrete path and had

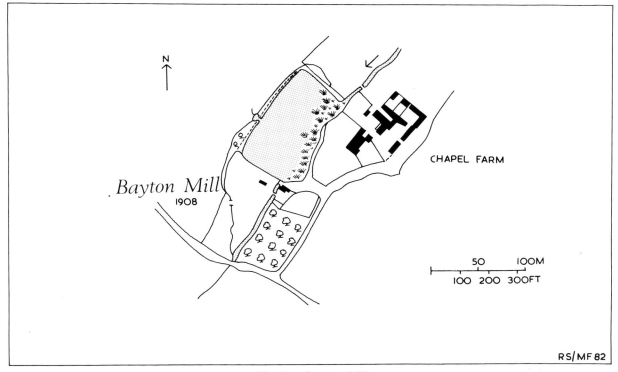

Fig. 8. Bayton Mill

had its eye filled with another, quite different, stone. This was most unusual for they are invariably filled with concrete or cement. The colour of the stone was a dark grey-blue, and the material was a fine texture, suggesting that it may have been what is called a Blue Stone. It was 39 in. in diameter.

Resting on a wall in the garden was a French Burr stone, 40 in. in diameter with an 8½ in. eye, and iron-bound to its full depth. Inside the eye was a cast-iron bar. Two other stones lay nearby, both 39½ in. in diameter with 10 in. eyes; one was 11 in. thick, the other was 8 in. thick at the skirt. The 11 in. stone had another iron bar, but the 8 in. stone had a cast-iron neck box. The material of these two stones was at first taken to be Derby Peak, but their texture was somewhat coarser and their colour was lighter than the grey of a Peak stone. Moreover, they had pieces and flecks of other stones in them, though not enough to suggest that they were man-made composition stones. They both had been bound on their edges with narrow iron bands indicating that they were liable to fracture.

BOCKINGFORD MILL, Loose. TQ 756 536   Surveyed 1971.

This mill ceased to grind corn just before the turn of the last century and, shortly afterwards, it was extended and converted to cottages (Fig. 46).

Mr Alan Wilson informed us that his father had worked this mill during this period but, in time, he had no wish to carry on working the stones. A letter in Mr Wilson's possession, dated April 1891, from a Mrs. Marsham, the owner of the mill, to his father confirmed that he wished to terminate his tenancy. Mr Wilson had occupied the mill for some time for she wrote of his 'lengthened tenancy' that had 'commenced in my uncle, the late Admiral Marsham's time', suggesting that he had worked the mill for at least a decade, possibly two or more. It is interesting to note that, in the letter, arrangements were made for a man to collect the 'silks', i.e. bolting cloths – clearly they were too valuable to be left in an empty mill.

After the mill stopped working, a Mr Rose took residence as foreman working at Ivy Mill, next up the valley. According to his son, Mr T. Rose of Southall, Middx., there was a man named Tom Bates in the mill-house before his father, also a foreman at Ivy Mill. The mill had not been closed very long for he had heard his father say that the water-wheel under the mill was still in working order because they had had to wedge it fast to stop it revolving, or else they could not get any sleep at night. Mr Rose could remember his father saying that they built two rooms onto the mill when they converted it into cottages.

This mill was far from obvious even when one passed close by, no falling water was to be seen or heard, no lucomb housing the sack-hoist showed, and the building itself was inconspicuous, two-floors high, and covered with a drab buff-painted weatherboard.

The mill-pond was about 300 ft. long and, at its widest point, was 70 ft. wide, but was very overgrown and muddy, as one would expect after at least sixty years neglect. For the last 80 ft. or so before the mill, the pond had been channelled between stone-lined banks. At the beginning of this section, the waste was taken off via a sluice connecting with the bypass. For many years, the stream's water had flowed through both sluices; in fact, the one nearest the mill could be clearly seen from Teasaucer Hill, some distance away but, recently, a falling Spanish oak had damaged the pond embankment and the upstream sluice, so that all the water had to take the less spectacular course.

In the garden of the mill was an underground brick and concrete chamber housing two 4 in. Easton automatic water-rams, which had been used to pump water from the mill-pond up to houses overlooking the valley. The maintenance of the rams in time became a problem, until main water was piped to the property concerned.

Beside the stone-lined head-race to the mill was a low wide concrete platform so arranged that if the stream should flood, all excess water would flow over the platform and be directed to a flood-gate above the bypass. In this way, damage to the wheel, machinery and mill fabric would be avoided.

Nothing was left of the machinery that once worked inside, though underneath the mill the remains of the water-wheel were still in place. Unfortunately, the tail-race was rather deep, but it was possible to gauge the wheel diameter as being some 12 ft., and its width, 8 ft. The wheel was an overshot with the usual compass-armed arrangement of eight cast-iron arms, in two 4 ft. bays bolted to a square cast-iron shaft. All the buckets, shields and backing had corroded away although no water was passing the trough-gate. Some years ago, perhaps in the war effort, the wheel was considered for scrap, but it was thought that the preparations for its removal would damage the mill foundations. The skeleton of this wheel, being under cover, will probably remain with us for as long as the mill is inhabited.

BOWLEY MILL, Boughton Malherbe. TQ 902 496   Surveyed July 1975.

The scant remains of Bowley Mill lay about two miles to the west of Charing village, and were set on the upper reaches of the Great Stour, within a few miles of the source of this well-known river. When the site was surveyed, in July 1975, the mill-house was the home of Mr and Mrs. Alexander. The early-nineteenth-century ragstone house stood at the far end of a private track that skirted the mill-pond. The site stood in a tree-lined valley, which with the rush and sorrel-lined pond complemented the gardens and made this an attractive rural setting. As with so many disused mill-ponds, this one was rather heavily silted up, although the owner hoped to be able to have it dredged out one day. Recent heavy rainfalls had raised the water level so that, in places, it had penetrated the pond bank, and some leaks were showing. The long, rectangular pond terminated, at what had been the head-race, in three separate exit channels that passed through the pond bank. The two exits furthest away from the mill were lined with brick, or brick and ragstone, and were clearly waste water, or overflow, channels. The further one was still in use, and held back the water with wooden sluice boards held behind sturdy angle irons, whilst the overflow water poured over it and down a dressed-stone spillway. At the bottom of the spillway, in a large depression, were some massive, lichen-covered, blocks of stone. The central exit, which was dry, was lined with brick and ragstone but, apparently, led nowhere, although at some time it must have served a useful purpose. The exit nearest to the remains of the mill continued alongside the remaining external walling, and was once the head-race that used to lead to the water-wheel, although nothing remained of its sluice gear or the wheel itself.

The existing walling of the mill building finished flush with the surrounding ground, thus leaving a ragstone and brick-walled pit in the ground that was the remains of the cog-pit. At the time of the survey, the pit was filled with tall, sturdy, stinging nettles, willow herb, thistles, and other wild plants that made a detailed inspection impracticable. However, from the upper regions, it was possible to see some of the equipment that had fallen into the cog-pit, which was itself almost half-full of débris and soil. The 8 in. square, cast-iron wheel-shaft was still in position, supported at the outer end by a bearing, and at the inner end by another bearing set into the wall of the mill. From its conjectural position relative to some features of the wall of the mill it was considered that the wheel was of the overshot type, and had measured approximately

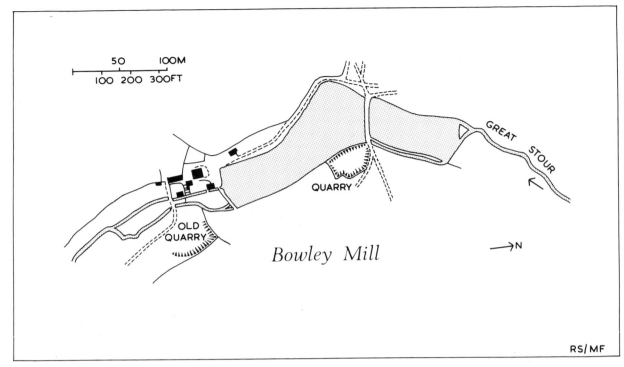

Fig. 9.   Bowley Mill

6 ft. in width and 12 ft. in diameter. There were no remains of the wheel itself. Within the cog-pit, the wheel-shaft supported the cast-iron remains of the pit wheel, which had formerly carried ninety-six wooden cogs, although all were broken off. The pit wheel had eight arms, and had been cast in two halves bolted together. The square wheel-shaft supported the pit wheel by means of its square hub, which carried short webs at each corner and midway along each face, and which in turn supported an octagonal outer hub on the corners of which were set the eight, T-section, single-tapered arms. Although the wheel-shaft was about a foot above the surface of the rubble partly filling the cog-pit, the space between the rubble and the shaft was filled with water. This had probably leaked from the pond, and the brick-lined arch that supported the shaft bearing where it pierced the wall had acted as an overflow or weir. Although it was not carrying any gears, a length of circular wooden shaft approximately 1 ft. in diameter may have been the remains of the main vertical shaft. A bridging box and footstep bearing on a short beam had fallen across a cast-iron layshaft and, nearby, were two cast-iron stone spindles. Both stone spindles carried solid, wooden, stone nuts hooped with metal bands at the top and bottom. An all-wood spur gear, much decayed, was of a clasp-arm construction, and may have been the great spur wheel. Also in the pit were two, hooped, French burr stones that measured about 46 in. in diameter, and it was suspected that two more may have been sighted in the luxuriant herbage. The last item of particular interest was a wooden sack hoist bollard with integral wooden gear teeth morticed into one end of the shaft. Of the superstructure and its contents nothing could be deduced from the rather pitiful items scattered around the cog-pit.

The remains of Bowley Mill were sufficient to allow us to picture a small, two-stone rural corn mill, the gearing of which, in view of the type and number of wooden gears, was of some antiquity when the building stopped work for the last time.

BRANBRIDGE MILL, East Peckham. TQ 673 485   Surveyed February 1982.

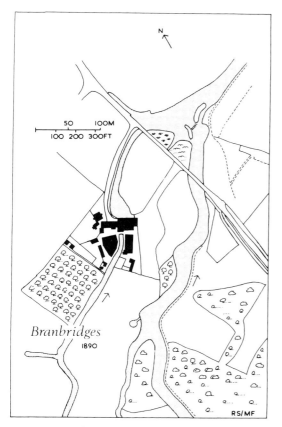

50   100M
100   200   300FT

Branbridges
1890

RS/MF

Fig. 10.   Branbridge Mill

The site of this former mill was in an area where no less than four well-known Kentish rivers met within a two-and-a-half mile length of waterway. These were the Rivers Medway, Beult, Teise, and Bourne. The region was level and low-lying and, in consequence, was prone to flooding, particularly when these four rivers were in spate. On the face of it, this was not a situation where a watermill would have been anticipated, and yet, in the middle of an industrial site to the immediate west and north of Branbridge itself, could be seen the unmistakable sight of lucams on a large Victorian industrial building.

Permission to visit and examine the site was generously given by Mr W.P.G. Arnold, of Arnolds (Branbridges) Limited – a company engaged here in medium/heavy engineering work. During our conversation, it was learnt that, although the site had indeed supported a watermill in former times, the lucams belonged to a warehouse, and not to a mill.

Prior reference to nineteenth-century Ordnance Survey maps had shown that Branbridge Mill (or Brandbridges, as it was then spelt) had been an oil mill before it became a corn mill. The oil milling operation would have consisted of the extraction of oil from seeds such as linseed and rape. The same maps had also shown the mill to be unusual for this region, in that the necessary supply of water had been diverted from the River Medway, which it rejoined downstream of the mill. The topography of this site was such that, when it was made fully navigable, it was necessary to employ two locks to accommodate the difference in level between the portions of the river at this point. Thus, the head of water available to the mill was quite significant, especially at a site so far downstream on a river of this size. It was estimated that the effective head of water at the mill was of the order of 8–10 ft. Presumably, prior to the installation of the locks, the head had been maintained by a weir.

Although the mill originally was powered by a water-wheel this had been replaced by a water turbine, which itself had been succeeded by a gas engine, which in turn had given way to an oil engine. The gas for the gas engine probably was manufactured on site, since the 1897 25 in. O.S. map showed a gasometer and a large rectangular building standing close to, but separated from, the mill itself. A coal wharf on the bank of the River Medway itself, on the far side of the main road, must have made the supply of coal for this operation particularly convenient.

There were no remains on the site that had any direct connection with the mill itself, but the warehouse had been used for storing either grain or ground products as necessary, was still standing, although its demolition was imminent. It stood against the edge of the head-race and, very unusually, had a lucam on both the land and water sides, so that barges could be brought

BRANBRIDGE MILL   (based on a photograph dated 1898)

mjfuller 1982

Fig. 11. Branbridge Mill

right up the head-race and be unloaded there. On the other side of the head-race was the large old stable block, in weather-board and brick, a reminder of the importance of horse-power in an earlier age, and the facilities that they required. Although the head-race still ran up to the mill dam there were no signs of any sluice gear or ancillary equipment. The tail-race formed a large pool at the base of the dam, and the remains of the upper works of a sunken barge stood above the water to provide a congregating place for a flock of friendly mallard.

Although the Arnold family is now in the engineering industry, Mr William Arnold started operations in this area in the corn milling trade. The family left Bartley Mill near Frant, on the Kent/Sussex border, and came to Branbridge in 1980. The mill was operated as two separate units – one for flour milling, and another for provender milling. Flour milling ceased in about 1916 after a fire caused severe damage, but provender milling continued until about 1946 when the business was sold to a Sussex company. The buildings were converted for engineering work, but another severe fire in about 1960 meant that the complete mill site had to be cleared.

A photograph taken of the mill in 1898 was kindly lent by Mr Arnold so that it could be examined thoroughly and be used as the basis for the sketch shown here. The building on the left is the engine room, and the single-storey building on the right is believed to have housed the water-wheel. It was the custom for W. Arnold and Sons to provide an annual excursion on a steam barge for many of their Sussex farmer customers. Refreshments were provided by the company, but it was a surfeit of liquid refreshment that, in part, led to the abolition of this quaint but charming custom. The problem was that some of the guests would become quite unsteady by the end of the day, and fall overboard! Concern for the safety of their customers led the organisers to withdraw their hospitality and make a sad break with tradition.

BURNT MILL, Lenham/Charing. TQ 913 492   Surveyed September 1978.

Burnt Mill lay in a remote valley which could be reached by footpath from Lenham Heath or Egerton or, for the more adventurous, by a tortuous back lane which culminated in a half-mile long rough track. The mill, built on the downstream-side of the mill-dam, was shrouded by trees; the nearby mill-house also had a back-cloth of trees on the flank of the valley, and, in its garden, tall old apple trees, long since trimmed by the pruning saw, cast shadows across the mill-pond. Several large willows on the edge of the pond sprang out horizontally several feet from the bank before turning skywards to support their graceful foliage. Do such trees fall towards the water in their early years their roots perhaps weakened by a brimming pond, or do they have some strange affinity for water? A tranquil setting, quiet save for the continuous sound of the waterfall in the bypass and the occasional call of a water bird from the undergrowth at the head of the pond.

The mill and mill-house were undoubtedly built at the same time, for they had common features of brick quoins, ground courses and window surrounds, with ragstone panels in the walls. The house had a solid, attractive appearance, nicely proportioned under a clay-tile roof pierced by two tall, brick chimneys. It merited attention in its own right, especially the kitchen with its massive brick chimney incorporating a baking oven. The chimney had delightful tumbling-in on its overhanging brick face and filled one corner of the kitchen. But it was to the mill that our attention had to be given.

Burnt Mill was built against the mill-dam and was served by an old road running across the dam which is now grassed over. It could be traced through the fields nearby as a sunken lane. The builders of the mill had taken advantage of the change in ground level and the unusual

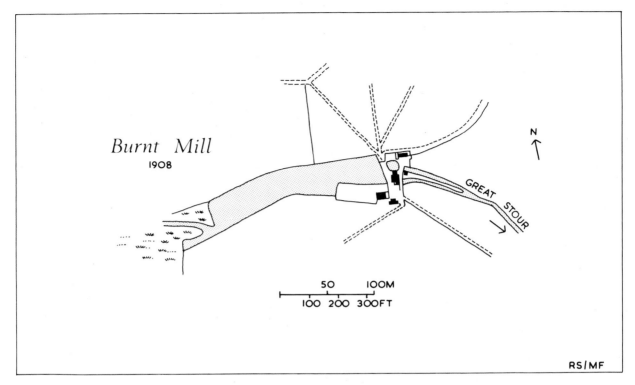

Fig. 12.   Burnt Mill, Lenham

width of the dam by providing one entrance off the top of the dam, into the first floor, and another one into the floor below from the tail-race side of the mill – both doors were of the usual stable-type half-doors. The lower walls of the mill, against the mill-dam, were built of ragstone and supported timber frames and weather-boarding under a clay-tile roof. The downstream wall of this lower floor had red brick quoins, door and window surrounds, and a string course just above ground level, infilled with ragstone panels.

Beside the mill, the water-wheel pit was mainly ragstone-lined, except on the mill-side downstream of the wheel-shaft where it was brick-lined, as was also the base that supported the landside or outer bearing of the wheel shaft. This base was of such a width as to give access to the bearing and the wheel side. The head-race was taken through the dam in a brick-vaulted tunnel, the bare top of which could be found amongst the grass in front of the mill. This tunnel fed a short trough with wooden sides and base which was much decayed. The wooden penstock had two cast-iron racks, which engaged with cast-iron pinions mounted on a square iron shaft projecting through the mill wall.

The overshot water-wheel, which was still in place though much decayed, was 5 ft. in width and 10 ft. 4 in. in diameter. It had two iron frames making a single bay, each frame having been cast in halves, and bolted together. Eight radial arms, + in section and tapered on both axes, sprang from a circular hub to support an L-section rim cast integrally with the arms. The $7\frac{1}{2}$ in. deep rim carried forty-eight L-shaped iron buckets on ribs cast on its inside face. Each bucket was 12 in. deep, unventilated and strengthened by three bolts and stays from the iron sole plate. Some three-quarters of the buckets had decayed and fallen away, and not more than half of the sole-plate remained. However, the wheel-pit was relatively clear of débris and deposit – perhaps facilitated by a good gradient, for the wheel was just clear of the small amount of water that had leaked through from the pond. A ragstone-lined tunnel took the tail-water beneath the path leading to the back of the mill, and made an attractive sight from the tail-race further downstream. The wheel was carried on a 9 in. diameter, hollow-ended, cast-iron shaft which had a $5\frac{1}{2}$ in. diameter journal resting on a cast-iron bearing and sole-plate. The sole-plate carried the following legend: J. HILL, ASHFORD, 1863. The shaft entered the mill via a brick bull's eye.

The mill had been abandoned when it had ceased to work in the 1950s, and in that relatively short space of time had become quite ruinous; the roof had fallen in, taking nearly all of the top floor with it, and this in turn had caused the collapse of most of the first floor onto the ground floor. Internally, only the massive timbers of the hurst frame with its ragstone- and brick-foundations had remained in place, still supporting the millstones on the floor above. The wooden walls and weather-boarding of the mill still stood precariously, weakened by beetle and damp. Being open to the sky and elements, the end of the mill was hastened, each storm was more harmful than several winters during its working life.

And so it is with fear of life and limb that such a mill is entered, and with the decay so advanced the visitor must begin at the bottom of the mill to prove each tread, and appraise from *below* the ability of the fabric to sustain weight at the higher levels. The survey of a mill in bad structural condition should always be planned to take place on a dry, windless day so as to reduce the chances of any structural collapse while the surveyor is within the building. At all times caution and commonsense must prevail, with observation providing a continuous appraisal of the conditions.

Entry to the lower floor of the mill was gained through one of the windows near the cog-pit. The glass and frame had long since disappeared and only the wooden cill remained, still in place between the wide internal splays of the brick surround. Dropping in onto the floor was not easy, for most of the floor-boards were missing and the joists were badly decayed. Investigation revealed that this corner was the only area of the floor that was safe to take any great weight, including that inside the cog-pit through a door immediately ahead. The torch-light inside the gloom of the cog-pit showed that the millstones and gearing were still in place. With such weight overhead, it was necessary to examine the frames and foundation for signs of weakness – luckily none were found, for the elements had not yet gained entry to this corner of the mill. The scantling that had been used in the box-frames and the bridge-trees was large – far larger than any elsewhere in the mill. In fact, the main posts of the mill walls seemed unusually light in section and were not hardwood, which no doubt had contributed to their rapid decay. It was not perhaps surprising that local memories recalled the building shaking noticeably when the mill was in use.

The pit-wheel was cast-iron, with eight, tapered, T-section arms that sprang from a square cast-iron hub to support a rim with eighty wooden cogs. Each cog was nailed from the back and was mounted in a rectangular hole cast through the bevelled rim. This gear, which was about 8 ft. in diameter, had been made from a single casting.

Two substantial wooden beams that spanned the pit supported a third beam over the wheel-shaft bearing, which in turn carried the footstep bearing of the vertical wooden shaft of the mill. This shaft was 14 in. square within the cog-pit, but above this it changed in section to become sixteen-sided. The gudgeon, which was probably winged, was held in position in the end of the shaft by two wrought-iron clamps. Close above was the cast-iron, single-piece wallower, which had a large square hub with eight radial webs carrying thirty-two bevel teeth.

The wooden great spur-wheel was approximately 6 ft. in diameter, and had four compass arms which passed through the vertical shaft in which they were held by locking wedges. On the

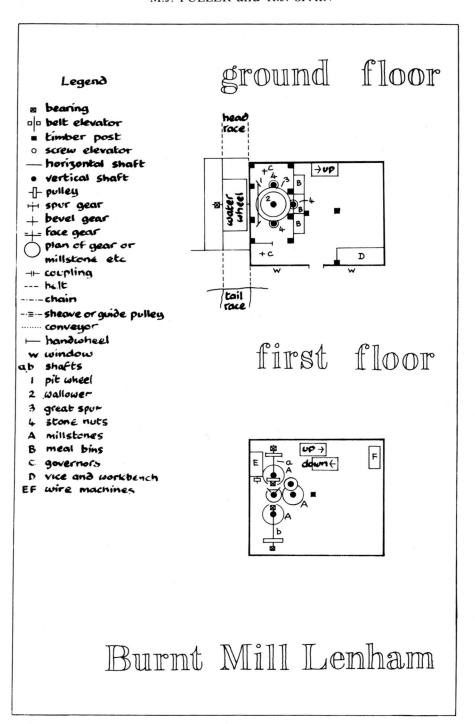

Fig. 13.   Burnt Mill, Lenham

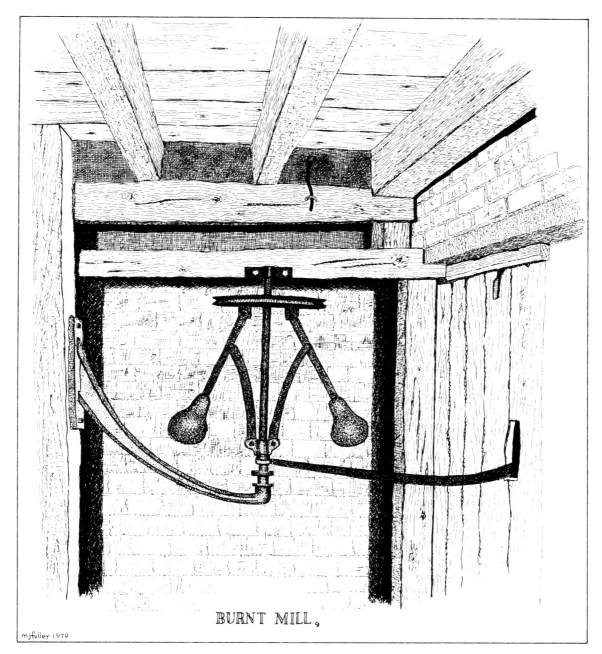

Fig. 14.   Burnt Mill, Lenham

underside of the arms there were four large cants which were bolted integrally with the rim, which was pierced for approximately ninety-two cogs.

The three pairs of millstones at Burnt Mill were driven via stone nuts; the one nearest to the pond was cast-iron, whilst the two others were wooden. Only the nut nearest the tail-race was accessible for inspection, although the middle one appeared to be of the same pattern with upper and lower iron hoops on a wooden hub that carried eighteen cogs – three of them slip cogs, which were absent. The third stone nut was taken out of gear by a lifting ring and yoke raised by a screw passing through the bridge-tree. All of the bridge-trees were made of wood, with the two outer pairs of millstones controlled by governors – apparently identical – each with two pear-shaped lead weights which, with the spindle, pulley and levers, were supported by a graceful, curved, cast-iron, cantilever bracket bolted onto the wall. One of the governors was outside the pit, and one inside, and both moved the bridge-tree via long steel-yards and iron links.

MECHANICAL RATIOS		
Element	Number of cogs/teeth	Revolutions per revolution of water-wheel
Pit-wheel	80	1.0
Wallower	32	2.5
Great spur-wheel	92 appr.	2.5
Stone nuts	18	12.8

Outside of the pit, against its long panelled wall, were the meal bins, (B) one for each of the meal spouts from the stones above. In one corner, beneath the window, a wooden work bench complete with a vice (D) stood on a small patch of floor, the remainder of which had rotted, and lay broken under the mass of débris which had fallen from the floors and roof above. The stairs were still in place and, behind them, the wall against the mill-dam had been boarded over, presumably to allow the sacks of meal to lean against it without becoming damp.

Of the first floor, only that portion over the hurst frame remained. All of the millstones were in place, with two spare ones standing on edge leaning against the outside wall of the mill. The stone nearest the pond was a French burr, 44 in. in diameter, with a 10 in. diameter eye, complete with an octagonal tun, horse and hopper. The other sets of stones were also French burrs, one of which was complete with tun, horse and hopper. The middle set had a 40 in. diameter runner with a 9 in. eye, while the tail-race set had a runner of 44 in. diameter. Both of the spare runner stones were 42 in. in diameter; the French one was 8 in. thick with a 9 in. eye, while the Peak had a $10\frac{1}{2}$ in. eye and was complete with its mace or rynd.

High on the main vertical shaft was a cast-iron single-piece crown gear with a square hub, tapered T-section arms and eighty-eight bevel teeth. Immediately above this was an 18 × 5 in. single-flanged wooden pulley which drove an adjacent similarly constructed 30 in. diameter pulley. This was mounted on the bottom of a $1\frac{1}{2}$ in. square iron shaft which passed through to the floor above. Two iron lay-shafts were driven from the crown gear, the one on the pond-side (a) was $2\frac{1}{2}$ in. square, with bevelled corners, and carried two cast-iron pulleys with crowned wrought-iron faces. One of these, measuring 40 × 6 in., drove a wire machine via a small, solid, wooden, crowned, single-flanged pulley. On the casing of the machine were numerous pencil notes, including the dates 1952 and 1954. The other lay-shaft, (b) which did not have a bevel gear on the crown gear, was $1\frac{1}{2}$ in. square and carried a single, solid-beech, canvas-faced pulley measuring $15\frac{1}{2}$ × 2 in.

Most of this floor had fallen in, but, scattered over the remaining portion, around the millstones, were the paraphernalia of milling, together with the domestic lumber which invariably may be found in a mill adjacent to a house. A portion of the upper floor above the

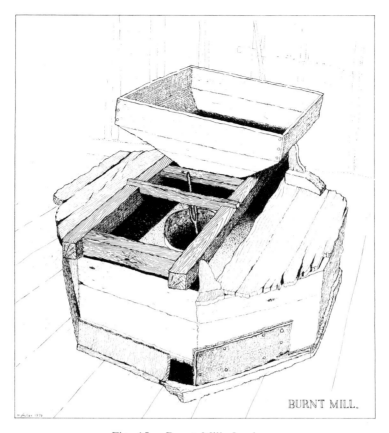

Fig. 15.   Burnt Mill, Lenham

millstones was still in place, but was inaccessible and was unsafe anyway. The remainder of the upper floor and the roof above had fallen in, and broken joists, posts and beams, together with masses of broken clay-tiles, lay scattered everywhere. Here and there, parts of the roof were still attached to the walls, enough to show that, very unusually, the mill roof apparently had had a hidden valley. Such a rain trap probably accelerated the decay of the mill for, once the rainwater pipes, which had to pass through the mill, had become blocked or started to leak, all of the water from this valley must have passed into the mill, with dire results.

Most of the top walls were boarded-out inside, showing where the bins had been positioned. Light to these areas was provided by small, high-level windows, some of which had been boarded over to make hatches.

CHART MILL, Chart Sutton. TQ 794 493   Surveyed April 1974.

Chart Mill was positioned on the scarp slope running east – west from Linton to Ulcombe and faced south overlooking the broad valley of the River Beult, and beyond, the Weald. The old mill and detached mill-house, where no doubt the miller lived, had become part of a private residence.

The mill was timber-framed, with brick walls up to the first floor and weatherboarding above,

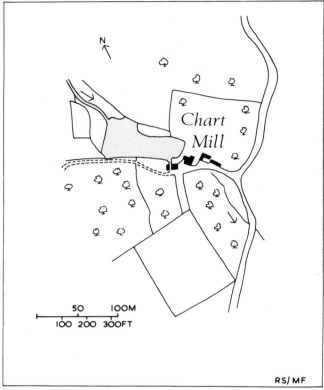

Fig. 16.   Chart Mill

under a pitched, clay-tiled roof with hipped gables. On the wheel-side of the mill, the gable wall was ragstone up to ground level, and the deep wheel-pit was lined with ragstone. Beside this end of the mill was a hollow in the ground, some 30 ft. square, with sides sloping down to the wheel-shaft which was well below general ground level. This hollow, which had become something of a sunken garden, was edged with a well-trimmed privet hedge which had neither gate nor entrance; the gardener pointed out the 'secret' entrance and sprang the hedge apart to allow access. The water from the pond above still fell down into the empty wheel-pit, which was quite deep, and down in this hollow the noise and spray were considerable. The wheel had been taken out during the last war but the cast-iron shaft and outer bearing were still in place. The shaft was 9 in. square, relieved in the centre of the faces, and turned down at the end to 6 in. diameter. On one face was the name W. WEEKS & SON — MAIDSTONE. A plummer block and bottom brass supported the shaft, and this in turn rested on a long sole-plate with shoulders, with the date 1875 cast on. A massive brick plinth supported this bearing.

The wheel, which was overshot, was deduced to have been 4 ft. wide and 24 ft. in diameter. This diameter was one of the largest in Kent. The wheel-pit was relatively free from deposit, thereby allowing a clear view of the tail-race tunnel. It is believed that this tunnel was lined with bricks throughout its length of 150–200 ft. The mill-end of the shaft still passed through the gable wall via a barrel vault which was round, but it had an additional layer of bricks at the bottom, tapered off at each side of the shaft, making the hole rather egg-shaped. Presumably this had been done to keep water out. No machinery remained in the mill, and the basement or lower chamber, which must have housed the pit-wheel and gearing, had been filled in with concrete up to ground level. The upstairs of the mill had been converted into an office. Outside of the door was a concrete path which ran in front of the mill and around one end of it and into this were bedded seven millstones. Four of these were French burrs, and the remainder were Peak stones, and all but one were hooped. They were all 4 ft. in diameter. Whilst measuring the millstones, a swarm of brown bees was noticed on the weather-board. They were busy coming and going between the boards and it was believed that they had nested there for ten years.

The old mill-pond had become overgrown some years ago, and had been cleaned out and an island formed in the middle. It formed part of a delightful garden, and was retained by a very low brick wall which had replaced an older ragstone surround. On climbing the grass face to look at the penstock above the wheel-pit a confrontation took place with an intent mute swan

Fig. 17. Chart Mill

with arched wings and erect tail. Not surprisingly, he received a lot of attention, and the examination of the pond was thereby reduced to a cursory glance. The water passed to the wheel between brick walls, some 2 ft. apart, and the brickwork appeared to be modern, being identical to that which skirted the pond. Turning away from the mill and walking briskly along the pond bank between polled willows, the extent of the pond was checked where it was hidden by the island. The swan, suspicious of the movement, swept through the water with powerful surges, its neck pressed even tighter to its body. This must have been the cob, for a demure, inquisitive and unruffled swan came across from the island to see what the fuss was about. They were left in peace, and the gardener sought to thank him for his help.

CHARTHAM MILL, Chartham. TR 097 554   Surveyed February 1974.

This old mill lay on the bank of the River Stour close to the main road from Chilham to Canterbury. It seemed likely that, in earlier times, this may have been a true river mill with an undershot wheel, which at some later date was moved to a position inside the mill and served by a watercourse coming from the river upstream of the mill. Such an arrangement could create a

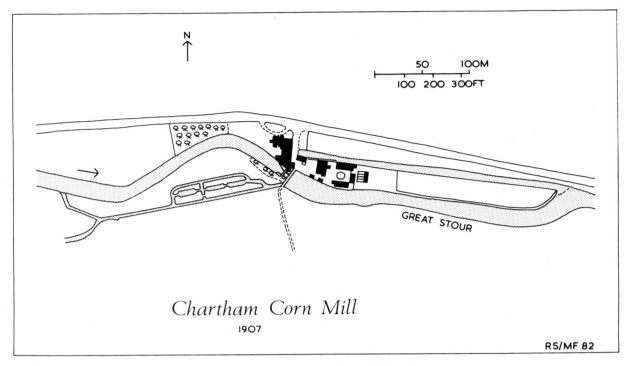

Fig. 18.   Chartham Corn Mill

head of water at the mill, the greater the length of the head- and tail-races, the greater the head of water. The water-wheel had gone, but the existing waterfall at its position, some 4 – 5 ft., showed it to have been a low breast-shot wheel some 10 ft. wide.

Close by the wheel-pit were two identical, vertical cast-iron frames, still in position, which had two cross-beams. The upper one of these had a circular, footstep-bearing emplacement complete with adjusting screws for taking the millstone spindle; the other cross-beam in the frames had a machined top face to take a bearing, undoubtedly to support a horizontal drive shaft.

Built over the river, and against the mill, was a turbine and pump house. The turbine, which was still in position deep in the water, was apparently used to drive a pump which served a 3 in. diameter iron fire main, part of which could still be traced passing downstream beside the mill. Whether or not this turbine ever drove the millstones is not clear. The turbine was some 4 ft. in diameter, but its height could not be determined. It was driven via a 6 in. diameter vertical iron shaft that passed through a gland in the top case, with a coupling just above the body. A 3 ft. diameter, cast, hand-wheel was used to regulate the flow of water through the turbine which, via a rim gear, opened annular ports in the turbine casing. All the gearing between the turbine and the pump was of iron. On top of the turbine shaft, below a top bearing was a sixty-eight tooth bevel with four T-sectioned arms, which engaged another similar bevel with forty teeth mounted on a horizontal shaft.

The drive from this was transmitted through a clutch to a six-armed iron spur-gear with 102 teeth which in turn engaged a ninety-three tooth spur-gear on the crank-shaft of the pump. The mechanical ratio of this gearing between the turbine and the pump was therefore 1.86 : 1. On the lay shaft was a 64 × 18 in. crowned cast-iron pulley with six oval arms, and this probably acted as a fly-wheel as well as a drive.

Fig. 19. Chartham Corn Mill

CHEGWORTH MILL, Ulcombe. TQ 850 527   Surveyed Summer 1972.

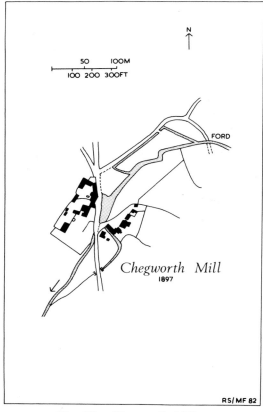

50   100M

100   200   300FT

N

FORD

Chegworth Mill
1897

RS/MF 82

Fig. 20.   Chegworth Mill

The name of Chegworth is given to a small group of agricultural buildings including two or three farms, a row of cottages and a mill and millhouse. It is hardly a hamlet, more like a small settlement which may have developed, in earlier centuries, around the watermill.

At Chegworth the River Len was dammed to create a small pond, now almost overgrown with watercress and rushes, which then passed through a culvert under the farm track to serve the overshot wheel beside the mill. The overflow or 'waste' water which was excess to the mill's requirements, passed through a penstock by the mill-dam against the road, ran under the road and on down the valley into the grounds of Leeds Castle. The head of water created was greater than at first appeared, for the wheel was 10 ft. 10 in. in diameter. As this watermill site is very old – we have archive evidence of at least an early fourteenth-century existence – the head had probably been improved several times during its history.

The mill had brick walls up to the first floor, with timber framing and weatherboarding above, under a pitched clay-tile roof. It had a pleasant appearance, with its hipped gables and cream-painted weather-boarding. In plan its shape was an extended oblong, perhaps six times as long as its width, with a slight kink half way along. On one side of the building was the water-wheel and tail-race, and it was interesting to note that among the ragstone foundations which occurred immediately above the water was some tufa. As this early building material is usually found in Norman masonry work – examples of it may be seen in some local churches – it is possible that some of the ragstone work in the mill was very old.

The water was carried to the wheel through an open iron trough with cast side panels, one bearing the inscription:

W. WEEKS

MILLWRIGHT

MAIDSTONE

Its apron was supported by a cast-iron frame. In the trough, just prior to the wheel, was a penstock controlled from within the mill via an octagonal iron shaft carrying two iron pinions engaging with a cast-iron rack. The overshot wheel, which was 10 ft. 10 in. in diameter and 7 ft. 6 in. in width, stood in backwater. Beside the wheel the mill wall was plastered, a feature which was common to many watermills.

There were three frames to the wheel, each with a single-piece cast rim carried by eight radial arms with tapered cruciform section. The rim, which was L-shaped in section ($7\frac{1}{2} \times 2\frac{1}{4}$ in.), and $\frac{3}{4}$ in. thick, had cast lugs to which the arms were bolted, and raised internal shoulders to which the

Fig. 21. Chegworth Mill

buckets were bolted. The wheel carried forty-four iron buckets, L-shaped, about 12 in. deep and 2 in. wide at the outer rim of the wheel. There was a sheet-iron sole-plate, and the buckets were not ventilated. The makers' name appeared again on the shroud:

W. WEEKS & SON LTD
MAIDSTONE

The wheel-shaft was square in section, and on the land side of the wheel the 6 in. diameter journal was carried by a large wooden block which rested on a brick pier.

The door to the mill, and the small window in the adjacent wall, both had splayed reveals. Inside the mill, on the ground floor, the gearing and hursting were contained within a wooden-walled chamber. The cast-iron pit-wheel, which was overhung, was split and bolted in two halves onto the $7\frac{1}{2}$ in. square iron shaft. It had square hubs from which sprang six T-section arms, each tapered on the flange and web, which supported a morticed iron rim carrying ninety-six lignum vitae cogs. The bearing arch which supported the footstep beam was in turn supported by iron sole-plates resting on a brick pier. The iron vertical shaft was square in section, nominally 5 in., but tapered at the top and bottom. It rested in the usual bridging box mounted on a cast arch and was supported by a bearing just below the floor above. Mounted low on the iron vertical shaft was the cast-iron wallower, which was a single-piece casting with eight radial T-section arms supporting a rim with thirty teeth. Close above the wallower was the great spur-wheel which was a single piece casting with eight radial ⊥ section arms, tapered on flange and web, that supported a morticed rim with 104 wooden cogs pinned inside at the top and bottom.

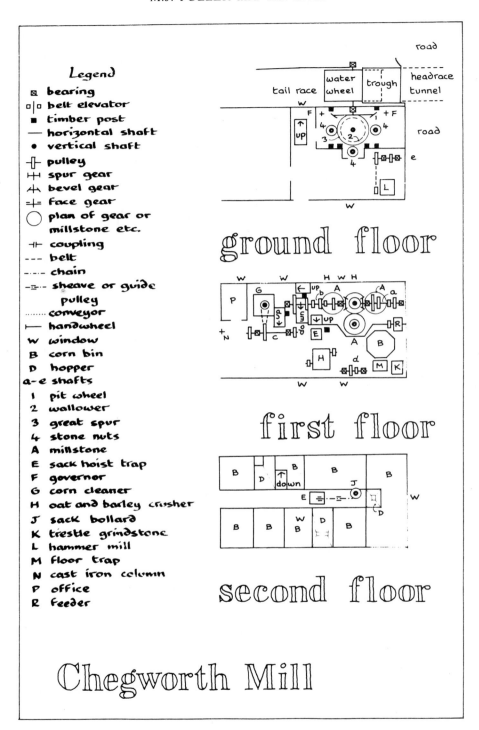

Fig. 22.   Chegworth Mill

On the periphery of the great spur-wheel were three equidistant stone nuts on the millstone spindles. The spindle nearest the pond was carried by a wooden bridge-tree with the usual bridging box and adjusting screws. Through this beam passed the two vertical rods of the jacking ring, which was screwed by handle from below to raise the eighteen-tooth cast-iron nut up the 3 in. square spindle to take it out of mesh with the great spur-gear. An identical arrangement existed on the cast-iron stone nut furthest from the pond, but the middle one, which was housed in a projection of the cog-pit chamber, had a cast-iron bridge tree with provision for the same type of jacking ring. This nut had twenty teeth, so that the speed of this millstone was slightly slower than the others. The mechanical ratios in this mill were as follows:

MECHANICAL RATIOS		
Element	No. of teeth/cogs	Revolutions per rev. of water-wheel
Pit-gear	96	1.0
Wallower	30	3.2
Great spur	104	3.2
Stone nuts	18	18.5
Stone nut	20	16.6

Just inside the cog-pit door was an old wall-mounted governor, a relic of the days when the mill produced flour. It had two pear-shaped lead weights and, on top, a single-flanged pulley 10 in. in diameter which was driven by belt from the stone shaft. A similar governor that existed in the far corner of the chamber was belt-driven from the pond-side stone shaft, but this one had two 5 in. diameter round balls. The driver pulley on the millstone shaft was 6 in. in diameter and the driven pulley on top of the governor spindle was 10 in. in diameter. For each revolution of the water-wheel the governor would have rotated 11.1 times. On the wall of the chamber outside was a quadrant slide lever which controlled the penstock above the wheel.

Upstairs, the floor adjacent to the millstones was at a lower level, by some 18 in., than the remainder of the first floor. The three pairs of millstones were still in place at the time of the visit, complete with their tuns and most of their top gear. The pair of stones nearest the mill-pond were French burrs, 44 in. in diameter with the maker's name,

HUGHES & SON
DOVER and LONDON

on three balance boxes and the eye plate. These stones had a four-beat damsel and were contained in an octagonal wood tun with horse and hopper on top. The middle pair of stones appeared to be a mixture, the runner a 42 in. diameter Peak, and the bedstone, by the plaster which could be seen underneath, presumably a French burr. These stones, which were well worn and rather thin, carried a four-beat damsel, shoe and horse but no hopper. The third pair of stones, within a round wooden tun, were 46 in. diameter Peaks, which also had a four-beat damsel, shoe and hopper but the horse was different, being made from welded angle-iron. On top of the tun were miscellaneous tools; a mill bit and shaft, metal scoop and a large wooden wedge used in raising the stones for dressing. The square-section iron vertical shaft terminated just below the floor above in a bearing. Below this bearing was a flanged wood pulley with two different diameter faces; the upper was roughly 20 × 5 in. and the lower slightly smaller. The larger one drove a 21 × 5 in. double-flanged wood pulley mounted nearby at high level on a 2 in. square iron shaft which passed through the floor above. This belt was tensioned by a wooden

Fig. 23.   Chegworth Mill

roller at the end of a pivoted beam. Below the double pulley on top of the main vertical shaft was a single-piece cast-iron crown wheel some 4 ft. 8 in. in diameter. Its square hub carried eight radial T-section arms, tapered on flange and web, which supported the cast rim morticed to hold the eighty-eight wooden cogs. The crown wheel drove two horizontal lay-shafts which transmitted the power to various ancillary machines throughout the mill. Shaft (a), nearest the pond, was driven from the crown wheel by a cast-iron bevel gear with nineteen teeth. It was taken out of gear by raising the bearing which was adjacent to the bevel. The various pulleys on this shaft in order from the driven end were:

1.   A flangeless pulley 35 × 5 in. which had a laminated, segmented and lapped wood rim carried on six, radial, + sectioned iron arms bolted to the rim.
2.   A wrought-iron faced pulley 30 × 6 in. split into two halves and bolted together, carried off a round iron hub by eight round-sectioned radial arms.
3.   An 11 × 2 in. solid wood single-flanged pulley split into halves and bolted together, and
4.   An 18 × 3½ in. wood rim pulley with four cants, split and bolted together.

Shaft (b) was driven by an identical cast-iron bevel gear, with nineteen teeth having the same method of disengagement as shaft (a). The various pulleys on this shaft in order from the driven end were:

1.   A wood-rimmed and framed pulley which was split into two and bolted together on the shaft. Its rim was made of seven laminates and had the remains on its face of a felt material, presumably to provide a better grip;
2.   A solid wood 11 × 4 in. pulley;
3.   A 22 × 5½ in. pulley built in the same style as the 18 × 3½ in. pulley in item (4) on shaft (a);

4. A solid wood 11 × 3 in. flangeless pulley;
5. A 26 × 4 in. solid wood flangeless pulley with a felt face; and
6. A pulley identical to (5) above which drove shaft (c).

Shaft (c) at high level, was 1½ in. in diameter and had three pulleys mounted on it, which were, from the driven end as follows:

1. An overhung cast-iron 9 × 3 in. single-piece pulley with a solid web and no flanges;
2. A 14 × 4¾ in. flangeless iron pulley with four arms; and
3. A 20 × 6 in. overhung single-piece cast-iron pulley with four arms.

Fig. 24. Chegworth Mill

The 14 × 4¾ in. pulley on shaft (c) drove a French corn cleaner or winnower with the name UREKA on it. On the floor near the millstones was a crusher for oats or barley, made by GANZ & CO. of Budapest, with the date 1885 inscribed on it. This was apparently one of the first eight in the country. It was driven from shaft (b) and may have been served by more than one pulley, probably depending on the type of corn being crushed. Close by the millstones nearest the millpond, at high level under the floor above, was what appeared to be a belt-driven feeder with an eccentric cam, which was probably driven from the 11 × 2 in. solid wood pulley on shaft (a). Underneath on the floor was a large octagonal wooden corn bin and behind it was a trestle grindstone. Shaft (d) was a short low-level lay-shaft with two pulleys. One was a 16 × 4 in. cast-iron pulley with four double-curved arms, and the other was an 11 × 6 in. pulley. This shaft was driven from the 35 × 5 in. pulley on shaft (a) and was used for driving a saw bench outside the mill.

Years ago, the previous miller, Mr Potter, apparently tried to drive the mill from a tractor outside. He used a small 2 in. diameter lay-shaft (e) at high level on the ground floor, connecting the tractor by belt to a 24 × 5 in. single-piece cast-iron pulley with four arms. Adjacent on the shaft a 7 in. diameter canvas-faced wood pulley drove the 30 × 6 in. pulley on shaft (a) on the floor above. We have been told that this arrangement was not successful, but whether for want of power or control we do not know.

On the second floor were the corn bins, arranged in the traditional manner on either side of the central gangway. All the bins were lined with boards, and two or three were self-clearing, with sloping bases. Natural light was admitted through small windows in each gable wall, and, half-way along the bins, was a small dormer window in the north flank of the roof. The pegged clay-tile roof was lined outside of the rafters with bitumenised felt. Above the gangway were curved wood braces, on one of which were carved the initials GPA, probably those of an earlier miller. The sack bollard was mounted at high level on the 2 in. square iron shaft coming up through the floor. It was some 9 in. in diameter, with a canvas-wrapped face to give better grip to the chain attached, which passed over an idle roller at high level to a 14 in. diameter, 2 in. thick, wooden sheave. This was positioned above the sack-hoist's trap-door on this floor and the floor below. The far end of the mill, away from the pond, was obviously built at some later date from the remainder, for its construction was somewhat different. It had ragstone walls and less timber-framing than the original, and had round cast-iron pillars at mid-span supporting the floor-beams. More obviously, the axis of this addition was different, and it was clear that it had been positioned hard against the tail-race, which had a deflection in its course at this point. The drain from the yard was taken under this extension through a small vaulted arch to the tail-race on the other side.

Lying in the yard between the mill and the house were the remains of several millstones. The following facts could be determined:

1. At the door of the mill, one half of a Peak Stone 41 in. in diameter, with a cemented eye;
2. A French burr 44 in. in diameter, with the eye filled-in;
3. A Peak stone 42 in. in diameter, with an 8½ in. diameter eye. This was a top stone, with the rynd emplacements to view;
4. A French burr 43 in. in diameter;
5. Another French stone with the working face upwards;
6. In front of the house, a Peak stone 31 in. in diameter, with a 9 in. square eye. This had the appearance of being an old stone;
7. Below the steps of the mill-house door, a 43 in. diameter stone with a 9 in. square eye;

In the yard adjacent to the newer part of the mill were the remains of foundations where a bakehouse had stood until recently. Attached to the bakehouse was a faggot store where the fuel for heating the ovens was kept. The present miller used the bakehouse for a farrowing house until its demolition several years ago. It was most unusual to have a bakehouse built beside a watermill.

This mill was a good example of a small rural watermill having a full complement of corn-milling machinery, which was working until quite recently.

CHILHAM MILL, Chilham TR 078 534   Surveyed 1975.

This watermill was one of the few in the south-east of England which was preserved, and contained most of its milling machinery and equipment. It was owned by the Mid-Kent Water Company who used part of the ground floor of the mill to house pumping control equipment. They kept the mill in good condition, the external weatherboarded elevations being regularly painted, and the floors and roof kept in good repair. The owners allowed private parties to view the mill by arrangement, and for anybody who had an interest in old buildings or industrial archaeology, this mill was certainly worth a visit.

Chilham mill was probably one of the most beautifully sited watermills in Kent. Its size was impressive and, for a rural mill, it was very large, having five storeys. Much of its charm was due to its setting; the attached mill-house and the outbuildings helped to detract the great height of the mill, which would otherwise have dominated the scene excessively.

The volume of water flowing past the mill was considerable, even in summer, but this was not surprising in view of the great catchment area which lay above the mill. The relatively large undershot water-wheel was typical of a river mill where the volume of flow is large but the head of water is slight. At Chilham (where the river was nearer to the sea than to its source) the

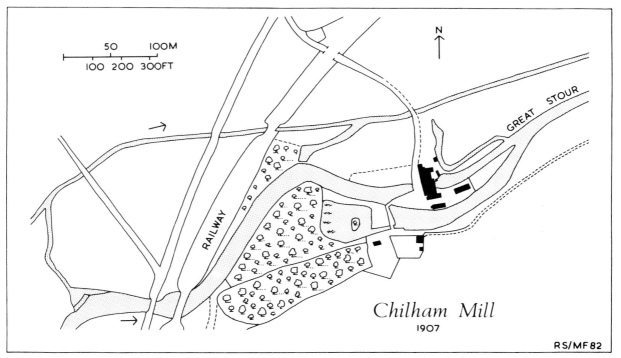

Fig. 25. Chilham Mill

gradient of the river bed was fairly shallow and, consequently, the problems associated with creating a head of water, enough for an overshot wheel, had been virtually insurmountable. In earlier times this valley had been swarming with watermills, as the Domesday Survey indicated, but, as time passed, the gradient of its course had lessened due to a combination of erosion, deposition, and land movement. In addition, the water volume had increased in recent times.

As already stated, this mill was large, and having six pairs of stones and numerous ancillary machines, it required considerable power. It was recorded that an engine had been required in addition to the water-wheel in order to keep the mill going during the last few decades of its working life.

The mill was timber-framed, with brick walls up to the first-floor level, and weatherboarded above. On the front elevation, access to the wheel chamber was facilitated by large wooden doors and, nearby, high in the brick wall, were several circular cast-iron plates installed to strengthen it where some weakness had occurred. Part of the mill, the south-east half, terminated under a slate roof at first-floor level, while the remainder, containing all the bins and much of the ancillary processing machinery, continued to rise another three floors beneath a pitched slate roof with dormer windows. At the top of the building the roof was extended over a lucomb on the front gable. Butted to the mill, on the north face, was the miller's house. On the first and second floor of the mill, the timber frames of the common wall had been filled in with brick. All of the structural timber inside the mill appeared to be oak. Six main posts could be traced passing up through the mill. These posts must have supported very heavy loads, for this mill was particularly large for a rural mill. One indication of this was that the corn bins at the top were over 6 ft. deep.

On the south face of the building an extension had been built at some later date, and this followed the same design as the main building, brick up to the first floor and weatherboard above. This new section contained only a ground and first floor under a slate roof which had two parallel ridges running north—south. It appeared that this extension had been built to house a new steam engine, but had the additional advantage of enclosing the water-wheel, hitherto probably unenclosed. On the corner of the new extension had once been built a chimney which was taller than the mill by 5 or 6 ft. It used to stand on a substantial brick base that was approximately 8 ft. square. Above this base, the stack was octagonal in section but, 3 or 4 ft. above this, it became circular and tapered to the top. A photograph had been taken of this mill before the chimney was taken down, and appeared in *The Kentish Stour* by Robert H. Goodsall in 1953. A historical study of the mill could no doubt tell us much more of how it may have been developed.

At the back of the mill the tail-race left the building through brick arches, and meandered down the valley to join the river some hundred yards downstream. On the 'island' created by the head- and tail-races there were two outbuildings belonging to the mill. The wagon shed adjacent to the mill had been, until recently, connected to the first floor of the mill by a high level passageway. Its plan measured some 15 × 47 ft. and it had one upper floor which was probably used as a hay store or mill store. The walls were of brick, and it was divided into several bays on the ground floor, all of which opened onto the elevation facing the river. The gable walls had single windows on the first floor and the whole building was covered by a slate roof.

The smaller building further away from the mill had been the stables. It was a brick building, measuring 16 ft. 6 in. wide and 39 ft. long and had internal stalls and access doors on the side furthest from the river. There were two main internal timber division walls, making three bays, each having two windows opposite each other. The stalls which were at each end of the building, had graded brick floors and feeding troughs on the gable walls. In the pitch of the tile roof there was a hay loft, which had a loading door in the gable nearest the mill. On the corner of the building nearest the mill there was a splay which had probably been made to stop the horses chafing their flanks as they passed by.

A low head and an enlarged sheet of water had been created on the river by a sluice gate above the mill. Upstream of the mill, on the opposite bank, water-cress beds could still be seen, though what relationship this industry may have had with the mill was unknown; it may have flourished after the mill ceased to work. The boards of the river sluice were no longer in position, though their emplacements could be seen on the inside faces of the concrete piers, which formed the sluice. When the boards had been in position and a head of water created, the river used to be diverted, undoubtedly via another sluice gate, through a head-race towards the mill. This head-race had been filled in not many years previously, although some water still followed the old course through a 20 in. diameter concrete pipe which the owners had installed to keep the tail-race flowing.

The water used to be admitted to the undershot wheel through an inclined control gate, which could be raised and lowered by an iron shaft carrying pinions which engaged cast-iron racks bolted onto the vertical members of the frame. Movement of the penstock was effected by a hand-wheel mounted on a spindle (b) which passed through the wall into the wheel chamber. On the end of the spindle was an eleven-tooth pinion which engaged a seventy-eight tooth iron spur-gear carried on the penstock spindle.

In order to have applied the water as effectively as possible to the wheel, the pit below the breast of the wheel was curved and had been rendered so that the gap between the wheel and the pit had been minimised. Originally, the width of the penstock would have matched the width of the wheel, so that water was applied to the full width, but with the abandonment of the old head-race, and the installation of the 20 in. diameter pipe in its place, the water application had

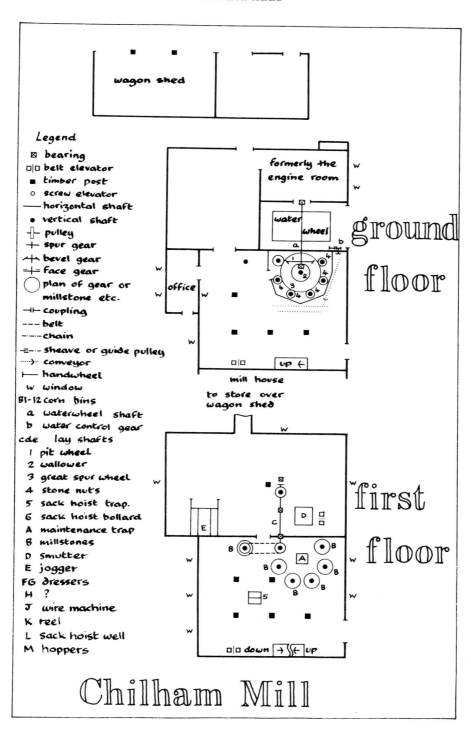

Fig. 26.   Chilham Mill

been much reduced. As the pipe terminated low down in the breast of the pit the effectiveness of applying water onto only part of the wheel width out of 94 in. was to be questioned, especially if it had been intended that the wheel should do anything more than idle in rotation. If this pipe was graded, i.e. sloped downwards towards the wheel, some advantage might have been gained from the increased velocity of water when it struck the wheel. However, even if this was the case, the volume of water that entered the wheel was still much less than with the original method, since it had to pass through a 20 in. diameter pipe instead of the original full section of the open channel head-race.

The water-wheel comprised three cast-iron frames each with eight radial T-section tapered arms which were bolted to a central hub. Each frame had been cast in halves, split along the arms, which had been bolted together but, surprisingly, were not staggered in their position on each of the frames. Each of the three cast hubs had an L-shaped rim section, to which the arms were bolted, an octagonal rim and bore, carried in turn by an octagonal single-piece sleeve. Both the hubs and the sleeves were carried on iron keys. The middle frame, hub and rim were cracked probably as a result of frost damage.

The rim had been cast with radial slots, which held wooden starts to which the iron buckets were bolted. There were some fifty-four L-shaped buckets which were lapped by about $\frac{1}{2}$ in. and which therefore were not ventilated. They were 9 in. deep and 9 in. apart, and were bolted to the starts in two places, and also to the rim. The width of the buckets was 94 in. and they overhung the frames on each side of the wheel. The overall diameter of the wheel, from bucket tip to bucket tip, was $14\frac{1}{2}$ ft. The iron wheel-shaft was unusual in being + in section, nominally 20 in. in diameter with $3\frac{1}{2}$ in. thick arms. It passed through a bull's-eye aperture into the cog-pit where it supported the bevelled cast-iron pit-wheel. This was 10 ft. 8 in. in diameter, had been cast in two halves and subsequently bolted together, and had eight, tapered, + section arms that supported a morticed rim which carried ninety-six cogs. The cogs were nailed at the back, top and bottom, with wedges in between. This gear had an octagonally bored hub and an unusual cast-iron sleeve between the shaft and gear. The iron vertical shaft, which did not pass through the floor above, was 7 in. square in section at the wallower, and tapered down to an octagonal section with alternate 3 in. wide and 2 in. wide faces above the footstep bearing. A single-piece, cast-iron wallower engaged the pit-wheel, and had eight T-section arms – tapered on both web and flanges – supporting a rim with thirty-four bevel teeth. Above the wallower was the great spur-gear, which had a single-piece, morticed, cast rim carrying approximately 114 cogs nailed at the back, top and bottom. It had eight, radial, T-section, tapered arms bolted to the rim, and these sprang from an hexagonal hub cast integrally with the arms in a single piece. This gear was packed off the square vertical shaft by an unusual casting.

The great spur-gear engaged six spur-gears equispaced on its perimeter; five of them were stone nuts. Originally, six pairs of millstones were driven on the floor above, but at some later date one had been moved and installed some distance away from the others, as this survey will show. Working in clockwise order from the wheel-shaft, the stone nuts were:

1.   A solid cast-iron nut with twenty two teeth;
2.   Ditto with twenty-one teeth;
3.   A cast-iron morticed nut with twenty-two cogs;
4.   Ditto with twenty-one cogs;
5.   Solid cast-iron nut with twenty-two teeth.

At the sixth position, in place of the original stone nut, was a cast-iron spur-gear with six tapered + section arms carrying thirty teeth. All of the millstone spindles were supported on pivoted cast-iron bridge-trees.

The bridge-trees and all of the main gearing were partitioned off by stud-and-panel walls. This partition had six faces, each one was adjacent to a bridge-tree and was open at the top between the frames, thus providing a 'window' to allow adjustment of the millstone spindles and stone nuts. One of the faces of the partition had a door in it to provide entry to the cog-pit. In front of the cog-pit partition were two screw conveyors, one at high level suspended from the beam above, and the other at low level supported from the floor. The lower one was quite long, having two separate screws, one feeding into the other. This must have received the warm meal from the stones above, and passed it to an elevator which took it up through the mill to the bolter (k) on the third floor.

On the first floor were six pairs of millstones, five of them were lying in a circle, but one pair was remote from the others. Five of the pairs were French burrs – all 40 in. in diameter, and the remaining pair was Derby Peaks measuring 46 in. in diameter. All of the runner stones were between 9 and 10 in. thick, with plenty of life left in them. Most of the stones still had their tuns in place, but nearly all the top gear – the horses, shoes and hoppers – was missing. From the predominance of French stones the mill presumably had spent its last few working years in producing flour. During the demise of the country mills most turned to producing animal feedstuffs; the stones remaining in the mills seeming to reflect this, i.e. a predominance of Peak stones. In many mills, French stones were abandoned, together with the governors, which had been necessary to give the fine speed control for successful flour production. If Chilham mill had ended its days in grinding animal feedstuff one would have expected to find more Peak, or non-French, stones. It is interesting to note here that this mill, in earlier times, had been called French Mill.

The remote pair of stones, which had been re-positioned, possibly when the building was extended, were overdriven. The runner stone was carried on an iron spindle supported from below the floor on a cast-iron bridge-tree, complete with the usual bridging box and set screws, suspended from the first-floor beams by cast-iron plates. Adjustment of this bridge-tree was from below, by single levers, and not by the more usual compound levers involving steelyard and brayer. The drive to this stone was provided via a vertical shaft coming up through the floor, which carried a 30 in. diameter pulley at high level, with a belt drive to another 30 × 8 in. pulley, single-flanged, with six double-curved arms, mounted on top of the independent shaft. This vertical shaft also provided power to a belt-driven smutter (D) in the other part of the first floor.

On the second floor were two old processing machines, one of them apparently a centrifugal dresser (G) with a revolving horizontal drum covered in fine wire, with the inner rotating brush arms independently driven. In the corner of the room, at high level, was a wooden-framed wire machine (J), some 4 ft. long and $2\frac{1}{2}$ ft. in diameter, whose spindle had a single-piece, solid, twenty-four teeth, bevel gear at the high end.

At high level were two lay-shafts, parallel to each other. Shaft (d) was driven from a bevel crown gear carried on top of the $3\frac{1}{2}$ in. square iron shaft, which came up through the floor from below. The shaft was cased, for safety, up to a height of 6 ft. Above the crown gear was a flangeless, iron pulley with four, straight, tapered arms, with a + section, carrying a thin rim some 24 in. in diameter. The crown gear had six T-section tapered arms carrying a morticed hub, and had forty-eight cogs, nailed at the back on top and bottom. The faces of the cogs still bore the centre punch and scribe marks where they had been marked for trimming. This engaged an overhung, cast-iron bevel, with a square boss and with four arms that carried a rim with twenty-four teeth. The shaft (d), which had a $3\frac{1}{2}$ in. square section, carried the following pulleys, described in order from the driven end:

1. A small wooden pulley, split into halves and bolted together;

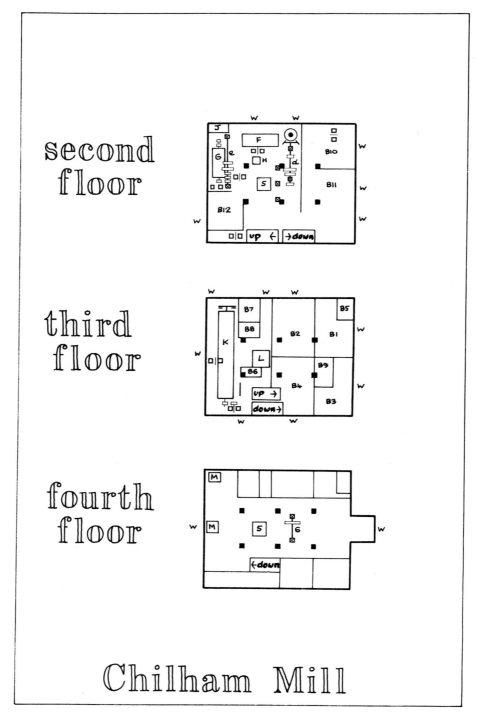

Fig. 27.   Chilham Mill

2. A 28 × 5 in. cast-iron pulley, made in two pieces and bolted together, with six single-curved arms. This probably drove shaft (*e*);
3. A 26 × 6 in. wide double-flanged wooden pulley with solid screwed-on faces. This used to drive the sack hoist on the top floor. The belt between the two pulleys had been boxed-in where it passed through the grain bin on the third floor;
4. An overhung, small, solid, cast-iron pulley.

Close to shaft (*d*), and parallel to it, had been another lay-shaft, since removed, but its three bearing blocks were still in position, the end ones being mounted on two pillars.

Shaft (*e*) was carried on two bearings resting on cast-iron slung brackets. The pulleys carried on this 2 in. diameter iron shaft, in order from the end above the wire machine, were:

1. A 26 × 4½ in. single-piece, iron pulley with six single-curved arms;
2. A 27 × 5½ in. iron pulley similarly constructed to (1) above;
3. A 9 × 3 in. cast-iron single-piece pulley with four curved arms;
4. As (3) above;
5. 18 × 3½ in. cast-iron pulley with four curved arms. This drove the machine on the floor below.

Fig. 28. Chilham Mill

Portions of the floor had been divided off with stud walls to make grain bins, indexed *B10*, *B11* and *B12* on the plan (Fig. 27). These were all lined on the inside, from floor to ceiling, with match-boarding. In the floor were numerous holes, many with tapered throats, communicating with wooden or sacking chutes below. As expected, there was a great number of chutes above the mill-stones on the floor beneath, but not being self-clearing bins, the grain must have required constant dressing to the holes when there was less than about a 3 ft. depth of grain in the bins.

On the third floor there was a very long reel (*k*) spanning the whole width of the mill, which was fed with meal at one end via an elevator from the ground floor of the mill. The middlings from the reel appeared to have been fed into the centrifugal dresser (*g*) on the floor below, whilst the tailings passed to the wire machine (*j*) below, where the last of the flour was removed from the bran. The remainder of this floor was taken up by nine bins, the five smallest ones being self-clearing, (*B5–B9*). All of them were boarded out, and each of the four largest bins (*B1–B4*) had high-level windows, complete with cover panels, so that they could take grain to a considerable depth. The floor-loading must have been terrific when these were full, a fact which was reflected by the cross-sections of the floor beams and vertical posts used throughout the mill.

All of these bins could be fed from the top floor, either by being part open, so that the sacks could be emptied by being discharged over the edge of the floor straight into the bin below, or access could be gained by trap-doors in the floor. The traps were complete with recessed brass lifting rings. Close to the edge of the floor in each of the four large bins were vertical step-ladders, bolted to the wall of the bins, thus giving access to allow the grain to be dressed to the various outlets in the flat floor. Between these bins, the internal sack hoist had been boarded out.

The sack hoist bollard – serving both internal and external hoists – was situated above head-height in the roof of the mill. It was belt-driven from the double-flanged wooden pulley (*3*) on a layshaft (*d*), on the second floor, and where the belts passed through bin *B2* they had been boxed out. Cloth and leather had been wrapped around the horizontal bollard to grip the hoist chains, and the pulley had an octagonal hub cast integrally with six, radial, T-section arms tapered on the flanges and webs. The wooden rim into which the arms were morticed and bolted had six straight cants which were dovetailed and pegged together. Two flanges were screwed onto the faces of the pulley. To transmit the drive, which relied on a slack belt system, the bollard and pulley were raised an inch or two by a compound lever system, operated by a hanging rope.

The mechanical ratios that existed in this mill are as follows:

MECHANICAL RATIOS		
Element	No. of teeth/cogs	Revolutions per rev. of water-wheel
Pit wheel	90 (approx.)	1.0
Wallower	34	2.65
Great spur	114 (approx.)	2.65
Stone nut (Peak)	21	4.4
Stone nuts (French) (underdriven)	21 and 22	14.4 and 13.7
Stone nut (French) (overdriven)	Via 30 tooth spur and two 30 in. dia. pulleys	10.1

CHRISTIAN'S MILL, Maidstone. TQ 768 557   Surveyed 1966.

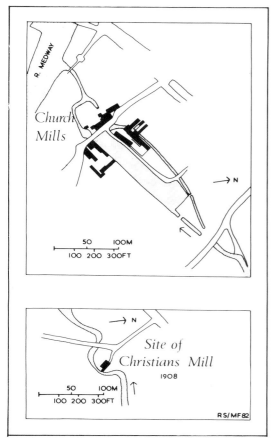

Fig. 29.   Church Mill and Christian's Mill

The mill building had long gone from this site, nor was any evidence to be found in the stream. The only physical evidence was an inscription on the existing building marking the site:

'Fulling Mill House 1567'

It seems likely that this mill was a river mill, for there is no evidence, on the landscape or written, that any pond existed to serve this mill. The water-wheel was probably a breast type. The mill was last used as a corn mill and apparently was demolished sometime prior to 1735.

CHURCH MILLS, Maidstone. TQ 758 555   Surveyed 1966.

At one time there were two watermills powered from the mill-pond beside Mill Street, but the last of them was demolished in 1902 to allow the widening of the road (Fig. 29). In the gardens where the mill stood was a wide penstock which marked where the water-wheel once worked. The level of the pond was maintained up to the height of an overflow cill by water gates in the corner of the pond, near where the other mill, called Little Church Mill, stood. It is odd that a mill should stand on the bypass of another. From what we know of their history, common ownership seems to have prevailed and, indeed, must have been necessary, for work in the smaller mill was very dependent on the excess water from the larger, particularly in summer.

THE COMB alias LOWER MILGATE MILL, Bearsted. TQ 802 552   Surveyed 1966.

This was the site of a house and small estate, which could be identified from eighteenth-century maps.

On these maps, a small tributary of the River Len that ran roughly south from Bearsted was shown dammed to form a large pond with a house placed midway beside its western flank. From the end of the pond, the stream rounded a small oblong sheet of water about the same size as the house, then passed on down the valley. This small sheet of water may have been a garden fish-pond, but we cannot ignore the possibility that a mill may have stood here.

Water still lay in the thickly wooded depression beside the road.

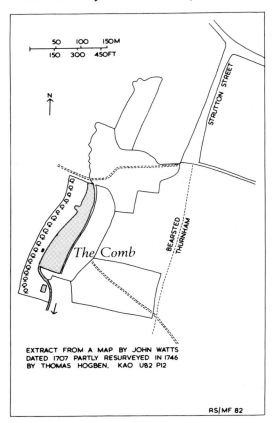

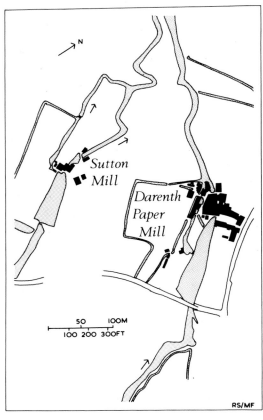

Fig. 30. The Comb, alias Lower Milgate Mill   Fig. 31. Sutton Mill and Darenth Paper Mill

DARENTH MILL, Darenth. TQ 558 714   Surveyed 1975.

The water-wheel and machinery that at one time existed at this old paper mill site had gone, and only a few of the buildings were old, the rest having been built since the manufacture of paper ceased. Another industry had taken its place, that of making flags. It was not difficult to find where the wheel had once stood, for the river narrowed, passed under a bridge, and then between ragstone and brick-clad banks, to fall over a cill some 20 in. high. In the east bank, a few feet downstream of the drop, there was a cast-iron wall box built into the brickwork. It was some 2 ft. above the level of the existing head-race, and probably marked the position of the wheel-shaft bearing. If this was so, the wheel was a breast-shot, most likely of the low breast type. At this point the river was some 8 to 9 ft. wide.

There was one other point of interest; on the east bank, beside the old wheel position, there was another cast-iron wall box built into the brick gable wall of a building. It was approximately 6–7 ft. above the ground and had been filled with cement. This box had been placed inside an old barrel vault, or, more exactly, an unlined circular hole in the brickwork. Whether the brickwork was pierced in this manner to allow the installation of the bearing box, we could not tell. It was not possible to reconstruct the lay-out of any drive machinery.

DUNSTER'S MILL, Ticehurst/Goudhurst. TQ 690 323   Surveyed 1974

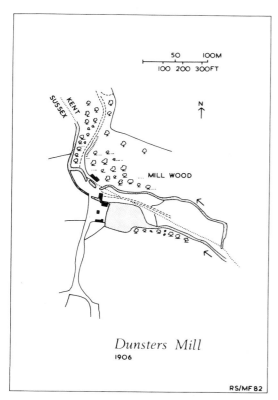

Fig. 32.   Dunster's Mill

This mill was in a remote valley on the borders of Kent and Sussex. Very little was left of the mill, some external machinery and an empty building. Probably the most interesting elements on this site were the remains of the water-wheel and gearing, which lay between the pond and the mill building.

The water was taken from the pond at one end of the mill-dam and was delivered to the wheel through a brick-edged 66 in. wide trough. Very little remained of the wheel, which probably had been overshot. The height of the stone apron, or cill, above the wheel shaft was 74 in. suggesting a wheel diameter of 12 ft. The wooden wheel-shaft, then very rotted, was octagonal in section, some 20 in. across the faces, with cross-head gudgeons in each end. One end of the shaft had three wrought-iron hoops, the other end had four, and in each case the end hoop appeared to be welded to the wings of the gudgeon which, in turn, was packed in the shaft with hardwood wedges. No bearings remained.

The single-bay wheel was mounted on cast hubs, each split and bolted together with octagonal bores. Each hub had eight cast boxes, complete with bolt holes, that received wooden arms – only two of which were still in place. Although the hubs were loose on the shaft, the wheel width appeared to be roughly 80 in. Nothing remained of the rim, sole-plate or shroud to tell what arrangement had existed.

At one side of the water-course was a brick-walled pit in which the pit gear had run. The gear was still in position on the wheel-shaft and was large, being some 10 ft. 8 in. in diameter. It was cast-iron, split and bolted in halves between the arms, with rim clamps, and had an octagonal hub that carried eight, radial, tapered arms of T-section, which in turn supported a morticed

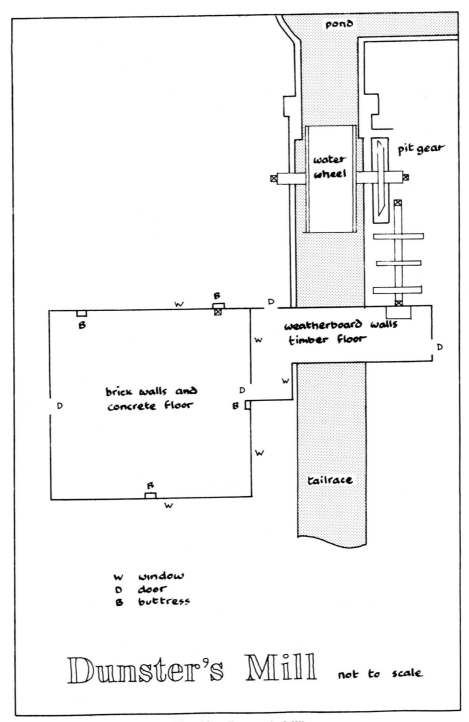

Fig. 33.   Dunster's Mill

cast-iron rim with one hundred and twelve cogs. The pit-wheel drove a horizontal lay-shaft, with gears, which probably drove millstones above – an unusual arrangement which was found in very few watermills. This iron lay-shaft, which was 5 × 5 in. in section, lay parallel with the water-course, and carried four gears. The driver gear, a bevel, was missing, but obviously had been 36 in. in diameter, with a $3\frac{1}{2}$ in. pitch. Mounted on the shaft were the remains of two gears, which were carried on the iron shaft by the same method, a cast-iron box mounted on eight keys – two per face – with radial webs and cast-iron face plates each side that measured 23 × 23 in. square. Wood clasp-arms, each split and bolted from face to face, were screwed to the face plates, and morticed part way into the wood rim which was supported by curved cants. The rim, which was very rotted, was split into eight sections which were lapped and dowelled together, and was morticed to receive spur-cogs of $2\frac{1}{4}$ in. pitch on a base diameter of 60 in., suggesting approximately eighty-four cogs. The adjacent gear, carried by the same face-plate arrangement of clasp-arms, but with straight cants, was much decayed on the rim; no cogs remained, but it was roughly the same diameter as the first.

At the end of the shaft was a cast-iron, morticed, spur-gear, with a diameter over the iron of 55 in., and which had been cast in two pieces and then bolted together on the radial arms. The square hub, with cast, moulded edges, was carried off the shaft on a square, hollow, cast box with radial flanges, which had hardwood packing between its faces and the gear bore, which was $14\frac{1}{2}$ in. square. Four, T-sectioned arms, tapered on both web and flanges and strengthened by curved webs from the hub that almost reached the rim, supported a cast rim, morticed to carry eighty cogs, $3\frac{1}{2}$ in. wide and of $2\frac{1}{4}$ in. pitch, which were nailed inside on both faces.

DUNSTERS MILL   FROM A SKETCH BY A. WELLS 1933   RJS 1982

Fig. 34. Dunster's Mill

No building fabric remained over or near these gears to help us determine what this part of the mill looked like. This section may have been timber-framed, without substantial foundations, so that, with decay and removal, nothing remained. The adjacent building, which was clearly part of the original mill, was in two distinct divisions or styles.

Bridging the stream was a narrow, weatherboarded room with a timber floor, under a slate roof. This communicated with a larger, brick-walled and concrete floor room, again under a slate roof, which had a bull's-eye light at high level in one gable wall, and a square light in the other. The only evidence that machinery once existed here was a large cast-iron bearing box, recessed into one wall.

Four millstones were embedded in the ground beside the end of the weatherboarded room, three Peak stones and one French burr. Three other stones lay embedded on edge. One stone was a dark-grey bedstone, $42\frac{1}{2}$ in. in diameter with a 10 in. diameter eye, and 6 in. thick at the skirt. The second was a Derby Peak, 48 in. in diameter, with a $12\frac{1}{2}$ in. diameter eye, $5\frac{1}{4}$ in. thick at the skirt, and had a cast-iron neck box. The third stone was a 35 in. diameter Derby Peak top stone, 6 in. thick at the skirt. In addition, beside the driveway to the mill, two French burr-stones were set on edge, and these bore the names of 'Hughes Dover Road, London' on cast-iron balance boxes. These stones were $46\frac{1}{2}$ in. in diameter and roughly 11 in. thick.

EYHORNE MILL, Hollingbourne. TQ 835 546   Surveyed 1966.

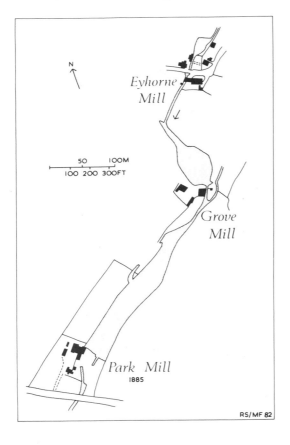

Being in a village this site was probably very old. Sometime during the last quarter of the nineteenth century the mill became abandoned, for the 1898 O.S. map shows the corn mill as being disused. The mill stood immediately south of Eyhorne Street. It was fed by a pond from the other side of the road. The remains of the mill – a small waterfall, some 6 or 7 ft. drop and 5 ft. wide – could be seen from the village street. Nothing else was left.

Fig. 35.   Eyhorne Mill, Grove Mill and Park Mill

FIELD MILL, Charing. TQ 915 483   Surveyed December 1974.

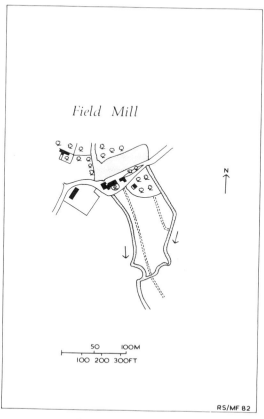

Field Mill

50   100M
100 200 300FT

RS/MF 82

Fig. 36.   Field Mill

The mill and mill-house, which was a charming residence, were joined together by a stone-floored room which was roofed over, rather like an internal courtyard. The tail-race passed under one side of the yard, then under the road outside the mill. On one side of this space, against the mill, was the water-wheel, which was open to the weather but separated from the yard by a glazed wall. This consisted of a low brick wall supporting windows overlooking the wheel, and beside the wheel-shaft bearing was a glazed door. Projecting beneath this door was a cast-iron sole-plate with the inscription 'HILL & SON ASHFORD 1877'. The wooden frames of the windows had suffered badly from the perpetual damp conditions, especially from the spray of the water cascading over the wheel, which was only some 18 in. away from the windows.

The water-wheel was an overshot and in surprisingly good condition. Its diameter was 10 ft. 6 in. and it was 5 ft. wide with approximately forty buckets. The unventilated buckets were of iron, and each consisted of a 15 in. long piece of straight sheet riveted to the sole-plate. Each bucket had a 'mouth' depth of some 4 in. and was braced in three places from the sole-plate with bolts and tubes. The wheel had a single bay and, on each side, the cast-iron frames were split in halves and bolted together at opposite arms. Both of the side-frames had radial, tapered + section arms cast integrally with the rim and shroud. The rim was 9 in. deep with a raised edge or bead along the inner and outer radii on the outside faces of the frames.

The wheel-shaft was cast-iron, 11 in. in diameter, having a common section throughout its length, with six equispaced key-like protrusions, parallel to the shaft axis, projecting from its surface. Each hub had a circular bore packed with six keys, one on each protrusion. The outer end of the shaft was reduced and carried in a bearing. The shaft passed through a round barrel vault which had a steel shield inside to keep out the spray.

The pit-wheel was the only gear remaining in the mill, all other machinery having been removed. It was a bevelled cast-iron gear, split into halves and bolted together. It carried sixty well-rotted cogs, nailed at the back, and had six radial arms, each having a + section, tapered on the longest axis. Rim and arms were cast integrally with a round hub having a round bore packed onto the shaft in the same manner as the water-wheel. Water still flowed over the wheel, which was prevented from rotating by a heavy chain holding an arm of the pit-wheel fast to an overhead beam. There was a cast-iron arch over the internal bearing of the wheel-shaft, which had a footstep bearing emplacement cast inside.

The vertical columns of the mill were still in place, though rotted at the bottom near the pit, but the bridge-trees had gone; only their cast-iron pivot brackets showing where they had been.

This mill apparently had contained two pairs of stones, but they had been removed many years ago for the flooring had been made good and it was not possible to tell what arrangement once existed. In a wall emplacement above the pit-wheel was an old governor which had two spherical iron balls for centrifugal weights.

Three of the walls of this floor were brick, but the wall towards the mill-dam was ragstone. In this wall was a curved recess from floor to ceiling, 32 in. deep and 87 in. wide. The most likely reason for this was that it allowed the installation of a large gear-wheel on the main vertical shaft but, if it had been built for this purpose, it antedated the present arrangement. This was because the centre of rotation for the curved recess lay some distance from the existing vertical shaft axis; moreover, at least two of the present timber posts would have been in the way of the gear-wheel suggested.

Upstairs, on the first floor, no machinery remained and all of the holes in the floor and ceiling had been boarded over and were difficult to trace, except those which were large and could be identified by the trimmers between the joists. On this floor all of the walls were weather-boarded with matchboard lining inside. The floor was divided into three bays by wooden posts and beams, which were braced in the upper corners by heavy section knees. This gave the effect of being between the decks of a wooden-wall ship. Several casement windows pierced the walls, both wood-framed and leaded lights. Some of them had novel old wrought-iron latches and stays.

The stairs in the old mill were not the originals, and had steps of near-normal treads and risers – much easier to use than the usual very steep open stairs of mills. The top floor, the old bin floor, had two rows of five wooden posts, which probably marked the bin divisions, ranged along each side of a central gangway. The walls were boarded out, including the gables which had been boarded up to the hips at each end of the mill. Pegged clay-tiles were on the roof which, at one time, had been lined inside, for all the rafters had galvanised clouts still embedded in them. A most interesting feature was that the roof-tiles, on the side facing the mill-house and on both hipped gables, were embedded on hay. This hay was made up of many fine grasses, a sign that it had come from a long-established meadow. Using hay for tile bedding was rather unusual, for clay or moss were normally employed. Presumably, this was to stop the ingress of wind-driven snow or water from dropping onto the bins below.

High in the roof at the road end of the mill was a large cast-iron pulley, with a horizontal axis, set in a morticed wooden block. This must have been associated with the internal sack hoist, which had disappeared. A short distance away was a small wooden pulley bolted onto a rafter, and on the roof flank was a small bearing-block bolted onto a block of wood positioned on top of a roof purlin. Natural lights took the form of a single window in each gable, together with two small roof lights, one on each flank. The mill had apparently been used for wood-working, for there were lengths of wood stored on one floor, together with a box of veneers and a wooden work bench on the middle of the first floor. At the top of the mill were many pieces of wood carving, old picture frames and a large box full of old printing blocks.

At the back of the mill a door led onto a small brick arch bridging the head-race. A large Muscovy duck sat squarely on the bridge amid several loose feathers, barring the way to the mill-dam. Edging towards him brought forth some gobbles; was it really only the wind that stirred his feathers? We stood together and communed for a while until it seemed that we had settled any differences and then progress was resumed. On the mill-dam near the mill was an embedded French burr stone 46 in. in diameter with an 11 in. eye and bar emplacement. It was made up of nine external segments and five internal ones. Nearby, close to an upturned skiff, was half a Peak stone standing on edge. This was 46 in. in diameter and had a 14 in. eye with a 7 in. thick skirt. Between the mill-dam and the house ran a deep, wide gutter or gulley, which had been rendered on the base and the inclined flank of the dam for a height of several feet. Inside the house, a millstone had been installed as a hearth. It was difficult to identify, as only a portion of it was showing; its grey, rather porous nature ruled out a Peak stone, and it did not seem to fit any of the variations of appearance that burrs exhibit. It may have been a composition stone.

FORD MILL, Wrotham. TQ 635 585   Surveyed 1976.

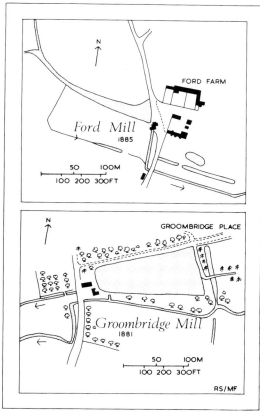

Fig. 37. Ford Mill and Groombridge Mill

This mill used to stand opposite Ford Place until 1970 when it was demolished as part of the construction work associated with the M20 motorway. All that remained of the site was the fairly small pond, running parallel to the ridge of the North Downs and fed from Wrotham Water higher up the hill. The downhill side of the pond had been heavily embanked to raise the height of the pond level with the uphill side. The overflow sluice was a modern one that incorporated part of a modern drainage system. At the head of the pond was the brick and concrete dam and wheel emplacement, the measurements of which suggested a wheel approximately 15 ft. in diameter and 3 ft. in width. The tail-race was almost completely dry, and the flow from the stream had been diverted out of the pond via the overflow course. This ran down the hill to the valley bottom, where it joined the waters of the Leybourne stream. At the foot of the mill-dam were the scant remains of the mill walling, but there were insufficient remains to permit any deductions to be made about the structure of the mill.

GROOMBRIDGE MILL, Groombridge. TQ 531 376   Surveyed October 1975.

This small rural mill was timber-framed and abutted the mill-house with a common gable wall. It had brick foundation walls, weather-boarding above, and was tile-hung at high level on two elevations (Fig. 37). At the back of the mill, where the water-wheel stood, the wall of the mill was weather-boarded up to the roof, which had clay tiles. It had a huge mill-pond which, for a mill with only two pairs of millstones, must have provided ample water. Unfortunately, the water-wheel had gone from this mill.

The wooden water-wheel shaft was 15 in. square, with a gudgeon held by three hoops, and

Fig. 38.   Ford Mill (*based on a sketch by A. Wells, 1933*)

was supported by a half brass bearing in the cog-pit. Where the shaft passed through the mill wall there was a barrel vault which had been cemented up. On this shaft the pit-gear was packed off with wood. It was a two-piece, cast-iron, morticed, bevel gear with a square hub and six tapered cruciform – section arms. The cast halves were bolted together along two of the arms which sprang radially from opposite corners of the square hub; the other arms were not truly radial but were normal to the cast faces of the hub. In the rim were seventy-two cogs, nailed at the back.

Mounted on the vertical shaft was a single-piece cast-iron wallower with a square hub and eight radial arms supporting a bevel rim with approximately thirty teeth. Above this was a large, all-wood, great spur-gear with a laminated rim, and square cants carried by four radial arms morticed into the square-sectioned, wooden, vertical shaft. Each arm was wedged at the top and bottom in the mortice. This gear, which carried approximately eighty-four cogs, nailed at the back, was very much decayed.

At this mill the hursting was unusual, for the two bridge-trees were not symmetrically arranged in the plan. One of the stone nuts was wooden, hooped, with three of its fourteen cogs arranged to slip; the other one was of similar construction but with thirteen cogs. Both of the iron millstone spindles were of rectangular section, one $2\frac{1}{2} \times 1\frac{1}{2}$ in., the other $3 \times 1\frac{1}{2}$ in., and both rested in the usual footstep bearing boxes with adjusting screws in each of the four walls.

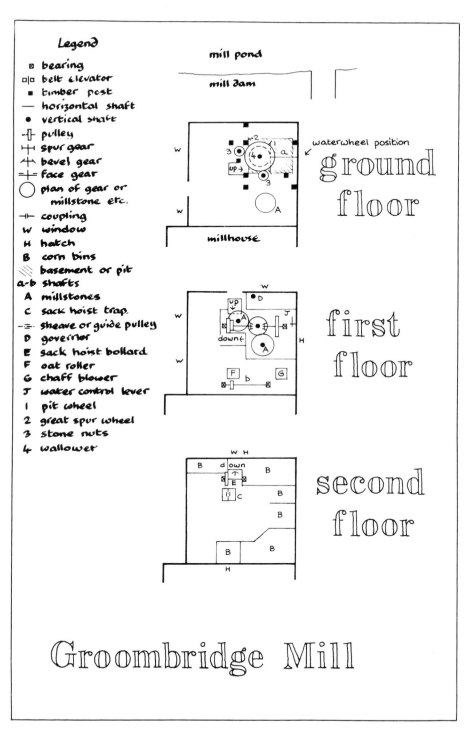

Legend

- ⊠ bearing
- ▢|▢ belt elevator
- ■ timber post
- — horizontal shaft
- ● vertical shaft
- ⊣⊢ pulley
- ⊦⊦ spur gear
- ⊬⊦ bevel gear
- ⊧⊧ face gear
- ◯ plan of gear or millstone etc.
- ⊣⊢ coupling
- W window
- H hatch
- B corn bins
- ▨ basement or pit
- a-b shafts
- A millstones
- C sack hoist trap
- ⊣☰⊢ sheave or guide pulley
- D governor
- E sack hoist bollard
- F oat roller
- G chaff blower
- J water control lever
- 1 pit wheel
- 2 great spur wheel
- 3 stone nuts
- 4 wallower

mill pond

mill dam

waterwheel position

ground floor

first floor

second floor

millhouse

Groombridge Mill

Fig. 39.   Groombridge Mill

On the floor beside the hursting was a 46 in. diameter French burr millstone. All of the walls on the ground floor were of brick, with some sandstone at the bottom of the gable wall remote from the mill-house.

On the first floor the walls were timber-framed and weather-boarded, with lath and plaster lining on all walls, except the one above the water-wheel position. All of the windows had leaded lights, which is unusual for mills. The wooden vertical shaft was sixteen-sided, with an all-wood crown wheel at high level. This had clasp arms with square cants holding a bevelled, morticed rim with approximately seventy cogs. This gear drove two high-level lay-shafts. The shorter one, a $1\frac{1}{2}$ in. diameter iron spindle, was driven by a wooden hooped bevel gear with thirteen teeth. It carried a single wooden pulley with a round hub and four flat radial arms that supported a $34 \times 5\frac{1}{2}$ in. rim, laminated with lapped segments. The other lay-shaft was a $3\frac{1}{4}$ in. square section wooden shaft driven from the crown wheel by an all-wood bevel gear with twenty-three teeth. On the end of the shaft were two wooden pulleys; one was cross-armed and measured 28×4 in., the other was solid, and measured 22×4 in.

Three millstones were in position; the pair on the mill-house side of the vertical shaft was 46 in. diameter Derby Peaks with 10 in. eyes. All of the top gear and tun was missing. The third stone was smaller, a 34 in. Peak bedstone set flush with the floor. Again, no tun, horse or hopper were present.

On the inside of the mill wall was a wooden lever for adjusting the sluice over the water-wheel. Adjustment was provided by a chain, the length of which was altered by the position of a pin in one of a number of holes in a board on the wall above.

To one side of the hursting the floor had decayed and apparently fallen-in; on the gable wall nearby was a bracket-mounted governor driven from a pulley on the top of the vertical shaft. At the other end of this floor, at high level against the mill-house wall was a wooden lay-shaft, square in section, carrying a single wood pulley that measured $7 \times 2\frac{1}{2}$ in.

There were two processing machines in the mill, one was a dressing machine with the usual external-framed circular wire screen and the other was a hopper-fed, belt-driven oat roller, inscribed 'E R & F TURNER IPSWICH'.

On the top floor were several bins, one was boarded out and two were open-fronted. There was a hatch in the gable wall which gave entry to the roof space of the house adjacent. The sack bollard had well-worn wooden slats on the surface and the shaft was hooped at each end. It was powered by a 48×5 in. clasp-arm, all-wood pulley which was driven, via a wooden jockey, from a large pulley below. Over the internal sack hoist was a single, iron, pulley wheel in a wooden sheave.

GURNEY'S MILL, Loose/East Farleigh. TQ 760 521   Surveyed 1971.

Only the foundations of this mill remained, close beside Salts Lane. The pond serving this mill was some 200–300 ft. upstream, but close to the mill was still a small sheet of water which was best seen from the viaduct carrying the Linton Road nearby. A small waterfall marked where the wheel once worked. We know it to have been an overshot wheel, 15 ft. in diameter and 9 ft. in width.

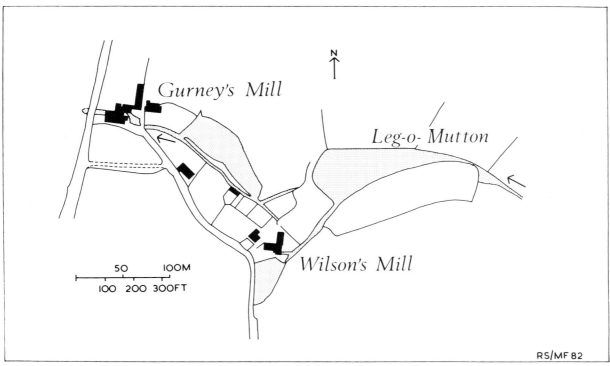

Fig. 40.   Gurney's Mill and Wilson's Mill

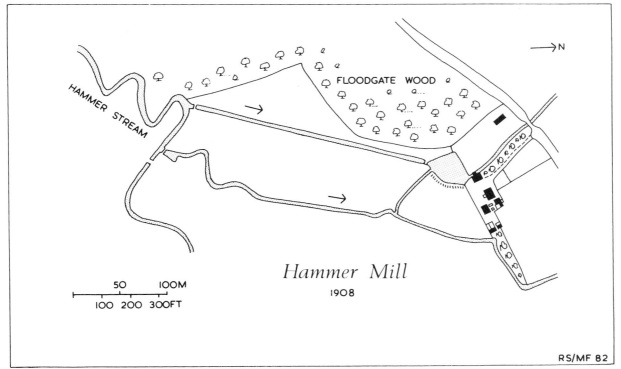

Fig. 41.   Hammer Mill, Sissinghurst

HAMMER MILL, Biddenden. TQ 820 383   Surveyed March 1974.

The first enquiry, after meeting the owner Mr F. Hall, concerned the mill-pond and waterways, for nothing was known about the physical layout of the site. A path passed the end of the mill and went along the top of what originally had been the mill-dam. The pond had long gone and the shallow basin showed signs of having been, at one time, a vegetable garden. No doubt, a very rich ground for a garden. It was rather surprising to see how flat were the surrounding fields. The tail-race was carried at least 100 yds. in a deep and wide cutting before disappearing under the road; this suggested that the natural head of water at this site had been augmented by the digging of a deep tail-race channel.

The original 'Hammer Mill' stood some 200 yds. away to the north-east and was, as the name implies, a water-powered forge associated with the Wealden iron industry. Sometime after that mill ceased to work, the present one was built and adopted the name of its predecessor, and water was diverted from the stream to the new mill-pond. A farm track crossed the stream where it entered the pond, and the water was taken through a nicely-shaped brick culvert, some 12 ft. long, built entirely of layers of stretchers and unrendered. The excess water was taken out on one side of the pond and passed back to the main stream via a control gate located in a brick-lined channel. It would have been much easier to let the bypass enter the tail-race but, presumably, this was avoided because it would have deposited more alluvium in the tail-race.

The mill building was rectangular in plan, with three floors, including a floor within the pitched roof, together with a basement. All of the walls were built of brick and supported a clay-tile roof with hipped gables. Each gable wall had weatherboard cladding above eaves level and below the hip. The basement walls were thicker than those above them and had internal brick piers, two on each of the long walls. There were several iron wall-ties, S- and X-shaped, on each main face and there was a bad vertical crack above first-floor level. The ties and the crack suggest that the mill may have been sited badly.

Where the water used to leave the pond and enter the trough, the earth had been raised along the line of the footpath. The entry to the trough was splayed, or bell-mouthed, with two brick walls. At the wheel-end of these splays, and at the beginning of the parallel trough, there was evidence that a water-gate had at one time been present. At each side, there was a substantial vertical timber set against a concrete shoulder, and on the faces of the timber where it touched the walls, it was cased in a lead sheet. The trough had a timber floor and brick walls at the pond end, but a timber trough was carried out over the wheel and was supported on a vertical timber pillar. At the end of the trough over the wheel there was a penstock operated by an overhead horizontal shaft. This carried two cast-iron pinions which meshed with cast-iron racks, each having twelve teeth, bolted onto the gate. This shaft was supported at each end on bearings with vertical, steel, sole-plates, and was turned by a double-flanged, solid, cast-iron pulley with four arms and square hub. An identical pulley could be seen lower down, above the tail-race, on the end of a spindle (b) which carried through the mill wall. The timber trough and penstock shaft had collapsed onto the wheel and the cast-iron racks were down in the wheel-pit.

The overshot water-wheel was 12 ft. in diameter and 6 ft. wide inside the shrouds. It carried thirty-six curved, unventilated buckets each consisting of two 1 in. thick wooden boards, secured at each end onto curved shoulders cast into the shroud sections. This was additionally stabilised by two intermediate iron straps bolted onto the steel backing sheet or sole-plate. Each of the cast-iron shrouds consisted of six sections bolted together with a bead on the outside curve, and a flange on the inside curve of the shroud onto which the sole-plates were bolted. There were originally eighteen sole-plates bolted together around the wheel but only one remained in

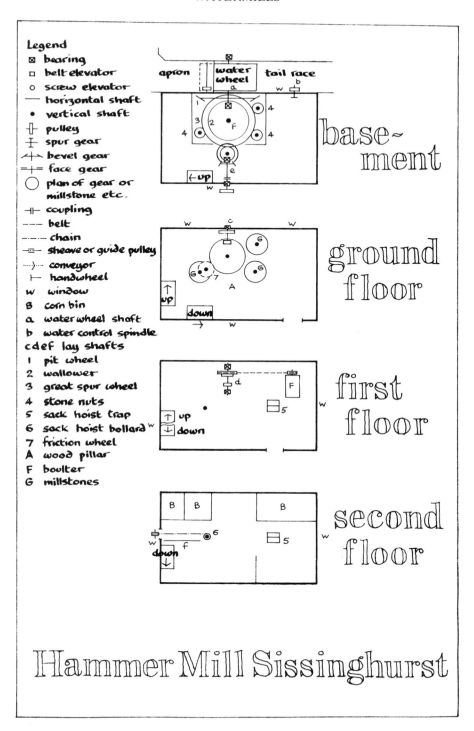

Legend

⊠ bearing
□ belt elevator
○ screw elevator
— horizontal shaft
• vertical shaft
⊩ pulley
⊤ spur gear
↳ bevel gear
╪ face gear
◯ plan of gear or millstone etc.
⊣⊢ coupling
--- belt
-·-·- chain
⊸ sheave or guide pulley
····)··· conveyor
⊢ handwheel
w window
B corn bin
a water wheel shaft
b water control spindle
cdef lay shafts
1 pit wheel
2 wallower
3 great spur wheel
4 stone nuts
5 sack hoist trap
6 sack hoist bollard
7 friction wheel
A wood pillar
F boulter
G millstones

base~ment

ground floor

first floor

second floor

Hammer Mill Sissinghurst

Fig. 42. Hammer Mill, Sissinghurst

position. Each section of the shroud was carried from a radial arm made of 4 × 2 in. iron channel mounted with webs facing outwards. These arms were bolted and registered between cast shoulders at both ends on the shrouds and flaunches. Nearly all the wooden buckets had fallen off their mountings, and the arms were badly corroded but still in place.

The cast-iron single-piece flaunches were curved hexagonal profiles (alternate concave-convex) with a beaded edge to view, and square bores with a similar beaded edge outside, and an internal flange. This flange facilitated the holding of eight keys or wedges in each hub, two per face on the $8\frac{1}{4}$ in. square cast-iron wheel-shaft. On the land side of the wheel the shaft, reduced to a relatively small diameter journal, was carried in a lower bearing-block with cast-iron sole-plate, supported in turn by a timber block. The wheel-shaft (a) passed into the mill through a square hole with a timber lintel.

The breast of the wheel-pit was vertical and the pit so full of mud that the bottom 3 ft. of the wheel was under mud with 6 in. of water on top. Above the trough, and overlooking the wheel, was a small window, and over the wheel itself was an inclined corrugated steel roof supported by a timber frame, which may at one time have had a covering fabric on the land side.

The half-doors of the mill led into the gloomy interior of the mill-stone floor. Resting on one of the stones, and elsewhere on the floor, were several large wooden casks which dominated the scene. On one side was a sack-jogging machine. All manner of lumber was present. If a man's library is representative of his academic ability and interests, then his lumber – the physical flotsam of life – must surely indicate his practical ability and interests.

The stairs leading down into the cog-pit were of the sort invariably found in mills – steep, with narrow, well-worn, treads. When there were signs of decay or long disuse, each tread had to be tested, while the hands and the other foot were well placed to take weight, just in case. It was gloomy down below with a little sunlight entering through small high-level lights, which were dimmed by dust and cobwebs. On reaching the bottom step it was natural to look to the floor nearby. On this occasion it was seen with dismay that there had once been a timber floor, but it had rotted and fallen in between the joists onto the earth below. Some of the joists had also given way. The atmosphere was dank and smelt strongly of decayed wood. One of the joists supporting the ground floor had rotted where it touched the wall and although a temporary vertical timber had been pushed in underneath, this too had given way. The cog-pit and gearing were contained in a massive hurst framing taking up a quarter of the floor with the remainder quite empty. By keeping entirely to the earth floor and avoiding, at all costs, touching any framing or main timbers, it was possible to survey this floor. Moving towards the framing it was easy to be awed by the timber sections, some of the largest observed during this survey. This framing had originally been covered with wooden panels and doors, but they had nearly all been removed – or perhaps fallen off.

There was no question of climbing through this framing to view the gearing at close quarters and so the examination had to be restricted to peering between the beams. As far as could be discerned, the pit was half full of water, which was not surprising in view of the amount of tail-water that had been seen outside. The cast-iron pit-wheel looked massive and was made in two halves, bolted together, with eight T-section arms – webs to the waterside – carrying approximately eighty-eight morticed cogs.

In this corner of the basement one end of the cog-pit had been enlarged, or connected to a larger square pit, large enough for one person to work on the face of the pit-wheel. This 'maintenance pit' was a rare feature. It was not possible to make out the wheel-shaft bearing, except to notice that it was not an arched bearing, since the footstep bearing for the main vertical shaft (f) was quite independent.

The pit-wheel engaged a cast-iron wallower having twenty-eight teeth and a square bore, and was probably split and bolted. This was carried on the vertical wooden shaft, which was supported on a footstep brass mounted on wooden blocks. The bottom of the wooden shaft was tapered and three wrought-iron bands held a gudgeon in place. Above the wallower was the great spur wheel, cast in one piece with approximately one hundred and twenty-eight morticed cogs in its rim. It had eight, radial, T-section arms, flanges down and had a square bore and hub which was wood-packed on each face of the square shaft. The spur-gear engaged three stone nuts, though there was some evidence that at one time this mill had four pairs of stones. The three nuts were all cast-iron, each with twenty-four teeth and seated on tapered iron shafts but the method of lifting them out of gear had disappeared. Each stone shaft was supported on a heavy wooden bridge-tree and was tentered by conventional threaded rods and hand nuts. Above these bridge-trees were the remains of spouts coming from the floor above.

MECHANICAL RATIOS				
	Pit-wheel	Wallower	Great Spur	Stone nut and mill-stone
Number of teeth or cogs	88	28	128	24
Revolutions per revolution of water-wheel.	1.0	3.1	3.1	16.8

The great spur-wheel also engaged a single-piece cast-iron spur gear with twenty-eight teeth and four + arms, keyed onto a vertical steel shaft. There was no sign of a mechanism for disengaging this gear. This shaft rested on a footstep bearing and also carried above the spur, at head height, a cast-iron bevel gear which had four T-section arms, carried thirty-two teeth and engaged a similar iron bevel gear carried on a horizontal steel shaft (e). This also had thirty-two teeth and four T-section arms, but was morticed. This high-level shaft passed outside the mill to an overhung cast-iron pulley wheel, with six double-curved arms. The pulley and shaft were used when a portable engine powered the mill, before the turn of the nineteenth century, followed later by a traction engine – presumably used in times of low water.

Up on the ground floor were three pairs of stones, two burrs of 40 in. diameter, with the hoops all rusted away, and a pair of Derby Peaks. On one side was a stone tun complete with horse. The main vertical shaft was rather nicely made, having sixteen faces which reduced to eight, and then to four, just below the crown gear which was at high level, close up under the first floor. This gear was made entirely of wood, having four felloes with straight cants – almost planked solid – carried by four radial arms which probably were morticed right through the square shaft. There were forty-eight cogs at approximately 3 in. pitch, cut flush with the underside of the gear and having well-worn profiles on top. The cogs were inclined so that they did not form a true face-gear. This gear had two shafts, one driven from the cogs and the other, a friction drive, from the rim which was faced with a canvas belt.

On the upturned face of the crown gear rested a small, morticed, wooden pinion, with an iron band at each end, giving the appearance of the nave or hub of an old waggon wheel. This pinion, having fourteen teeth, was carried on a short horizontal spindle (c) pivoted and supported at the end furthest from the main vertical shaft by a small, upturned, pedestal bearing. The arrangement allowed the end of the spindle carrying the wooden pinion to be lifted clear of the

Fig. 43. Hammer Mill, Sissinghurst

crown wheel. On the other end of the shaft was a pulley with a cast-iron hub and four T-arms carrying a wooden rim which appeared to be of box section instead of the usual laminates. The belt drive from this pulley was absent but, clearly, it used to pass through the floor above.

The friction drive for the vertical shaft of the sack hoist passed through this floor. It consisted of a 30 in. diameter, $4\frac{1}{4}$ in. deep, wooden-rimmed friction wheel having a cast-iron hub, four T-arms and flange rims. The parellel iron rims held the forty-eight, radial, wooden segments making up the friction rim. The top side of the hub of this wheel was a small cross-head gudgeon cast integrally with it, and this was morticed into the vertical shaft and clasped with two iron hoops. Both vertical shaft and friction wheel were carried on a horizontal wooden beam pivoted at one end to allow the working of the friction drive.

On this floor, in the middle of the mill, was a vertical wooden pillar supporting a roof timber. The pillar had been turned on a lathe, tapered to the top where it was 5 in. in diameter, grooved and finished with a carved capital. On leaving this floor and climbing to the one above, another unusual feature was noticed. On this floor the stairs to the second floor were of the normal wooden treads and stringers but, close beside them, was a wooden H frame from floor to ceiling. The frame was so positioned as to act as balustrades to both sets of stairs – between ground and second floor – and the horizontal bar was a hand-rail. It was made of oak, dowelled together, and where the verticals were liable to be held by the hand, the wood was turned from the square section and ornamented with rings at the ends of each element. To have such quality and detail in the fittings of a mill was unusual and showed that the millwright or carpenter took pains to maintain a relatively high standard of work.

On the first floor was a single lay-shaft (d) with several pulleys mounted on it. It might be more accurate to describe it as a 'compound' pulley, i.e. a forerunner of the modern cone pulley, because apparently the pulleys were all integrated. There were two wooden pulleys – possibly a third rope pulley – mounted on iron cores and shaft, together with a small wooden eccentric with double flanges, presumably to drive a jog-scry or vibrating machine. This whole assembly was belt driven from below. Some distance away was an inclined dressing machine set at a high level. This was parallel to the lay-shaft and was no doubt driven from one of the pulleys on it.

A climb to the loft above revealed the usual corn bins, two small ones with flat bottoms and a larger one with inclined boarded faces. The underside of the roof was boarded-out over the walk areas, but above the bins the laths and clay tiles were exposed to the view. The sack hoist bollard came up through the floor and its upper end was wrapped in steel sheet to reduce wear by the chain. Its diameter was 7 in. A small cast-iron grooved pulley was positioned over the sack hoist, and a horizontal lay-shaft with a small pulley was set at high level between the bollard and the nearest gable wall. It was not clear how this had been driven.

When back on the ground floor, Mr Hall thrust his penknife into the wood of the main vertical shaft to show how rotten it was and said he thought it was elm and not oak. Many of the wooden gears and pulleys were rather rotten, which was not surprising as they were last used in 1932.

An invitation from Mr Hall to drink a glass of cider with him in his kitchen was received with apprehension as the potency of farm cider can be quite devastating. This was no exception!! When the mill was working, the wheel could just turn two burr stones, although when they were grinding Sussex ground oats on the Peak stones, they demanded such power that no other stones could be used at the same time. The mill sometimes ran short of water, but when there was continual heavy rain, the tail water sometimes backed up and stopped the wheel. In those days, when they produced flour and grist, they had a horse-drawn covered van, an open van and a flat-bottomed van. The mill stopped working during the First World War, but later Mr Hall and his brother worked the mill from about 1927 to 1932. Mr Hall was the third generation at Hammer Mill.

HARTRIDGE MANOR MILL, Cranbrook. TQ 774 395   Surveyed April 1974.

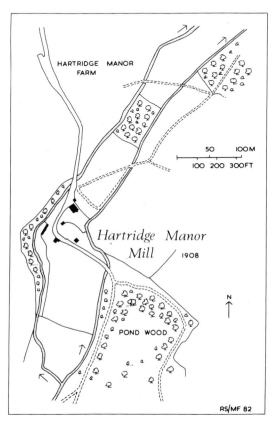

Fig. 44.   Hartridge Manor Mill

This mill site was found by following the farm road past Hartridge Manor Farm. Beyond the farm, it became an unmetalled track, generally without fencing, which eventually crossed the mill-dam, and then carried on up the valley through the woods towards Hockers Edge. Neither Mr Burdge, at the farm, nor the tenant of the old mill building, had any memory of milling at this site.

The old mill, called 'Watermill House', lay close up against the mill-dam. It was a very small building, brick up to first-floor level, and black weatherboard above, with hipped gables and a tile roof. It had been probably a small corn mill, possibly with two pairs or, at the most, three pairs of millstones. All machinery and fittings had long since been removed. There was no sign in the wall fabric of where the water-wheel may have stood, and the head- and tail-race had disappeared. The water left the pond some distance away from the house, and the ground around the house was a garden.

The track was followed onto the mill-dam where it overlooked the pond and mill-house. A more unromantic mill-pond it would have been difficult to find, yet it was in an attractive setting within a shallow valley with woods behind it. The water level of the pond was very low, and it was understood from Mr Burdge that he normally had the pond empty, but periodically let it partially fill. At the time of this survey the water lay in a large, shallow, saucer-shaped, dried-earth depression, completely devoid of any herbage. The absence of grass right out to the boundary fences had been caused by numerous pigs that could be seen rooting and snuffling about. Making the scene more unusual were several large trees growing up out of the water, confirming that the old mill-pond had been mainly dry for several decades.

A fruitless search was made for some sign of where the water was taken from the pond to the mill. The low water revealed nothing, suggesting that the pond profile had reverted to a dry terrain by natural erosion – and hogs? Slowly walking back along the rough track between the pond and the mill the only fabric worthy of note were many bricks, but these were not level and were quite unaligned – probably hardcore for a bad winter road, judging by the deep wheel-ruts.

Whilst no evidence came to light showing where the water-wheel stood, it must have been on the south-east face of the building. The head of water that may have existed was difficult to ascertain due to the low water-level, the absence of a high water-level, and the fact that the mill-dam was banked on the cottage side, but it is suggested that it had been fairly low, and turned a breast-wheel probably.

HAWLEY MILL, Sutton-at-Hone. TQ 553 718

Surveyed February 1975.

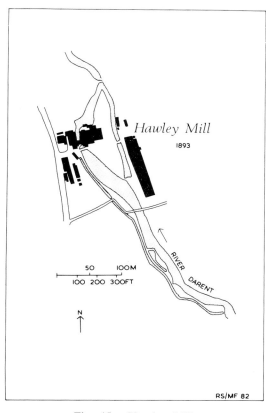

Fig. 45.   Hawley Mill

There were no remains of this mill, or its machinery, which had been removed several years previously to allow a prefabricated office block to be built on its site. In the reception room of this building there was a good aerial photograph which showed the old mill, a long, thin, black weatherboarded building set along the east bank of the river. There were no signs as to where the water-wheel had been positioned, although the aerial photograph suggested that it was against the east bank. The banks and the bed of the river in this region had been rebuilt with brick and concrete, and the only testimony to the fact that a head of water had once been obtained here, was a steep, inclined section of the river bed, down which the water raced.

This site, which covered several acres, had many brick-built buildings, most of mid- to late-nineteenth-century origin – some in ruins. The bypass, or waste water-course, then dry, could still be traced through the site. Sections of it had been filled in, but part of it had a concrete bed and sides, which ran beside open sheds – perhaps used as a convenient loading platform for lorries. When the river flooded, water rose up in this old channel.

Mr Amos, who lived in the Mill House on the west bank of the river, kindly acted as guide. The Mill House was believed to be of seventeenth-century construction, and was probably the oldest fabric on this site.

HAYLE MILL, Loose. TQ 756 538

Surveyed 1970.

This watermill, like many others in this valley, had been at work for many centuries. Since the early years of the nineteenth century, when it was rebuilt, this mill had been a paper mill. It still produced first-class hand-made papers, one of the last to do so in the country.

When this mill was visited the water-wheel was still in use though relegated to the mundane

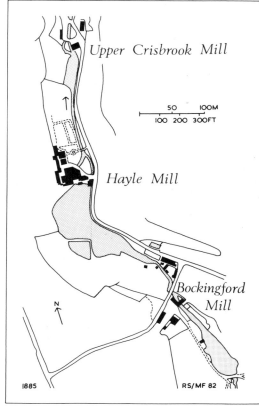

Fig. 46.   Upper Crisbrook Mill, Hayle Mill and
Bockingford Mill

task of driving the cooler fan for sizing the paper
and driving a felt washing machine. Some years
ago the wheel drove two small beaters.

The wheel measured a fraction over 12 ft. in
diameter, with eight cast-iron compass arms
mounted on a square shaft with eight keys. Three
bays, each 3 ft. 3 in. wide, made up the width. No
maker's name appeared. Water was applied by
two gates, an unusual arrangement, one overshot
and one pitchback on the opposite side. The overshot application was closest to the pond and was
undoubtedly the original method. A deflector
plate was employed with the pitchback, but the
water serving this was no longer running, and was
stagnant. It was last used some twenty years ago,
and the old quadrant gear that used to raise the
gate was broken.

In June 1968, the wheel was relieved of all work
and was left to stand idle. The owners would
gladly have been rid of the wheel and its extensive
cast-iron troughs for it took up much valuable
room in the mill. Hayle mill-pond was cleaned
once a year in the area close to the wheel and
waste, though the pond generally had some 12 in.
of clear water above 5 ft. of mud. When work was
required in the wheel-pit a couple of buckets of
ashes were thrown behind the gate to make a
watertight seal. The trash rack consisted of vertical bars and the waste
boards were all within
the mill and could be
raised by block and
tackle.

Fig. 47.   Hayle Mill

HOPE MILL, Goudhurst. TQ 708 372   Surveyed March 1974.

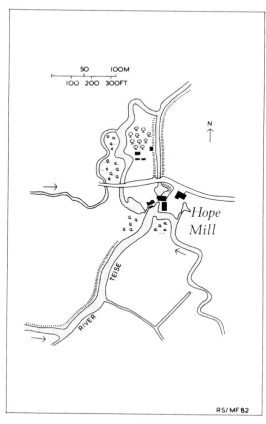

Fig. 48.   Hope Mill, Goudhurst

Most people travelling east from the direction of Tunbridge Wells towards Goudhurst must surely have seen Hope Mill. It lay just to the south of where the road crossed the River Teise, at the bottom of the mile-long rise up into the village of Goudhurst which overlooked the valley.

The mill building had been tastefully converted into a domestic dwelling; it was predominantly brick-built up to the first floor, with weatherboarding above, all under a clay-tile gambrel roof. The west gable wall lay against the water and it was through this wall that the wheel-shafts ran. This wall had been extended beside the tail-water to form a substantial buttress some 13 ft. high and 3 ft. wide. The half of the mill against the stream formerly had had a lower floor, below the surrounding ground level, which contained all the lower gearing. When the present owner acquired the building this lower floor was full of decayed building fabric and rubble which covered the gears. All of this, including the gears, was removed and filled in and the lower of the two barrel vaults, admitting the water-wheel shafts, was bricked in. There had been a lucam at the east end of the mill, but this had been removed. The mill was oak-framed, and although all internal hardware had been removed, except for one pulley wheel high in the mill under the roof pitch, the beams remained to view in the living quarters.

There used to be two water-wheels at Hope Mill, one presumably replacing the other. The oldest of the wheels, and no doubt the position of all previous wheels, was adjacent to the mill wall. All that remained of this wheel was the wooden shaft, which was octagonal approximately 18 in. in diameter, and two arm-hub castings. These castings showed that there had been eight radial wooden arms on each side of the wheel. The end of each arm would have been bolted into an open socket on the hub, and each hub arranged so that the sockets were open to the outside faces of the wheel. The hubs were wood-packed onto each of the wheel-shaft faces, and some of this packing was still in place.

The wheel-shaft had a cross-head gudgeon at the end furthest from the mill, and four iron hoops strengthened the end of the shaft. A plummer block was still attached to the gudgeon, or rather corroded onto it, for its base was vertical and the shaft hoop irons were bearing onto the support wall. At the other end of the shaft was the barrel vault, still open, its curved top and bottom showing that the other bearing had been on the landside of the cog-pit.

This wheel had been a breast-wheel, approximately 13 ft. 9 in. in overall diameter and 6 ft. wide. From a photograph in the owner's possession, the wheel appears to have had approximately forty-eight iron, or steel, L-shape floats mounted on cast-iron rims. No sole-plate could be seen, so that the buckets were very probably of the ventilated type. The breast of the

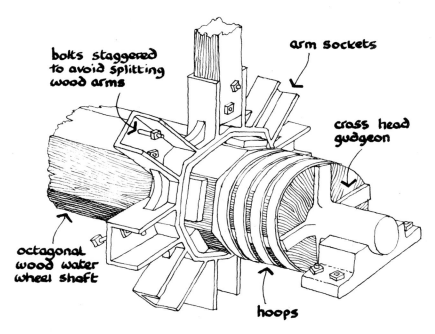

Fig. 49.   Hope Mill, Goudhurst (Detail of water-wheel shaft)

wheel-pit was curved and one interesting feature was that where the floats had run close by the pit sides, the brickwork projected out by about 4 in. to reduce water leakage. The water had been applied to this wheel close to the level of its shaft, and old timbers recessed into the walls of the waterway immediately above the cill showed where the gates had once been.

Several other photographs of this mill, many of them internal views, show how the mill once looked. A view of the mill-stone floor revealed that there had been at least three pairs of stones in a straight line, which would have been unusual. A further view looking down the cog-pit, showed the morticed cast-iron pit-wheel. It had eight T-section arms and was probably cast in halves and bolted together. Approximately forty-eight teeth were held in its rim, which may have had a slight bevel, or alternatively, it may have been a face-gear. The wheel-shaft bearing beside the pit was underneath a 'sprattle' or an arched thrust bearing which carried the vertical shaft. This cast-iron arch remained beside the mill-house. It had a cast box on top of the arch with adjusting screws in the walls and it measured 20 in. across the inside faces of the arch. No strengthening webs or fillets existed, making it a very plain casting.

The wallower was entirely of cast-iron, with twenty-eight teeth and eight T-section arms radiating from a square cast hub. The vertical shaft had a square section.

The second water-wheel was an overshot one, 9 ft. 2 in. in diameter and 9 ft. 3 in. wide. It had three bays formed by four sets of cast-iron hub, arms and shroud assemblies. Each had eight tapered arms with a + section, which were cast integrally with the hub and shroud, and the whole was cast in halves and bolted together. Most of the steel buckets and sole-plate had corroded away, but it could be seen that there were thirty-two L-shaped unventilated buckets, and the shroud was $8\frac{1}{2}$ in. deep. The wheel was carried on a cast-iron shaft, approximately 8 in. in diameter, which had two bearings outside the mill, one on the landside and one carried on a cast-iron, A-bracket standing in the water some 6 ft. from the mill. On the wheel-side of this bracket there was a coupling in the shaft. The wheel shaft was unusually long, for it passed over the tail-race of the breast-wheel before passing into the mill. When the mill was visited, this wheel was standing in at least 2 ft. of backwater.

A curious feature of this wheel was that the concrete trough serving it was some 18 in. narrower than the wheel, which suggested that either the millwright had made a mistake or, and this alternative seems more likely, the wheel came from another mill. The trough was 29 in. deep, and a series of $\frac{3}{4}$ in. diameter wrought-iron stay bars spanned the water at 3 ft. intervals.

There were at least six old millstones embedded in the paths around the mill, both runner and bottom stones. They varied from 43 to 48 in. in diameter and all, except one, were French burrs. This group showed very well how the colour of burrs could vary.

HORTON KIRBY PAPER MILL, South Darenth. TQ 563 695   Surveyed 1975.

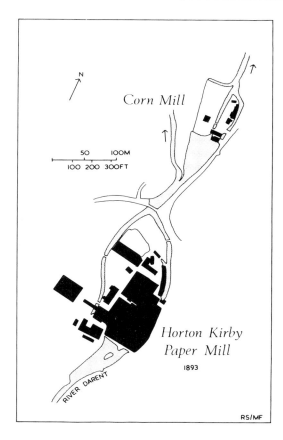

This was a large modern paper mill which had undoubtedly expanded considerably since the days when water power was employed. There were no remains of the water-wheel or associated machinery and the occupiers considered that it was not possible even to tell where the water-wheel may have stood.

Fig. 50.   Horton Kirby Paper Mill

HOTHFIELD MILL, Westwell/Ashford. TQ 989 450   Surveyed April 1975.

This mill stood about two miles north-west of Ashford, to the north of the A20, and was situated on a tributary of the Great Stour. It was easily seen from the A20; and its clay-tile, half-hipped roof, white weatherboarding and lucam, and red brick ground floor combined to make this a classical Kentish watermill, especially when seen against its screen of green foliage set at the foothills of the North Downs. It stood at the end of a short private track from the main

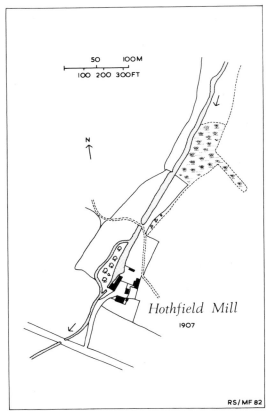

Fig. 51.   Hothfield Mill

road, in the company of several tile-hung cottages, a barn and outbuildings, all clustered into a compact group. At the time of the survey, in the summer of 1975, the mill was owned by Messrs. Denne and Sons Ltd., agricultural merchants, who had offices in Canterbury and Ashford and also owned Wye mill. When first visited Hothfield mill was crammed full of grain, seeds, and agricultural chemicals, and small saucers of rat and mice bait were everywhere, thus making a detailed survey impossible. Another visit was made later in the year when the mill was nearly empty of stores.

A dismantled silk, or flour grader, was stored in the nearby barn, and considerable site levelling was being carried out over what had once been the mill-pond. Nothing remained of the pond, although part of one of its sluice gates still stood, and the water tumbled unchecked over its sill. The sluice comprised two vertical timbers, set one each side of a gap in a low brick wall, and a horizontal timber, set at the upper end of the verticals, carried a metal block fitted with a square-shanked pinion gear and a small horizontal thrust roller. A heavy, vertical, wooden beam, fixed to the sluice boards at its lower end, carried, at its upper end, a metal plate on one face, and a 3 ft. long cast-iron rack on its opposite face. The roller ran against the metal plate, and the rack meshed with the pinion which, being turned by means of the square shank, raised or lowered the sluice boards thus allowing more or less water to pass.

The overshot water-wheel was still in place beside the end of the mill. It was an all-metal wheel 11 ft. in diameter and 7 ft. 6 in. wide, having two bays between three frames. The two frames nearest the mill were identical, being single-piece castings including the hubs, arms and the shroud, which was unusual. Each of these square hubs were carried off the square section 7 × 7 in. cast-iron wheel-shaft which was relieved on all four faces. These two frames had eight radial + sectioned tapered arms that sprang from the hub corners and mid-faces. One of the arms on the middle frame was split and had been clamped together near the rim – probably broken as the result of frost action. The landside frame had a two-piece square cast-iron hub bolted together with cast arm sockets on the corners and mid faces. This carried eight radial flat iron arms, $3\frac{1}{2} \times \frac{5}{8}$ in. in section, which were split in two, curved apart, and bolted to the shroud. Each of the cast-iron shrouds was 7 in. deep and $\frac{1}{2}$ in. thick, beaded on the outer edge and with a web on the inner edge to which the iron sole-plate was bolted. On the inside faces of the shrouds were machined cast lugs to which the forty-eight unventilated iron buckets were bolted. Each of the buckets was stayed in the mid-bay positions.

Inside the mill the cog-pit was boarded off as a separate enclosure adjacent to an office in the corner of the mill. The overhung pit-wheel appeared to have been cast in one piece, with eight, radial, T-section, tapered arms springing from a square hub. The morticed rim carried

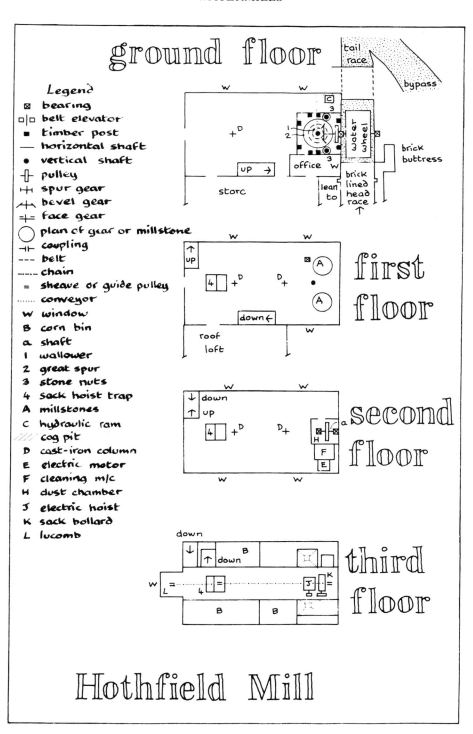

Fig. 52. Hothfield Mill

approximately eighty-eight cogs but they had all been stripped, testimony of some accident. The pit extended outside the cog-pit enclosure to the corner of the mill where a small hydraulic ram was positioned down in the pit water.

The main vertical shaft, which passed up through the mill, was $6\frac{1}{2}$ in. square, with relieved faces. A single piece cast-iron wallower engaged the pit gear, having four radial T-section arms carrying thirty teeth. Immediately above this on the shaft was a two-piece, cast-iron, bevel gear with eight radial T-section tapered arms carrying a morticed rim with ninety-six cogs.

Higher on the shaft was the great spur-gear some 70 in. in diameter. Its square hub was carried on the shaft by eight keys; from this hub sprang eight, radial, T-section arms, tapered on the web, to support the single-piece cast rim into which one hundred and twenty well-worn cogs were morticed.

An unusual feature in the cog-pit was a large iron pulley mounted on the wheel-shaft between the pit-gear and the mill wall. This was 5 ft. in diameter, 6 in. wide, and had eight curved arms.

The hursting told an interesting story, the eight vertical posts, spaced in pairs to support the bridge-trees showed that this was originally designed as a four pair mill; but it ended its days with only two pairs of mill-stones. Each of the two millstone spindles was supported by curved ⊥-section cast-iron bridges, both cast with a central footstep bearing-box. Both of the cast-iron nuts had twenty-five teeth, and were taken out of gear by wrought-iron rings driven up from below the bridges by the usual hand screws. All of the ironwork associated with the missing millstones, furthest from the water-wheel, was absent, except for some brackets on the posts. Above the hursting, where millstones once stood, the floor had been boarded over.

Up on the first floor, the walls were all boarded with matchboard up to a height of 4 ft. from floor level. The two pairs of millstones which remained were provided with natural light from two long narrow windows, one above the other. The runner stone nearest the head-race was a hooped Derby Peak 44 in. in diameter with a 10 in. eye, and was some $10\frac{1}{2}$ in. thick at the skirt. The bedstone was little more than 2 in. thick. The other pair of stones were French burrs; the runner was 42 in. in diameter with an 11 in. eye, and had four cast balance boxes let into the top face, each with the legend HUGHES DOVER & LONDON. All the top gear (tun, hopper, shoes, etc.) was missing from these stones, except for an off-centre wooden frame, some 4 ft. high, which was bolted to the floor around the French stones. This was presumably part of the horse, although it was unusual for it to have been floor-mounted.

The vertical shaft had a coupling immediately above the floor; above this it was 4 × 4 in. in section. It was made of cast-iron, with relieved faces and chamfered corners, and was supported by a top bearing bolted to the floor beam above. No pulley or gears were on this shaft, and the only other evidence of power transmission on this floor was a single bearing which had at one time supported a horizontal lay-shaft, driven from the vertical shaft.

The main frames of this mill were timber, with the usual post and truss arrangement, but on each floor, except the top, there were two cast-iron columns $2\frac{1}{2}$ in. in diameter. These lay on the centre line of the mill, below the ridge, and were spaced apart on each floor, obviously arranged to support the bressumer beams and to distribute and transfer the floor loads, including the grain bins, to the mill walls and foundations.

The gable wall next to the water-wheel was brick-built up to the second floor, but above that the whole mill was covered in unlined weatherboarding. On the second floor there was no machinery, except for what appeared to be a cleaning machine at the water-wheel end of the floor, which was driven from a floor-mounted electric motor. It bore the makers' name of Robert Boby Ltd. of Bury St. Edmunds, and incorporated a blower, brushes and a sieve. It had a feed hopper, which was fed from the floor above and was positioned against a small enclosed chamber which probably acted as a dust screen.

On the top floor, the grain bins were set on either side of a central gangway, with a central division wall under the floor. They were all boarded out, and the lower parts of the roof over the bins were similarly boarded. There were six bins, two of them self-clearing. The electrically-powered $2\frac{1}{4}$ cwt. hoist was adjacent to the sack bollard at one end of the floor. The sack hoist chain was carried over a grooved cast-iron pulley at high level, and passed along under the ridge of the roof on a board to another pulley over the internal sack hoist, which passed down through the mill floors. A brake rope was still in position passing down through small holes in the floor boards close beside the hoist flaps. On the gable wall furthest from the water-wheel was a lucomb, accessible from the bin floor, to which the sack hoist chain could be extended. Under the roof of this external hoist was a single-grooved cast-iron pulley.

Close to the gable wall, next to the water-wheel and projecting up through the bin floor, was a large cast-iron pulley with eight radial arms. This was supported by a short horizontal shaft under the floor, so that the greater part of this pulley projected into the chamber at the end of the floor below. This large pulley probably powered the sack hoist via the pulley on the wheel shaft at the bottom of the mill, prior to the change over to an electrically-driven hoist.

It was interesting to observe that some of the pegged clay-tiles were bedded on hay, a feature rarely met with in the South-east. This was a cheap and effective method of reducing the entry of wind-blown water or snow, especially on north-facing roof flanks.

This mill once had a donkey engine. It has also been learnt that the grounds were floodlit as a tea garden, and that dances were held on the first floor. Nowadays most of the feet that pass across the floors belong to mice and rats, forever searching amid the trays of rat poison.

HYTHE MILL (SPRING GROVE MILL), Hythe. TR 167 350   Surveyed April 1975.

This mill was served by a small stream running down the short steep valley cutting through the highlands behind Hythe. At one time there had been three watermills on this stream, but no buildings remained of the two higher up the valley. An indication of the steepness of this valley was given by the relatively large diameter water-wheel, which was served by an average size mill-pond.

Many years ago, soon after the owner, Mr Stuart Brown, acquired the mill, he had made a steep cutting around the west side of the pond to act as a bypass and remove water from the wheel. This had not been very successful, for the pond remained full with reeds and resident wildfowl at the upstream end. The bypass penstock comprised an upper horizontal shaft with a hand crank, on which was mounted a single-shroud cast-iron pinion of eleven teeth, which engaged with a cast-iron spur gear having six arms and fifty-seven teeth, mounted on a lower shaft. This had two twelve-tooth pinions, which engaged the usual vertical cast-iron racks bolted to the main timbers of the gate. The bypass water dropped down an impressive waterfall in a tree-shrouded corner of the owner's garden, then skirted the west side of the mill and mill-house, and passed out of sight under the road.

The mill and mill-house had been built together, with the mill lying between the house and the mill-dam. Hythe mill was relatively large, having an irregular shape, with five main floors, including the ground floor. It had brick external walls up to the third floor, with timber-frame and weatherboarding above, supporting a clay-tiled roof. The walls were pierced by many wood-framed windows. A main internal wall, running east—west, which divided the mill more or less into two halves, north and south, had a brick at high level in its north face bearing the

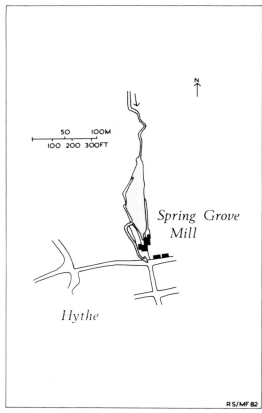

Fig. 53.   Hythe Mill

date 1773. This was probably the date when the original mill, adjacent to the house, had been built. It was this older part of the structure which stood five floors high. Some time later, a large two-floor extension had been built on the north side, hard against the mill-dam. The ground floor of this extension apparently had cut deep into the mill-dam, for the north wall of the 'basement' was built of ragstone, rather crudely dressed with an irregular vertical face. Indeed, the workmanship of this extension did not exhibit the same quality as the old mill; it was noticeable that the earthen floor had a considerable slope up towards the west.

From the mill-pond, the water had been delivered to the water-wheel in a brick trough running alongside the west wall of the mill. The cast-iron overshot wheel, which was still in place, was surprisingly large, especially when viewed at close quarters. It was 5 ft. 4 in. wide, inside the shrouds and 21 ft. 4 in. in diameter. The two side frames were virtually independent of each other due to the corrosion of the buckets and sole-plate, making it difficult to obtain an accurate width measurement. In each cast-iron frame there was a single-piece flaunch bolted to twelve + section radial arms, which were tapered on both aspects and which in turn carried a 7 in. deep shroud in six sections bolted together. On the inside of the shrouds were large, square cast lugs, which sat in shoulders cast into the ends of the arms. The L-shaped wood buckets were held in place at each end by a $\frac{3}{4}$ in. wide channel with raised edges cast on the inside face of the shrouds. The wooden sole-plates were recessed into the inside edges of the shrouds and bolted to cast lugs. The buckets did not appear to be ventilated.

The iron flaunches were interesting castings, 32 in. in diameter, 2 in. thick at the rim, with recessed face and radial gussets and they were hung on a $6\frac{1}{2}$ in. square, cast-iron, shaft supported by a stepped outer bearing. The wheel-pit was deep, but contained only a few feet of water and mud; it was possible that some complete buckets and sole-boards remained under water.

Access to the mill was by a narrow footbridge hard against the breast of the wheel. Entering a strange mill is always a pleasure, and this mill was no exception. The floor had been used as a store for, around the walls, were stacks of timber, chests of drawers, gardening tools and equipment, all sorts of hardware, collections of old rusty lanterns hanging up on the beams, sacks and stencils and so many different things that a survey of them would have been quite fascinating.

One other very obvious fact was that the scale of the machinery was very large, so that a platform had been built some 5 or 6 ft. above the ground, to support the vertical shaft and, surprisingly, an additional pair of millstones.

The overhung pit-wheel was cast-iron, split in halves and bolted together and approximately 10 ft. 3 in. in diameter. Rim, arms and hub were a single casting. It had eight, radial, + section

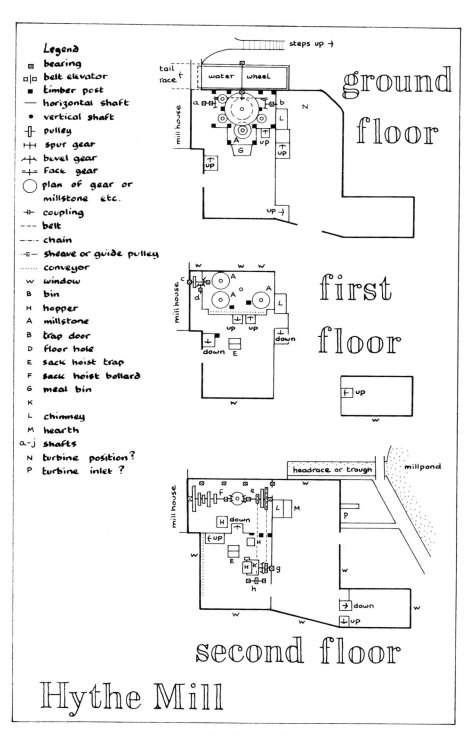

Fig. 54. Hythe Mill

arms tapered on both aspects, carried on a square hub, hung off the shaft with eight keys, two on each face. The rim had one hundred and twenty eight cogs, which engaged with the thirty-eight cast-iron teeth of the wallower. This was a solid, single-piece bevel gear bolted onto the underside of the great spur-gear. The vertical shaft was of cast-iron, 7 in. square, carried in a footstep bearing, and the bottom 40 in. of the shaft was tapered with an octagonal section from a comparatively small diameter up to 7 in. square.

The great spur-wheel was at high level and was approximately 110 in. in diameter. It was cast-iron, morticed, split into halves, and the external wall had been recessed to take the rim. Eight, radial, T-section arms, tapered on both aspects, sprang from a square hub and bore, and carried one hundred and sixty-eight cogs nailed at the top and bottom. These cogs, which were spurs, not bevels, engaged four stone nuts. The pit-wheel, as well as engaging the wallower, drove two horizontal shafts, one to the south (a) and one to the north (b). The southern shaft was 2 in. square, of iron, and was driven by a solid, wooden, bevel gear carrying sixteen cogs pinned through the rim, and its edges were bound with iron. No other pulleys or gears were on this shaft, and it was not possible to determine what it had driven. On the north side, the iron shaft (b) was driven by a solid, cast-iron, bevel gear, with four arms having a + section tapered on face view, that sprang from a hub with a round bore. It carried thirty-eight teeth and its shaft disappeared through the wall into the next room.

On the perimeter of the great spur-wheel were positioned four stone nuts, three serving under-driven millstones and one an overdriven pair of millstones. There was limited evidence suggesting that, in earlier days, a fifth pair of stones had stood in the corner above shaft (b). All of the stone nuts were cast-iron, with twenty-one teeth. The two bridge-trees serving the two underdriven stones on the inside of the mill were cast-iron, with pivot plates recessed into the vertical timbers. Both nuts were taken out of gear by parallel push rods that passed up through the casting and were driven from below by a screwed spindle and handle.

The overdriven stones rested on an extension of the platform; their stone nut was taken out of gear by a pivoted, flat, cast-iron arm which allowed the nut to swing away from the great spur-gear. This stone spindle, which had a coupling at high level, was $2\frac{1}{4}$ in. in diameter and drove a pair of 42 in. diameter, iron-bound, Peak stones. Above the stones was an octagonal wooden tun and a hopper, but no horse or shoe. In front of this pair of stones was a meal bin (g). Against the inside wall of this room were wooden rubbing-strakes.

On the first floor, the millstones were mounted on a platform 4 ft. higher than the remainder of the mill floor, giving the effect of a mezzanine. This 'displacement' also occurred on the floor above the millstones and was obviously intended to accommodate the large scale of the power transmission machinery. The pair of millstones furthest from the mill-house (upstream) were complete with eight-sided vat, hopper, shoe and a horse supported by turned legs. These were French burr stones, approximately 48 in. in diameter. The pair of stones nearest the wheel were also French burrs, but all of the top gear, including the tun, was absent, and the runner had been lifted off the bedstone and was leaning against the mill wall nearby. The bedstone, which lay almost flush with the platform, was 45 in. in diameter, and still bore traces of fine stitching on its grinding face. In the top surface of the runner were four, equidistant, circular, cast-iron balance boxes let into the plaster of Paris, each with the inscription 'Clarke and Dunham 1859 Patented millstone balance'.

The remaining pair of stones, probably 48 in. in diameter, were still in their round vats, and their smooth, dark grey surface suggested them to be Derby Peaks. A horse was still in place, and a four-beat damsel could be seen protruding through the top stone. A shoe lay nearby, and mill bits were scattered everywhere. On the edge of the platform nearest the mill-house was the

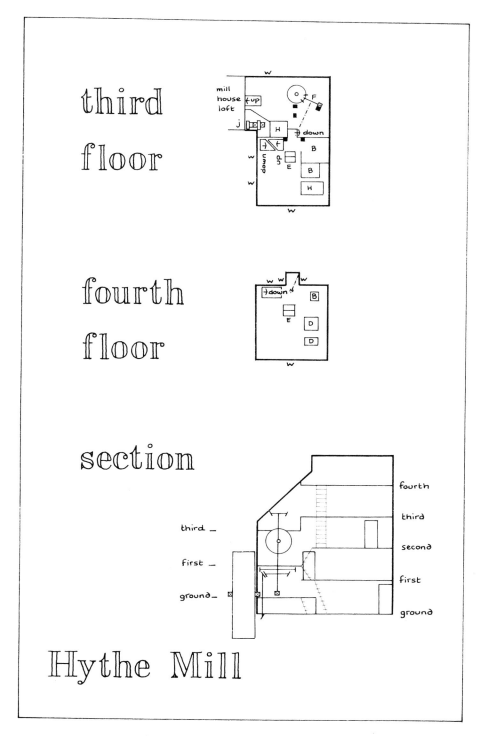

Fig. 55.   Hythe (Spring Grove) Mill

governor with two, pear-shaped, lead weights which controlled the adjacent Peak stones. It was powered by a 12 in. diameter rope pulley, but it was not possible to determine from where it had been driven. The iron vertical shaft which passed through this floor to the one above was square-sectioned, tapering from 3 × 3 in. at floor level to 4 × 4 in. at head height. It was guarded up to a height of 4 ft. from the floor by a wrought-iron cage, which was split and bolted together.

At the front of the platform was a horizontal, encased, iron, screw conveyor which picked up meal from both front stones and delivered it to a chute. At low level, beside the platform against the mill-house wall, was an 1½ in. diameter horizontal spindle (c) which carried a 12 in. diameter single-piece cast-iron pulley with four radial arms and a small cast-iron bevel gear. This bevel gear engaged with a similar gear mounted on a broken shaft (d). Some of the small windows overlooking the water-wheel had leaded lights.

Having thus surveyed the main gearing within the mill, it is convenient to define the mechanical ratios of the main items as follows:

MECHANICAL RATIOS		
Element	Number of cogs/teeth	Revolutions per rev. of water-wheel
Pit-wheel	128	1.00
Wallower	38	3.37
Great Spur	168	3.37
Stone nuts	21	26.90

The high level lay-shafts which were above the millstone platform have been shown on the second floor plan for clarity. They were driven from a single-piece cast-iron bevel gear carried on the vertical shaft with a square packing piece and eight keys. It had eight, radial, + section arms, tapered on both aspects, which supported a cast-iron rim with ninety-four cogs. This engaged two horizontal lay shafts (e) and (f).

Shaft (e) was an iron 2¼ in. square shaft which carried in order from the driven end:
1. A twenty-tooth cast-iron bevel gear with four arms, driven on the underside of the main bevel on the vertical shaft;
2. A 26 × 3 in. solid wooden pulley, with a grooved rim for a rope drive, that carried a leather belt which drove spindle (h);
3. A 52 × 5½ in. crowned, cast-iron, single-piece pulley with six, radial, oval-sectioned arms that sprang from a round hub;
4. A 58 × 6½ in. single-piece, cast-iron pulley with six radial oval-sectioned arms carried on a round hub. This drove shaft (g) via a leather belt.

Shaft (f) was 2 in. in diameter, iron and carried, in order from the driven end:
1. A twenty-tooth, solid, cast-iron bevel gear with four arms, driven on the underside of the main bevel on the vertical shaft;
2. An 11 × 3 in. single-piece, crowned, cast-iron pulley with four, curved, oval-sectioned arms and circular hub set-screwed to the shaft;
3. A 28 × 3 in. single-piece, crowned, cast-iron pulley with six, oval-sectioned, tapered arms and circular hub keyed to the shaft;

4. A 6 in. diameter cast-iron pulley, with a solid web, keyed onto the shaft;
5. A $10 \times 3\frac{1}{2}$ in. cast-iron pulley with four, curved, rectangular-sectioned arms;
6. A $60 \times 3\frac{1}{2}$ in. wood-rimmed pulley carried on eight, cast-iron, tapered, oval-sectioned arms that sprang from a circular cast hub. The rim was segmented and had two laminates, which were lapped and dowelled together.

Both this shaft and shaft (e) had the same bearing support arrangements; one was carried on a heavy-section, cast-iron beam immediately behind the driven bevel, and the other bearing at the end of the shaft was held in a drop hanger close to the wall. In both cases, the drive to the shaft was discontinued by the cast-iron beam being lowered at one end, thus taking the driven bevel out of gear on the underside face of the crown gear. There was evidence of an earlier shaft parallel to shafts (e) and (f) nearer the wall; the bearings have been marked on the floor plan.

Spindle (h) was a 1 in. square, short shaft at high level, carrying a solid wooden pulley and an overhung eccentric crank at one end, with the remains of a belt attached. This apparently provided the reciprocating motion necessary for the inclined screen in machine (k). Shaft (g), supported at one end by a wall bearing, was part of the sifting machine, and carried an integral, $15\frac{1}{2}$ in. diameter driven pulley and bevel gear with forty morticed cogs. This engaged with a small, sixteen-tooth bevel underneath, which was carried on an inclined spindle passing through the machine. At the front end of the spindle was a worm gear engaging a 6 in. diameter plate

Fig. 56. Hythe Mill

Fig. 57. Hythe Mill

gear, with twenty-three teeth, carried on a horizontal spindle which supported two, overhung, solid wooden pulleys at one end. These provided a belt-drive to feeding mechanisms in the hopper above the sifter machine.

On the third floor, the main 3 in. square, vertical shaft terminated in a crown friction bevel some 48 in. in diameter. This had a morticed, cast-iron rim supported on four radial + sectioned arms, and had additional strengthening plates bolted across the flanges of the arms. The rim carried fifty-four T-shaped cogs which had been shaped to provide the continuous, bevelled, friction-face, $9\frac{1}{2}$ in. wide, for a sack hoist bollard. The friction-driven bevel had thirty-six similarly shaped cogs carried in a single-piece, solid, cast-iron body mounted on a 2 in. square iron shaft. The sack hoist bollard (*f*) was of solid wood, with eight, parallel, cloth-wrapped wooden strips on its face to provide friction; this shaft was pivoted at the end remote from the vertical shaft, and power transmission was actuated by a rope, which lifted the driven friction bevel against the underside of the crown bevel. The sack hoist chain was still in place around the bollard, and passed to the hoist via a high-level, horizontal, wooden roller.

Shaft (*j*) carried a 20 × 4 in. four-armed, cast-iron pulley between bearings, and, overhung at one end, a 10 × 3 in. and an 18 × 3 in. cast-iron pulley. The last-mentioned pulley was driven from the 10 × 3½ in. pulley on shaft (*f*) on the floor below. Underneath shaft (*j*) was a small spindle (not shown on the plan) which transmitted power from (*j*) to a conveyor.

LEEDS CASTLE MILL, Broomfield. TQ 835 532   Surveyed 1966

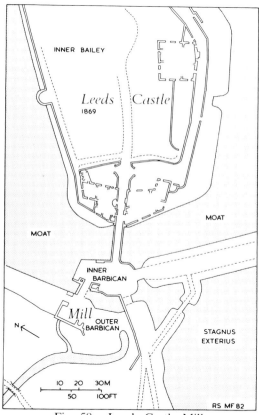

Fig. 58.   Leeds Castle Mill

The Castle mill was built into the outer barbican of Leeds Castle. Nothing remained except the massive crumbling walls, for the floors and roof had all gone, leaving only broken masonry in the water-course below.

The water was led from the moat via a small penstock in a low wall, through a tunnel beneath the ground floor of the barbican to the wheel. An examination of the tunnel floor showed no trace of wear, as one would have expected after centuries of being subjected to running water. This may be an indication that the water was delivered by an inclined wooden trough, probably caulked, to the wheel apron, thus producing a greater head of water. A second explanation is that the floor may have been renewed at a later date, as suggested by C.W. Martin in *The History and Description of Leeds Castle, Kent* (1869). No matter, a wooden chute must surely have been adopted in time, for operation of the sluice boards in the end of the tunnel warranted the use of a dry walkway of some kind to keep the operator from the water; furthermore, the existing sluice gate width was far less than the width of the lower and narrower end of the tunnel, suggesting a channel or trough to maintain control and gain efficiency. Needless to say, this may have been supplied by an earlier floor, and perhaps the moat level was lower then than it became later.

Whatever the method employed, the wheel diameter must have been close to 10 ft., or 11 ft. at the most, a figure supported by the height of the masonry cavities used by the first-floor timbers. The width of the wheel could only be guessed. The tunnel entrance was 6 ft. wide so, to allow comfortable entry, the wheel and water channel could not have been over 4 ft., probably nearer 3 ft., in width. The wheel was a breast-wheel – the height of application being in question. Most of the River Len's water passed through a sluice some 75 ft. away from the mill, but for how long this had been employed it was difficult to say.

At the bottom of the water-course in the wheel-pit were the remains of two Derby Peak millstones. Although they were in many pieces, they were obviously a pair. The upper stone had an eye diameter of 12 in. and a rynd displacement of 17 in. in length, approximately $2\frac{1}{4}$ in. in width, and $1\frac{1}{2}$ in. in depth. The thickness of the stone at the eye was $5\frac{1}{2}$ in., and 5 in. at the skirt. The bedstone had a 10 in. square eye, but no trace of the eye-box remained. Both stones were about 4 ft. in diameter, and had feathered grinding surfaces. All the grooves were straight, and there seemed to be eleven or twelve segments – all very shallow and well-worn. The runner revolved clockwise as viewed from above. By their design, the stones appeared to be no older than of early-nineteenth-century manufacture. This raised the question as to which mill they belonged. They must surely have come from nearby. Perhaps they were intended for Chegworth or Abbey mills, both corn mills, and in the later part of their lives appended to Leeds Castle estate.

LEG-O-MUTTON, Loose. TQ 762 521   Surveyed 1971.

Leg-o-Mutton pond, so called because of its shape, was a fairly large sheet of water, which could be reached by the footpath running from Salts Lane, beside Springhead Pond up the valley towards Quarry Wood (Fig. 40). It lay in a well-defined valley and had clearly been man-made, for at its western end, downstream, the water was held by an earthen dam, which had been raised across the stream bed. In the centre of the dam, water passed through a semi-circular trash grille and, then, between two dressed stones each bearing the inscription 'WW 1873', testimony to the Wilson family ownership when they occupied Upper Mill nearby. Behind the stones, the water dropped into a vertical stone-lined shaft, passed under the dam and came to view some 10 ft. away. Immediately beside this water-course, on the south bank close under the dam, were the remains of a building which, in the light of the following evidence, was very probably a watermill.

The physical evidence supporting the suggestion that a mill stood here was, by itself, very strong. Clearly, a head of water had been created to serve a mill close by. An inspection of the site will reveal that the water left the pond by two routes, one through the centre of the mill-dam, and the other via a 4 ft.-wide brick-lined water-course running towards the site of Upper Mill, which used to stand beside Springhead Pond. This culvert was man-made, for it did not follow the true valley, but instead took a direct line contrary to natural drainage.

The foundations of ragstone below the dam stood some 6 ft. high beside the water. There was no evidence that the fabric had ever supported a mill-wheel, nor were there remains of an apron or associated constructions, but this was not surprising when considering that in its later life the mill was converted to three cottages and subsequently reduced to foundations only. Mr Alan Wilson, whose father owned Upper Mill nearby, could remember his father's work-people living in these cottages. The cottages were of black weatherboard and he was always of the opinion that the end nearest the pond was constructed for the use of water-power. He recalled an overhang which was used as a changing-room when, as a lad, he swam in Leg-o-Mutton pond. A springboard was mounted on the mill-dam close by, and he remembered the water being very deep, for he could not touch the bottom when diving in. The fall of water at the dam was some 12 to 15 ft. Mr Wilson thought that the cottages were of eighteenth-century construction. His father was never able to shed any light on their origin.

The old mill-pond had become very shallow and was only 2–3 ft. deep at a point some 10 ft. from the mill-dam which, in the light of Alan Wilson's diving activities in 1908, proved that the rate of deposition had been very high. The western end of the pond, at the mill-dam, had a brick retaining wall which Mr Wilson said was always kept clear of weeds with the help of the resident swans. In only one part had reeds and rushes encroached on the water margin. At one time the pond had been well stocked with fish such as roach, bream, gudgeon, tench and pike, and had been let for fishing rights, but then the water became devoid of life. Several large willows, very ancient and polled long ago, skirted the pond, their decaying arms lying in the water.

LE NETHERTOUNE MILL, Leeds, TQ 823 534   Surveyed 1966.

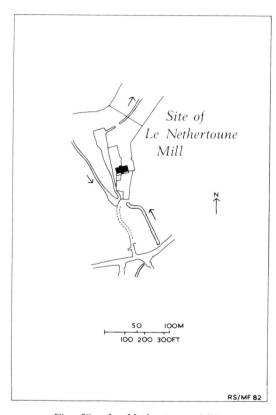

Fig. 59.   Le Nethertoune Mill

The first clue to the possible existence of a mill on this site was the pond size and shape, which may be seen on an O.S. map as the third from the source of the Priory stream. Its straight man-made end with a side exit suggests a mill-pond, although no masonry remains could be found nearby. The whole pond had become covered with reeds, and its triangular shape was virtually indiscernible. If it was ever in use, it probably delivered a 4 ft. head of water, possibly 5 ft. if the wheel was 20–30 ft. away, thus indicating a low breast-wheel or under-shot wheel.

It seems likely that this was the site referred to in the Fine Rolls of 1466 (Calendar of Fine Rolls, 6 Edward IV, 185, membrane 10, 14th October, 1466) thus:

'Commitment . . . to John Rogger, . . . by mainprise of Wm. Hardes of Ledys Kent, gentil-man, and Richard Stokes of London "gentilman", of the keeping of certain void ground lying in "Le Nethertoune" in the town of Ledys Co. Kent on which 2 cottages and a fulling mill [which are now completely in ruins] were sometimes situated, and a small cottage there, called "Le Hoggestye", with a parcel of the King's demesne land there, 35 yds long by 12 yds broad . . .'

By virtue of its position in the village of Leeds, this site, assuming it was in use, was probably very old. That it was in ruins by 1466 is surprising, as the Wealden cloth industry was building up in this period to reach a plateau of production before the last quarter of the fifteenth century. Perhaps its low head of water finally proved inefficient in comparison with the more powerful fulling mills in the valley.

LOOSE VILLAGE MILL, Loose. TQ 758 522   Surveyed 1971.

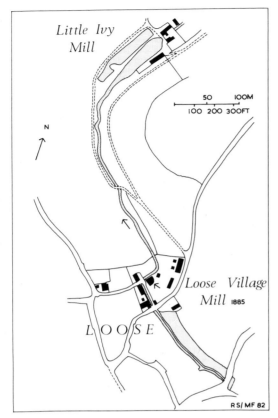

Fig. 60.   Loose Village Mill

Although this mill and water-wheel were working up to the First World War, we do not know when it was demolished. There was nothing to see at the site, apart from the waterfall where the wheel once stood.

The mill-pond was most unusual in shape, and was well worth seeing, for a public footpath passed alongside it. On the other side was the stream, so that the path was, in effect, on a long narrow causeway. At the downstream end of the pond, where the water passed under the path to join the stream and become the head-race, there was a millstone bridging the tunnel on the pond side. Its projecting lip revealed that it was a barley stone, some 40 in. in diameter, and worn down to some $2\frac{1}{2}$ in. in thickness. The furrows could clearly be felt by hand on the underside. This stone probably came from the village mill.

LOVEHURST MANOR MILL (STILL'S MILL), Staplehurst. TQ 780 414   Surveyed March 1974.

This small country mill was found beside a back lane some $1\frac{1}{2}$ miles south of Staplehurst. It was set close beside the entrance to the manor, and the long drive up to the house ran parallel to the mill stream, or, to be more accurate, the long narrow sheet of water which formed the mill-pond. The manor house was on an island at the end of the pond, and the surrounding waterways gave a moated effect, which lent considerable charm to the situation. While talking to the owner, it was learned that one of the three mill-stones that had come from the mill had been a Derby Peak and that this was later embedded in a nearby path. Across the water, near some oasts, were the remains of a French burr stone that had recently fallen apart out of its hoops. The mill-pond had recently been cleaned out by a mechanical excavator. As evidence of this, large areas of rich, black alluvial mud lay at regular intervals along the banks of the pond and over the adjacent fields. Mr Steel, the owner, said that he intended to stock the pond with fish and, during the survey, a lorry parked in the drive, and tanks of fish were tipped gently into the pond.

The mill-building was rectangular in plan, timber-framed, with three floors, and was brick-built as far as the first floor, with weatherboarding above on all faces. A corrugated asbestos pitched roof had replaced the original cover. The water-wheel and gates had disappeared, and no external iron or woodwork remained to suggest what arrangement might have once existed.

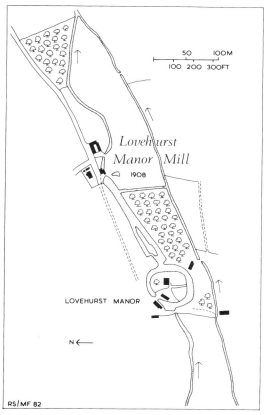

Fig. 61. Lovehurst Manor Mill

At the time of the visit there was a good head of water held back, it was believed, by temporary means. At the head of the pond, the concrete and brick fabric that once supported the pentrough was considerably broken up, and the brick walls that supported the outer wheel-shaft bearing were leaning away from the wheel-pit. In this wall was a 6 in. thick stone slab acting as a sole-plate, but the bearing was absent.

The water-wheel probably had been an over-shot one, but it is possible, although less likely, that it could have been a pitch-back wheel. The position where the wheel-shaft passed into the mill could still be seen. In earlier days, this aperture had been larger, apparently, but had later been bricked-in to make a smaller hole. The original gap had probably been a bearing position as it had the usual curved top and flat bottom associated with this use. The smaller, square hole, bridged with a small stone lintel, was presumably designed to accommodate only the shaft. Measurements from this position to the vertical brick breast of the wheel-pit suggested that the wheel may have had a radius of 83 in. The head of water at the time of the visit measured nearly 86 in. above the mid-shaft position. It was interesting to note that the plan view of the breast was definitely slightly curved – by design, as far as could be told. The maximum width of the pit measured 102 in. but, allowing for the leaning outer support wall, and for a running clearance, the wheel had probably been 8 ft. in width and about 14 ft. in diameter. The pit was some 4–5 ft. deep in silt, rubble and decayed vegetation.

All of the machinery that would normally have been seen adjacent to the water-wheel had gone. Only the heavy, vertical timbers remained – some with mortices and cuts where the bridge-trees had been supported and adjusted. There had been perhaps two pairs of stones. The area of floor between these vertical timbers – at least a quarter of the ground-floor area – had been boarded over. At the pond-end several of these boards had collapsed, revealing brick supporting piers underneath, but it was not possible to see into the cog-pit. Midway along this boarded area could be seen the top of the old barrel vault in the external wall. A single cast-iron hand-wheel, some 6 ft. up on the wall adjacent to the main frames, probably controlled the flow of water to the wheel.

Upstairs, on the first floor, there was a heavy covering of dust everywhere. This was not merely general dust, it was white meal, and this, together with barley, was scattered on the floor. Several sack sleeves hung down from the ceiling, with their ends tied up with string. They were sausage-shaped, and were heavy to the touch, clearly still holding grain. On one side was an old Avery scale with a cast-iron platform, an ornate pillar, an extended balance arm and sliding weights. Nearby was a wooden grinding unit of indeterminate type, but clearly regularly used. Very little remained of the old mill machinery. Near the head of the stairs was a small

LOVEHURST MILL   BASED ON A SKETCH OF THE BUILDINGS BY A.WELLS IN 1933   RJS 1981

Fig. 62.   Lovehurst Manor Mill

rotary screen, at high level, and driven from a lay-shaft nearby. The screen was inclined, and
had a wooden frame with curved ribs braced with parallels, and covered with a fairly coarse wire
mesh having some ten threads per inch. The whole was suspended inside a wooden box hanging
from the floor timbers above. The box was about 18 in. square, and some 30 in. long, and the
screen was supported on a shaft that passed through one end and out of the other. Entry to the
screen was above one end of it. The shaft had two solid wooden pulleys mounted on it; one was
10 in. in diameter, and the other one was 16 in. in diameter. Parallel to this shaft and some 3 ft.
away was a 2 in. square, wrought-iron lay-shaft, suspended at one end by a bearing mounted on
a wall timber, and at the other end by a timber suspension frame with an adjustable horizontal
member. On this adjustable shaft was a solid wooden pulley which was driven from above
through slots in the floor. At the other end of this shaft was a combination pulley, which drove
the rotary screen. This pulley had a cast-iron hub and four T-arms that carried two wooden
pulleys, and into one of which the arms were morticed. One pulley was 40 in. in diameter, and
the other was 60 in. in diameter and was carried off the face of the larger one. This arrangement
allowed the screen to operate at either of two different speeds.

A climb up the last flight of stairs revealed the roof with its central wooden floor running the
full length of the mill, from gable to gable, with grain bins on either side. Some of the bins were

subdivided, making a total of eight, all of which were flat-bottomed, as far as could be ascertained. Five of the largest bins still contained grain – a long-grained barley. Above the central gangway was the sack hoist bollard with the old chain still wrapped around a worn wooden drum. It was driven by a wooden pulley with four morticed wooden arms, flat-faced and planked in on the side of the arms so that a section through the rim looked thus: ⌣. The belt drive rose up from below and could be made to drive the drum by raising the shaft with a long wooden lever. This was pivoted, and worked in a long slot within the timber frames on either side of the walkway. Near the other end of the mill were the flap-doors of the vertical sack hoist and above them, to facilitate the chain movement, was a solid wooden wheel with a deep grooved rim. Overhead could be seen the curved wooden beams that braced the vertical beams on each side of the walkway.

LOWER MILL, East Malling. TQ 698 576   Surveyed 1971.

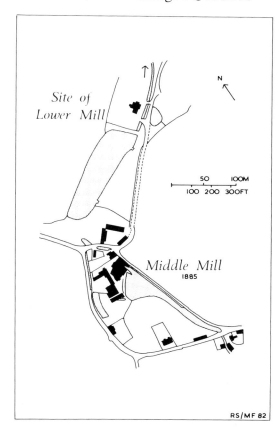

Fig. 63. Lower Mill, East Malling

There were no visible remains at all of the mill itself, although the mill-pond was in fine condition, and measured some 50 yds. in width and 200 yds. in length. At the head of the pond the water flowed over a large rocky ledge before plunging some 10–15 ft. into the tail-race, the bottom of which was itself some 12 ft. below ground level. The rocky ledge at the crest of the waterfall carried two narrow parallel grooves suggesting that this had once supported part of the pen-trough. If this was the case, the dimensions of the waterfall suggest an overshot wheel, measuring about 12 ft. in diameter and perhaps 6 ft. in width. Documentary evidence points to the mill, a paper mill at that time, having closed down in about 1850.

MAPLEHURST MILL, Frittenden/Staplehurst. TQ 803 417   Surveyed April 1974.

This mill was particularly worthy of a visit from the mill enthusiast or industrial archaeologist because it was almost complete, and was in good condition. The oldest part of the mill was built by David Papillon, whose initials and the date 1756 could be seen moulded in brick on two faces

Fig. 64. Lower Mill, East Malling

of the mill. The brick walls were extra thick below first floor level, and the roof was a peg-tiled gambrel with half-hipped gables. The later part of the building was entirely timber-framed, with weatherboard cladding, and was protected from the elements by a slate roof. A steam-engine shed had been built onto the mill in about 1890, using brick and slate. Another addition was a domestic property, probably the miller's, and this had been extended in more recent times.

The pond was long and narrow, and reached back from the mill along the length of three fields. Saplings and young trees overhung the water's edge along much of the northern bank. To reach the top of the mill-dam, a flight of millstones had been laid as steps. At least eight were counted, but there may have been others concealed by the long grass. All the stones to view

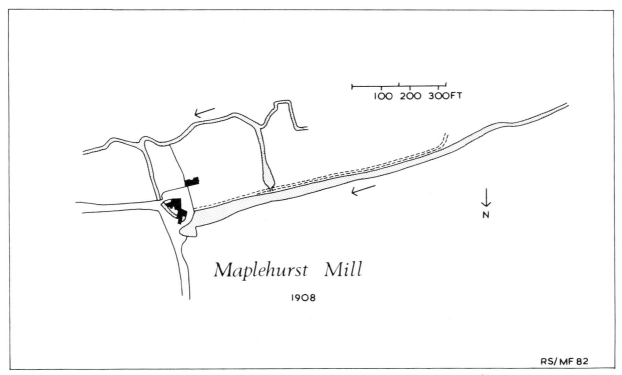

Fig. 65.   Maplehurst Mill, Frittenden

were well-worn Derby Peaks, and another one had been set in the ground outside of the mill. This was a bedstone, with a diameter of 45 in.

In the following description of the mill we have, for variety, chosen to 'follow the grain' rather than the machinery. The bin floor was entirely open to view in both the old and new parts of the mill, and there were no dividing walls. The plan of the floor shows the positions of the bins – large and small, and mostly flat-bottomed and unlined. There were even one or two small bins set beneath trap-doors in the walkway itself. Sacks of grain were no doubt stored in the large open area. The mill had two hoists, one internal and one external, both of which were served by chains from the vertical bollard (8). The external hoist chain was supported at three points by 4 in. diameter pulleys suspended above the open area, and the chain rested on planks between these pulleys. This was probably a safety feature. The changes in direction were achieved by passing the chain around twin vertical rollers. Set above the hoists was another pulley somewhat larger in diameter than the support pulleys. The bollard consisted of a 6 in. diameter, vertical, wooden shaft protected with metal strips to form a wearing face. There were numerous holes in the floor, and these probably marked the positions where flour and grain chutes had since been removed. In the rafters was a section of a screw conveyor complete with its wooden boxing, although rather rusty around its metal blades.

On a lower part of the bin floor, beside the walkway, was a flour-grading machine made by William Gardner of Gloucester. The drive for this machine had once been taken from shaft (e) on the floor below, but had since been disconnected. For control of the hoists from this part of the floor a lever was positioned beside the head of the stairs. The sack hoist bollard was driven from below via a friction-wheel that allowed the drive to be slipped, if a load had to be lowered.

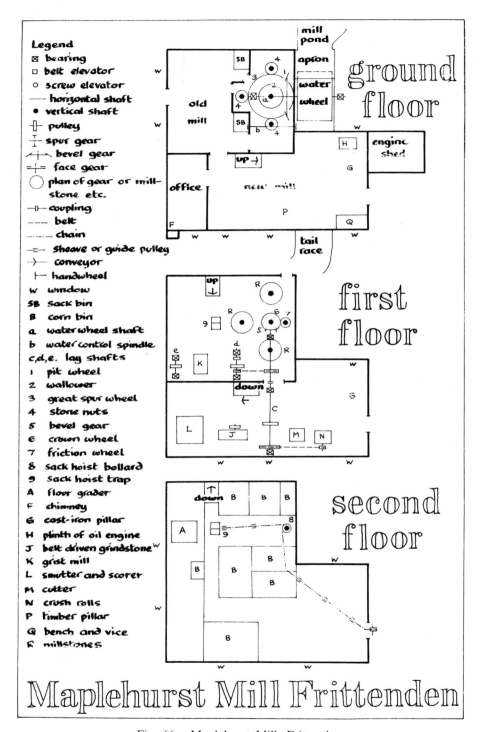

Fig. 66.   Maplehurst Mill, Frittenden

On the first floor, the old and new parts of the mill were divided by what had once been an external wall. The doorway had been removed and, at high level, there was a 2 in. square, horizontal lay-shaft made of wrought iron. The drive to this floor from the ground floor was provided by a substantial, 16-sided, vertical wooden shaft that was approximately 12 in. in diameter. This shaft carried a cross-head gudgeon at its upper end, and was bound with split and bolted hoops at this point. Near to the top of this shaft was a large, single-piece, cast-iron, morticed crown wheel having eight + section arms. The rim carried seventy-two teeth, each held in position by steel pins on the underside. This crown wheel was mounted on a tapered, octagonal wooden sleeve, and drove all the ancillary machinery, including the sack hoist. The hoist took its power from a friction-wheel (7) that turned against the outer face of the crown wheel. The friction-wheel was made of wood, and measured 28 × 4 in., and consisted of six radial segments mounted on a vertical shaft. This was supported in a thrust, or footstep, bearing, and contained a gudgeon. The shaft was strengthened at this point by iron bands. The bearing was attached to a hinged lever, which could be raised via a cord, accesible from either this floor or the bin floor above, thus allowing the miller to activate the hoist from either floor.

The lay-shaft (c) carried a cast-iron, four-armed bevel gear (5) having eighteen teeth. Three pulleys were mounted on this shaft. The first, which drove lay-shaft (d), was a 29 in. diameter, flat, wooden-rimmed pulley. It had a cast-iron hub with a square bore, wooden keys, and four + section cast arms morticed into the rim. The second pulley, in the middle of the new mill, was similarly constructed, except that the wooden rim was segmented and laminated. The third pulley, at the end of the shaft, was a large, single-piece, cast-iron pulley with six oval-section arms. At one time, these last two pulleys had driven the various machines remaining in this area of the mill, including a belt-driven grindstone (J) for sharpening the tools. The smutter bore the words 'Barnards New Horizontal Adjustable Size O, speed 500'.

In the new area was a large cast-iron pillar (G) supporting the floor above, and, for additional strength, the floor-joists adjacent to this pillar were cross-braced with wooden struts. An identical pillar and bracing were below this one, on the ground floor.

Lay-shaft (d) was 2 in. square and was made of wrought-iron, with turned end-supports set in bearings slung from the floor timbers above. There were three different diameter pulleys on the shaft, and this arrangement was the forerunner of the three-cone pulley. The pulley nearest the wall had a square, iron hub with four keys, and four arms of tapered + section were morticed into a segmented and laminated wooden rim. Overall, it measured 13 × 6 in. The pulley was coupled to that on shaft (c) with a leather belt. Adjacent to this was a 21 in. diameter pulley of identical construction, while, on the other end of this rather short shaft, was a 9 × 3¼ in. solid wooden pulley. In one corner of this floor, suspended from the ceiling timbers, was another short, square-section, horizontal shaft (e) carrying a single, solid wooden pulley measuring 13 × 3 in. This was probably the drive for the flour-grading machine on the floor above. Close by, on the floor, was a 48 in. diameter and 9 in. wide pulley with a solid segmented and laminated rim mounted on four, tapered, + section arms. This was set onto a square hub having a square bore. Nearby was a set of platform scales and a sack barrow. Between the two short lay-shafts was a grist machine (K) inscribed 'Feltons Patent American Grist Mill'. This was hopper-fed, with a side outlet, and had a fly-wheel mounted on one end of the drive shaft.

Maplehurst Mill had three pairs of mill-stones (r). There were two pairs of Derby Peaks – 48 in. in diameter and with 10 in. diameter eyes; and one pair of French burrs for grinding wheat. This pair was 44 in. in diameter, and the eye was 11 in. across. Its runner stone, being 10 in. thick, was still fairly new, and was still bound with four iron hoops. It had, on its upper surface, three, equidistant, flush, edge-plates with the name 'Hughes, Dover & London' cast on them.

The eye had a cast-iron rim plate bearing the same inscription. This pair of stones was without a casing and feed system, but the Peak stones were generally complete, each with its tun, horse, hopper, shoe and damsel. The steel springs for tensioning the shoe were still in place, but the wire or cord for these and the feed alarm were absent. Nearby stood a millstone crane.

The entry to the mill was a stable door, and on the upper half of the lower door was a scratch dial put there by a previous miller. The shadow cast by the door-jamb moved across the dial to give a rough idea of the time of day but, as with all such dials, they become almost useless on a cloudy day. Inside the mill, and some 8–10 ft. from the door was a most unusual feature. On one of the main ceiling beams were carved two letters, a few feet apart; 'F' for Frittenden and 'S' for Staplehurst, confirming the passage of the parish boundary through the mill itself. A suprisingly large number of watermills have parish boundaries running nearby, usually through the mill-pond and along the course of the stream, and this reflects the boundaries having been founded or delineated by physical features. Also, where a mill stood partly in one parish and partly in another one, it paid rates to both parishes; thus there may also have been some interest of a pecuniary nature. Boundary stones may therefore be found close to such mills, but it is rare that such internal marks were made.

The cog-pit in this mill was divided off from the remainder of the building by a partition wall of beams, studding and boards. A normal-width door admitted one to the right-hand portion of the chamber, and two additional doors allowed access to the gearing in the pit.

The octagonal wooden water-wheel shaft was supported by a bearing on the mill side of the pit. It had a cross-head gudgeon and four hoops, thus comprising the same arrangement as existed at the other, external, end of the shaft. The pit-wheel was of cast-iron, morticed, split in halves, and bolted at the rim and hub. It had eight T-section arms, and the cast-iron rim carried ninety-two wooden cogs which, as well as having been driven into the mortices, were each locked in position by two nails driven one into each side of each cog at the rear of the casting. The gear was held in position on the wheel-shaft by wooden packing pieces running the full length of the octagonal faces. Between this and the octagonal bore of the pit-wheel were numerous pieces of wood. This arrangement, combined with the separate cast-iron octagonal sleeves inside the hubs of the water-wheel, suggested that this shaft may have been a replacement for a larger original shaft. During the severe winter of 1947 the mill-wheel froze solid, and attempts to free it resulted in damage to the gearing. Evidence of this was seen during the survey, for the pit-wheel had obviously moved in towards the water-wheel by several inches.

The wallower, which no longer engaged the pit-wheel because of this damage, was a single casting and had thirty-four teeth. It had an octagonal bore and hub, and eight flat arms, or braces – for they were only a few inches in length, radiated from the corners of the hub towards the rim. The bore of the wallower was packed with wood onto the wooden, octagonal, vertical shaft. At its lower end, it was circular in section and housed a cross-head gudgeon, and was strengthened with three hoops. There was also another iron hoop higher up the shaft, on the octagonal section. The gudgeon was supported in a footstep bearing housed in an open-top emplacement box having an adjusting screw in each of its four faces. The box was cast into the top of a broad iron arch that spanned the water-wheel shaft. The arch had a flat section which was carried through to the feet on either side, and did not have any strengthening ribs or webs. It appeared to be of the same pattern as the arch seen at Goudhurst mill, and they may therefore both have originated from the same foundry.

The great spur-wheel was a single casting, and had one hundred and twenty cogs morticed into the rim, with nails driven into the back end of each cog, at the top and bottom. These served to prevent any movement of the cogs should the joint have become loose. The rim was supported by eight T-section arms radiating from the octagonal bore hub, which was packed with wood onto the vertical shaft. The great spur-wheel engaged three cast-iron stone nuts (4), each having four + section arms and twenty-four teeth. The stone nut nearest to the mill-pond was pushed up out of gear by a large metal collar via a forked arm that was screwed up by a hand-wheel. The footstep bearing was housed in the usual type of bridging-box, having adjustable bolts, mounted on a timber bridge-tree which was pivoted at one end, and levered at the other end for tentering the millstones. Both of the other bridge-trees were made of cast-iron; that furthest from the water-wheel was flat, and had the same arrangement for disengagement as previously described. The other one was curved, and had the footstep emplacement cast into it. In this case the disengagement was carried out by a yoke raised by parallel, vertical, threaded rods controlled by a hand-screw below the bridge-tree.

Above the great spur-wheel was a pulley having a wooden, segmented rim supported on a single, cast-iron flange and rim. The pulley had a circular bore which was packed with wood onto the vertical main shaft. This was probably used to turn a governor that had since been removed.

A steam engine was installed next to the mill in about 1890 or 1900, and its driving belt entered the mill through the external wall of the cog-pit. This belt drove a pulley and lay-shaft within the cog-pit, but both the engine and its drive had since been removed, and all that was left was the concrete pedestal for one of the bearings in the cog-pit.

Between the floorboards in one corner of the new mill the tail-race could be seen gleaming, and nearby stood a plinth for an oil engine that had been installed to drive some of the crushing equipment. The flight of wooden steps from the ground floor to the first floor had become so badly worn by the feet of countless millers that they had been inverted so that the undersides of the treads could be used. They must indeed have been bad for this work to have been carried out; stairs in mills are not noted for their flat treads at the best of times.

The overshot water-wheel measured 8 ft. in width and 10 ft. in diameter, and it was made with two bays. There were thirty-six, unventilated, L-shaped buckets that were about 12 in. in depth, and the wheel had a steel sole-plate or backing sheet. There were three sets of arms and hubs, and each set was integrally cast in halves and bolted together. Each set had eight + section arms. The buckets were bolted onto inclined lugs cast into the internal faces of the shrouds, and also onto the sole-plate which was, in turn, bolted to the underside of the shrouds. The hubs had circular bores and were mounted onto octagonal, cast-iron, split packing sleeves which, in turn, were mounted on the octagonal, wooden, water-wheel shaft. This shaft was supported at the end furthest away from the mill by a cross-head gudgeon, and it was reinforced at this point with several 18 in. diameter hoops. The gudgeon shaft reduced to a diameter of $3\frac{1}{2}$ in. where it was supported in a three-sided bearing cup that was recessed into a large wooden block. The pond water used to be carried to the wheel by a wooden trough supported at the wheel end by a single vertical timber, and by a horizontal timber morticed into the wall. The vertical timber had rotted away, allowing the end of the trough to bear upon the wheel. Moreover, under the trough, the ragstone breast of the dam had collapsed into the wheel-pit. On the landside of the pit a substantial brick buttress had been built against the end of the dam, suggesting that an instability of the fabric had been recognized in earlier times.

The penstock consisted of a vertical wooden gate raised by two racks and pinions mounted on a square iron shaft carrying a cast-iron pulley on the end nearest to the mill. The pulley was between 2 and $2\frac{1}{2}$ ft. in diameter and had four + section arms. It was turned by a belt running to it from a 9 in. diameter, flanged, cast-iron pulley on the end of a spindle set at high level on the ground floor. At the time of the survey the wheel was standing in about a foot of backwater, doubtless due to a partly-blocked tail-race.

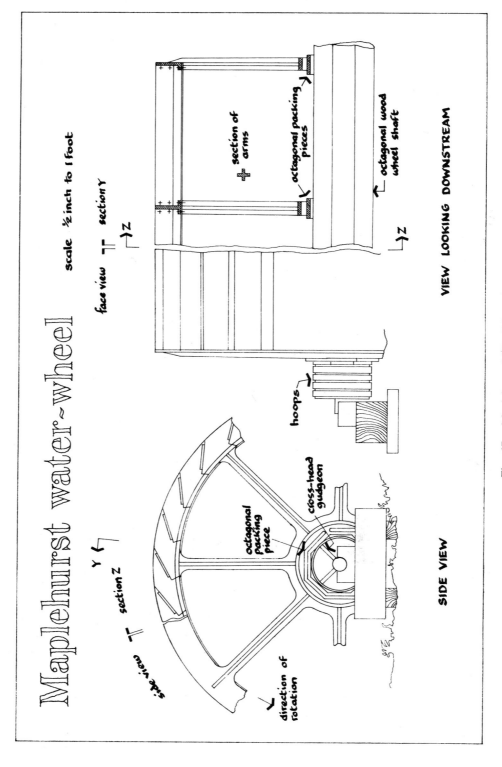

Fig. 67. Maplehurst Mill, Frittenden

MEREWORTH MILL, Mereworth/Wateringbury. TQ 673 535   Surveyed 1975.

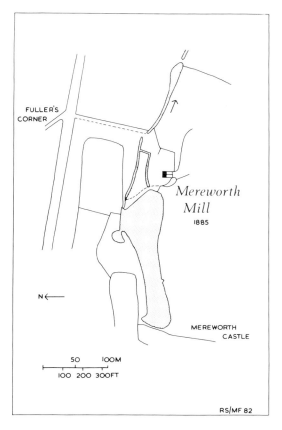

There were no visible remains of the mill or its associated equipment, which once stood at the eastern end of what were ornamental lakes in the grounds of Mereworth Castle. It is not known when the mill ceased work, but it is believed to have been between the years 1860 and 1885.

Fig. 68.   Mereworth Mill

MIDDLE MILL, East Malling. TQ 697 574   Surveyed 1971.

The site had been extensively developed since the closure of this paper mill in about 1932, and was owned by Messrs. Goldwell Ltd. in 1980 (Fig 63). Although many of the nineteenth-century paper mill buildings were still standing, there were few indications of their earlier use, and there were no visible remains of the water-wheel or pond. The East Malling stream had been piped below ground through the site, but it is known from documentary evidence that the mill-pond used to be in the south-eastern corner of the property. From the gradient of a footpath beside the eastern boundary wall, running between the tail-race and the old pond area, it appeared that the available head of water was likely to have been at least 10 ft. A débris grid protected the outlet of the short tail-race, immediately prior to its passage below a cart track, and into the head of the mill-pond, that used to supply Lower Mill, the next mill downstream.

MILL HALL MILL, Ditton. TQ 715 588   Surveyed 1969.

All that remained of this mill was the heavily embanked mill-pond, itself bisected by the M20 motorway. The mill, formerly a paper mill, but latterly a corn mill, last worked in the mid-1920s

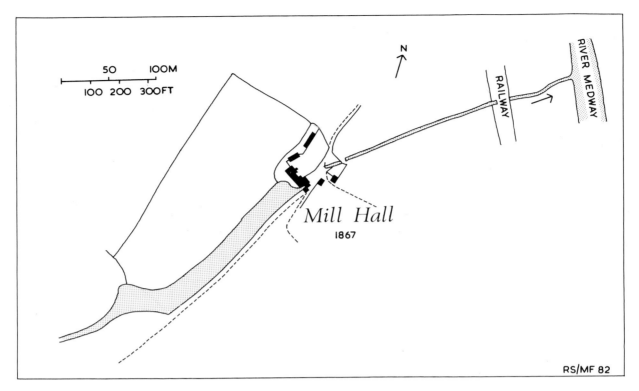

Fig. 69.   Mill Hall Mill

and was demolished in about 1950, although the overshot water-wheel and pentrough stood until 1969 when they were removed as part of the motorway construction work. It used to be a three-storey building, and contained two pairs of stones. The wheel was 14 ft. in diameter, 6 ft. in width, and carried sixty L-shaped buckets, and was mounted on a 9 in. square cast-iron axle. The wheel was made of iron – including the sole-plate and shrouds. The pentrough was 6 ft. in length and width, and 2 ft. in depth. It was made of cast-iron and carried a casting with the following inscription: 'W Weeks, Maidstone, 1887'. The sluice gate was in position and still retained its two racks, and the two pinions by which it was raised and lowered. The pentrough had been extended to the head of the pond by means of dressed stone slabs joined with tongues and grooves, and made watertight with lead seals.

MOAT MILL, Mayfield. TQ 592 248   Surveyed June 1975.

The mill lay in a shallow valley amidst secluded meadows; trees and hedges effectively screening it from the nearest public highway, and a length of unmetalled road had to be travelled before the mill was reached. The mill itself adjoined the mill-house and, although they retained their individual characters, they formed a charming, well-kept residence. Both structures had brick walls up to the first floor, and were under clay-tile roofs. However, the upper elevations of the house were tile-hung, whilst those of the mill were weatherboarded. The mill, understandably, stood higher than the house, and that portion of its gable wall that overlooked the house was

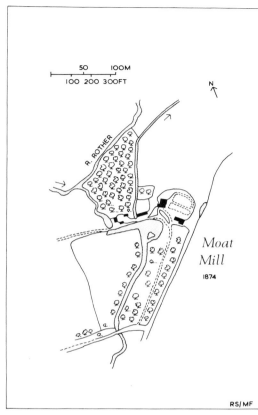

Fig. 70.   Moat Mill

tile-hung. Large wooden-framed windows, com-plementary to its new domestic function, had been built into the three main walls of the mill. In the roof of the mill, the old corn bins had been found to be ruinous and much decayed and, with reluctance, the owners had them removed. Each flank of the single-pitch roof had been pierced with two, large, flat-roofed windows.

The old water-wheel, which was still in position, had been served by a head-race – since filled in – from the river which flowed by some 20 ft. away. The trough, apron, and penstock were missing, and no water flowed to the wheel, although two drainage pipes projected from the breast of the dam towards the wheel. The pit was full of mud, topped by some 12 in. of water that spread out behind the wheel to form a small pond. There was no sign of the outer bearing and block that once supported the wheel-shaft, but whether it had been removed, or swallowed by the pit, was not apparent. Its absence probably explained why the wheel had settled, and tilted away from the mill. The water-wheel was of the overshot type, 11 ft. in diameter, and 4 ft. 3 in. in width, and had a single bay between two cast-iron frames. Each side-frame consisted of a circular hub with eight, radial, tapered + section arms. These supported an 8 in. deep rim with external flanges on the inside and outside diameters of the rim. Each frame was split into four segments between the arms, with the hub, arms and shroud cast as a single unit, and bolted together. This was very unusual, and no other examples were discovered during the survey. On the arms, the internal web was deep at the hub and ran out before it reached the sole-plate. The sole-plate was bolted to a flange projecting inside from the bottom of the shroud. Nothing remained of the sole-plate, although there may have been part of it below, in the mud. The wheel carried forty, L-shaped buckets, each 12 in. by $3\frac{1}{2}$ in., and these were probably of the unventiltated type. Each bucket was bolted to a projecting shoulder or lug cast on the inside face of each rim. They were stabil-ised by a single, mid-span stay bolted between the lip of one bucket and the heel of the next. Approximately one half of the buckets remained, although very badly corroded, but others, probably in better condition, may have lain below in the mud. Cast into the shroud was the legend 'NEVE BROS. MAKERS'.

The cast-iron wheel-shaft was 9 in. in diameter, and was reduced at the outer end for a journal. Where the shaft passed through the wall the circular barrel-vault had been bricked in, which, with a sinking wheel and shaft and a missing landside bearing, could have been causing bad stresses on the wall near the shaft.

The pit-wheel was overhung, rather unusually, and the wheel-shaft bearing was close to the mill wall. Between the pit-gear and the shaft was a hollow, octagonal, cast-iron sleeve, with internal radial webs and wooden packing strips between its face and the octagonal bore of the pit-gear. The gear itself was some 8 ft. in diameter and was a cast-iron morticed bevel that carried approximately eighty-four cogs, nailed at the back. It had eight radial + section arms, and the whole casting was in two sections, bolted together.

The vertical wooden shaft had two hoops at the bottom, and was octagonal up as far as the wallower. It was 12 in. square above the wallower, but changed to a circular cross-section again where it passed through the floor above. The footstep bearing arch was an interesting casting, and clearly had provision for containing a wheel-shaft bearing, if necessary. The wallower was made entirely of wood, except for the pins which passed down through each of the twenty-nine cogs, and the bolts that held the two parts of the body together. The split was a horizontal one, and thus passed through all the mortices. Between the wallower and the shaft was wooden packing, supported underneath by stops nailed to the faces.

Above the wallower was the great spur-gear, some 6 or 7 ft. in diameter, which had been cast in halves and bolted together along two of its eight arms. Its square shaft was wedged on the shaft at each face, and had a curved wooden block, nailed to the vertical shaft, hard up under each face of the hub. The arms were tapered on both flanges and web, and one of them bore the inscription 'new Dec 1893'. Its rim was morticed to receive one hundred and four cogs, which were pinned top and bottom, on the inside. The hursting showed that the mill had originally held two pairs of stones, but these had been removed, together with the spindles and stone nuts. Both the wooden bridge-trees remained, but the brayers and steelyards were absent. At some time a hydraulic ram had been installed to one side of the hurst, where its remains could be seen to have been fed via an inclined, 4 in. bore, earthenware pipe.

All of this ground-floor machinery was open to view, and was maintained, with the cast-iron work kept painted. At high level was a strategically-placed spotlight that showed the machinery to advantage. On the first floor, the vertical shaft, crown gear and two lay-shafts had been left in place, whilst the space had been most tastefully converted into a lounge. The old mellowed wood of the shafts and pulleys blended well with the fabrics and textures of the room, making it a most pleasant room to be in.

The vertical shaft was sixteen-sided up as far as the crown wheel, but became square within the gear. The morticed rim was segmented and laminated, with lapped and dowelled joints, and was supported from below by clasp arms. The remains of thirty-six old mortices could be seen in the $3\frac{1}{2}$ in. thick beech rim, but at the time of the survey it carried sixty cogs which had been cut flush at the back of the gear. On top of the crown wheel were two lay-shafts driven by wooden bevel gears, each with sixteen cogs. One of these gears was hooped on the edges, with the cogs pinned right through its solid body; the other one was split into halves across the mortices and bolted together. The split and bolted bevel was mounted on a wooden shaft which was octagonal in section for most of its length, but which changed to square at the further end, where it carried a single $32\frac{1}{2}$ in. × 7 in. crowned cast-iron pulley. The other lay-shaft was a 5 in. × 5 in. square-sectioned wooden shaft that carried the following pulleys in order from the crown gear:

1. 20 × $4\frac{1}{2}$ in. composite wooden pulley, without flanges, with a double-laminate cross-jointed and bolted body, with a segmented and nailed rim;
2. 23 × 5 in. double-flanged wooden pulley with a solid body, and with the segmented flanges dowelled into position. On the face of the pulley, hard against one flange, was a quadrant-sectioned, raised, wooden strip that suggested that the pulley may have been used for a narrow belt or wide rope drive;
3. Hard against the foregoing pulley was a small round pulley with a central, square, block core with segments nailed onto the four faces to produce a circular working face;

4. A 28 × 5 in. all-wood, flangeless pulley with a segmented body, and a rim composed of continuous slats.

No other machinery remained at this mill, and the corn bins had all been removed. Some distance from the mill, where the river turned, was a penstock which had the usual cast-iron frame bolted to the top beam, and a slide for the vertical, cast-iron rack, driven by an eleven-tooth shrouded pinion. The gate was held in position by a pawl running on the rim of a cast-iron, single-piece, 33 in. diameter spur-gear with one hundred and twenty-six teeth.

NEWBRIDGE MILL, Hartfield. TQ 456 328　　　　　　　　　Surveyed September 1975.

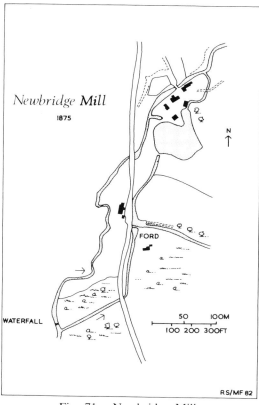

Fig. 71.　Newbridge Mill

The small, Y-shaped mill pond reflected the mill standing at the end of one of the two branches. The old mill had been converted into a dwelling, and all the internal machinery and the paraphernalia associated with corn milling had been removed. Sandstone foundations and walls up to the first floor supported a timber frame with weatherboarding under a clay-tile roof. Beside the mill the overshot wheel was still in position but, although the water still flowed over the apron, it was not applied to the wheel. A cast-iron trough, which was bolted together in sections and supported on reinforced concrete beams and pillars, carried the water over the wheel and then delivered it into the tail-race down an inclined trough. Standing over the head-race, just where the pond entered the trough, was an open-sided timber-framed shed with a clay-tiled roof, supported on brick piers. It was not clear what purpose this served but, being abutted to the mill, it may have been used as a store.

The water-wheel was made entirely of iron, being 10 ft. in diameter and 6 ft. in width. It had a single bay, between identical side frames composed of six, radial, cast-iron, tapered arms of + section. The shroud was split into six sections, which were lapped and bolted, each section having been cast integrally with an arm. Each hub had a groove cast in it into which the arms slotted. The heel of each arm had been cast and machined so that it fitted into the annular slot and was bolted to the next arm. The cast hubs had circular bores packed off the 9 in. diameter iron wheel-shaft by iron strips. The 10 in. deep shroud held thirty S-shaped, unventilated buckets bolted to curved lugs cast onto the inside faces of the shroud. Twelve, iron, sole-plates were carried on the underside of the shrouds, and each bucket was bolted to the sole-plate in six places across the width of the wheel. Further stability was provided by two stays placed between the rim of each bucket and the one behind it. Unfortunately, the wheel was in poor condition, for two arms at each side had lost the segments of the shroud that were once attached, and only about one third of the sole-plates remained.

Three water control devices remained in operation on the site; the sluice above the wheel had a drop-board gate which ran in vertical channels in each side of the trough. It hung on two chains carried on grooved, cast-iron, pulleys mounted on the control spindle which passed into the mill. Control was effected by a cast-iron, six-armed, hand wheel with a deadweight pawl. Not far from the water intake to the wheel was an overflow cill, square in plan, with brick and stone walls, which had grille bars on top, and a round wire-basket surrounding it in the water. The third sluice was remote from the mill, on the other branch of the pond above the mill-dam. When the crank was turned, the whole frame rose or fell, and carried both of the separate boards with it. Each of these could be removed and regulated by hand, independent of the main frame.

OLD MILL, Borough Green. TQ 606 565   Surveyed 1980.

The only indication that there had been a watermill here was the remains of a rusty sluice set across what had once been the head of the mill-pond in a heavily wooded steep valley. The mill-pond was dry, and greatly overgrown with nettles and grasses that softened its outlines, but it was about 75 yds. long and was triangular in shape, with gently tapering sides. The waters of the infant River Bourne flowed along the bed of the pond and below the fully-raised double gates of the sluice, which was set on a dressed-stone plinth between walls of the same material.

OLD MILL, Hollingbourne/Leeds. TQ 820 541   Surveyed 1966.

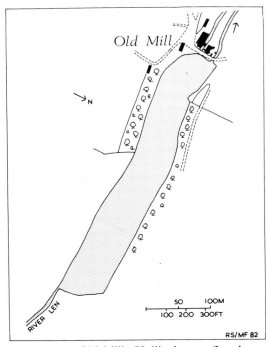

Fig. 72. Old Mill, Hollingbourne/Leeds

After leaving its meandering course through Leeds Castle grounds the River Len was joined in rapid succession by three streams, including the Priory and Hollingbourne brooks, at the head of a deep and narrow valley. Between the steep, wooded banks was the mill-pond, a quarter of a mile long, shallow and marshy at its eastern end, upstream, where there had long been a sanctuary for wildfowl.

At the mill-dam the water divided into two courses, thus forming an island. The head-race — the southern limb — became the Hollingbourne/ Leeds parish boundary. Throughout the centuries, the mill-dam, with a farm road running along the crest of it, had been built up until, by the turn of the last century, it was providing for the most powerful mill that the Len valley had ever seen. The mill had been demolished several decades earlier, and all was quiet save for the two water-courses splashing around and over the overgrown masonry.

The water still took both courses unchecked, the bypass having no adjustment because of several jammed boards. Where the wheel had once stood, the water poured over the apron and thundered down into the stream far below. It had undoubtedly been an overshot wheel, at least 12 ft. in diameter and 7 ft. in width.

PALEY MILL (HAWKRIDGE MILL), Cranbrook. TQ 777 400   Surveyed April 1974.

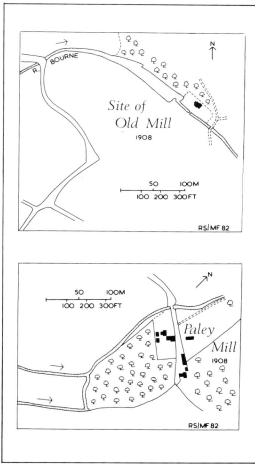

Fig. 73.   Old   Mill   (Borough   Green)   and
Paley   Mill

Had it not been for the fact that the mill was shown on earlier maps, it would have been easy to have walked past this site and not given the buildings a second glance (Fig. 74). There was no obvious physical evidence that a watermill had once stood here, although all the buildings that formed the mill were still standing! No waterways passed near the buildings – the nearest was an insignificant stream some 50 or 60 yds. away – there was no lucomb, no mansard roof, or water-wheel position, not even a depression in the land to show where the pond had once been. Were it not for Mr Tremenheere, the farm manager, our notes would have ended here. But he informed us that the easternmost building was called Paley Mill, and that the other one was called Mill Cottage. He could not recall any details that might have indicated a mill, except that, down-stream, and across the road from the mill, there had once been an orchard that had had a distinct depression running across from the mill to the stream. Moreover, he thought that there had once been a pond on the land currently inuse as a hop field. Prior to the field being levelled and planted with hops there had been some banking running across part of it. It therefore seemed as if all the water-courses had been filled in earlier in this century.

Great changes had taken place inside the buildings, and at least two periods of renovation and modernisation could be identified. Unfortunately, no further details as to what had once existed could be ascertained. Near the farm was a single, 44 in. diameter Derby Peak mill-stone with a cemented eye, and this stone had probably come from the mill.

FROM A SKETCH BY A. WELLS 1933   RJS 1981

Fig. 74.   Old Mill, Hollingbourne

PARK MILL (BATEMAN'S MILL), Burwash. TQ 670 236   Surveyed March 1975.

This watermill used to be owned by Rudyard Kipling and formed part of his estate, called Bateman's, which later became controlled by the National Trust. It was a small mill and formed part of a larger building containing the old mill-house and a converted oast. The mill had three floors and was wood-framed with weatherboarding on three of its elevations, except for a brick wall on the water-wheel face and a low brick wall on the mill-dam side. The elevation facing the main approach was painted white, as was most of the mill-house, but the other two elevations were painted black. The walls were pierced by very small windows, one or two of them being metal framed, and the clay-tile roof over the mill had two ridges, one at right-angles to the other.

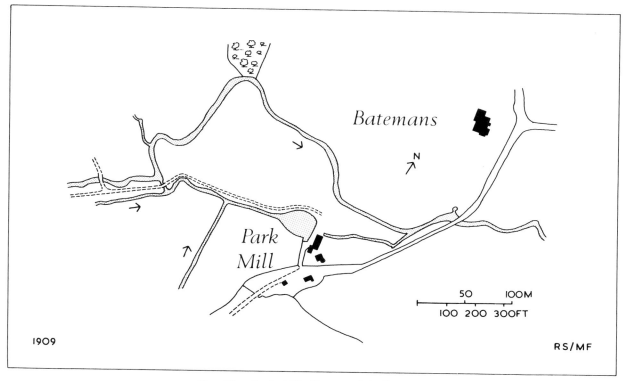

Fig. 75.   Park Mill (Bateman's), Burwash

The mill-pond was very small, and the dam was edged with brick at the water's edge. Between the dam and the building was a 6 ft. deep gulley, some 3 ft. wide, with a ragstone wall on the dam side. A back door in the mill led into this gulley and there were steps adjacent, which went up to the top of the dam. The head-race passed under the surface of the ground near the edge of the wheel-pit where it was retained by a large vertical cast-iron bulkhead carrying two gate valves set beside each other, controlling separate orifices. The plate had the following words cast on its outer face:

W. WEEKS AND SON LTD. MAIDSTONE AUGUST 1928

The orifice furthest away from the mill was circular, some 14 in. in diameter, with a spigot and flange. The one nearest to the mill was rectangular, some 30 in. wide by 12 in., and was the feed to the wheel. Between the cast plate and the apron, the head-race though was made of wood and was covered over so that the visitor could walk on top of it. At the end, immediately above the wheel, was a water-control gate, consisting of a metal guillotine plate that was operated by a pivoted lever from within the mill.

The present water-wheel was overshot, 10 ft. in diameter and 2 ft. 6 in. wide, and it was fairly new, having recently been made by a local Industrial Archaeology group. It replaced an earlier, wider, wheel which had been removed many years ago when the turbine was installed. A clasp-armed construction was adopted for the new wheel, and wood had been used throughout, except for the bolts and tie-rods. There were twenty-four buckets, unventilated, and rebated into the shrouds. They were straight, and were not radial to the wheel axis, but tangential to a circle of smaller diameter than the wheel itself; each cavity was therefore approaching a V shape. The wooden sole-plate was made up of numerous segments, each fixed to the inner

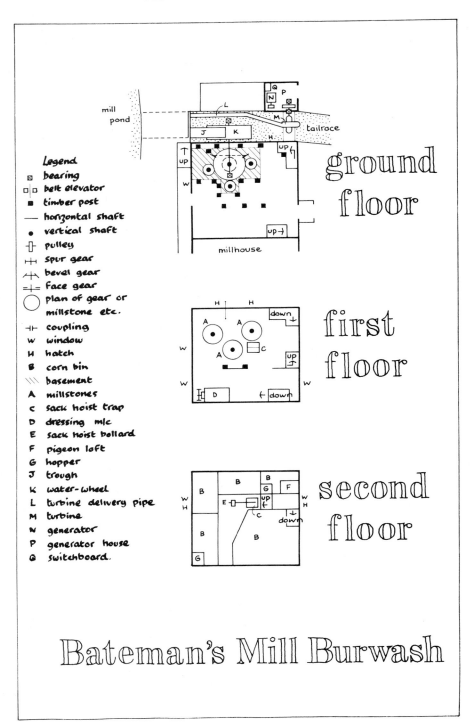

Fig. 76.   Park Mill (Bateman's), Burwash

radius of the shrouds, which were also segmented, and bolted together on their edges. Tie-rods passed between the shrouds to clamp the whole assembly together and the rims were also bolted and rebated into the arms.

Each parallel pair of arms was cross-halved into the other pair, thus giving a flat-sided wheel and each arm was packed off the oak wheel-shaft. This shaft had been made at the same time as the wheel and was roughly hewn except at each end, where the insertion of a cross-head gudgeon and three wrought-iron hoops had necessitated the formation of a circular shoulder.

Inside the mill the pit containing the pit-wheel was fairly large and this had been called the basement on the floor plans. All of the wooden posts associated with the hursting were sprung from wooden sole-plates resting on the low brick walls and cills surrounding the pit. Nearly all of these beams were new and made of oak. Two or three spotlights had been strategically placed on the beams to illuminate the pit which could be inspected in comfort from the ground floor. The pit-wheel was original, but had eighty-eight new apple-wood cogs driven into its cast-iron rim. This rim was single piece, approximately 7 ft. 6 in. in diameter and was bolted onto the eight radial, cast-iron arms which were cast integrally with an octagonal hub and bore. The arms had a T-section which was tapered on the web. Wooden packing, some 3 in. thick, had been inserted between the hub and the shaft, showing that the original shaft was considerably larger than the present one.

The wooden vertical shaft was new, nominally 10 in. square, and did not pass up through the first floor. It reduced to a circular section and was bound with three wrought-iron hoops at the top and bottom where cross-head gudgeons were inserted, and was supported by a new footstep bearing with the usual cast-iron square box and four adjusting screws. At the top of the shaft, below the hoops, there appeared to be a split, possibly a large shake, which had necessitated placing a two-piece wrought-iron clamp around the shaft. This clamp was square and bolted together on opposite corners. Near the bottom of the shaft the section had been modified to a hexagon, by the addition of shaped wooden blocks and the reduction of some of the square faces. On this hexagonal section was positioned the cast-iron bevel wallower with its radial arms and bolted-on rim carrying thirty-one teeth. At high level on the vertical shaft was the new great spur-wheel, which had four pine arms supporting beech cants and rims which were fitted with ninety-two apple-wood cogs, pinned inside at the top. The cants were straight and each one had been made from two layers of timber which carried an additional layer on top, at the edge of the wheel. Thus, the rim consisted of three laminates and the cogs were morticed between the upper ones.

This mill had three pairs of stones, two French burrs and one Derby Peak. The pair of stones nearest the pond were the Peaks and these were driven from a new cast-iron stone nut having nineteen teeth. The stone nut had four, thin, radial arms, with a tapered bore and key, and was raised off the quant by a welded ring on two push rods, which passed up through the bridge-tree. A handle on a screwed spindle raised a bar with the push rods on each end. When the mill was visited, this pair of Peak stones was being used to produce a wholemeal flour, which is unusual. The other two stone nuts were new and identical. Each was made of wood, bound top and bottom and carried twenty morticed apple-wood cogs. In each nut three slip cogs had been removed and the nut was held firm by a long, pivoted, wrought-iron latch, which registered in a large staple on the nut. The body of the nuts was split into two, the cogs being morticed into each half and the whole assembly clamped together by four bolts passing right through. Oak wedges held these two nuts on the stone spindles. Tentering on all the stones was achieved by the conventional compound lever arrangement. All of these beams were new, as also were the wrought-iron fittings, which differed slightly in detail from beam to beam. The adjustment at the left-hand end of the middle bridge-tree, i.e. where the bridge-tree and brayer joined, was interesting to see; it consisted of a set of wedges which controlled the adjustment in three planes.

At high level, beside the middle bridge-tree, there was a small, horizontal, double-flanged, cast-iron pulley or bollard, turned by a windlass which controlled the gate on the head-race. Between the windlass and the nearby window was a new cloth sleeve from the tun on the floor above. Hanging from the beams was a pair of sackboys. At the time, there was no crown wheel on the main vertical shaft, but it was intended that one should be installed in the future.

There were two sets of stairs to the floor above, one at each end of the mill, and like all stairs in the mill they were new. It is unlikely that there were two sets originally in such a small mill and the additional one was probably introduced to improve the circulation of visitors. On the first floor, or stone floor as it might be called, were three pairs of millstones. Two of them were 46 in. diameter French burrs and the other was a 48 in. diameter Derby Peak. They all had 10 in. diameter eyes. The two pairs of stones nearest the water-wheel had octagonal vats or tuns and both were complete with hopper, shoe, horse, damsel, etc. Nearly all of the woodwork around the Peak stone was new. The third pair of stones had no tun and the runner stone had been raised on wooden wedges whilst various tools associated with stone-dressing lay on the face of the bedstone. This runner stone had the date 1836 cast (or carved) in the plaster between the hoops. Augmenting this display was a rack of mill bills and thrifts on the wall.

In the corner of this floor was a dresser, hopper-fed from above, with the usual inclined shaft carrying six rotating brushes which dressed the meal against the circular wood-framed sieve. This machine still had the divided hoppers below, the longer one for flour, at the high end, and a narrow division at the low end for the middlings, supers or thirds, as they may be called. The high end of the inclined shaft was driven from a solid, wooden, combined pulley and bevel wheel with approximately forty-four cogs dowelled through the rim; the pulley was 16 in. in diameter with a 6 in. wide face. This bevel engaged with a small, solid wooden spur-gear, mounted on the dresser shaft. It had about twenty teeth and was hooped on both sides of the cogs.

MECHANICAL RATIOS		
Element	No. of cogs	Revolution per rev. of water-wheel
Pit-wheel	88	1.0
Wallower	31	2.8
Great spur-wheel	92	2.8
Stone nuts	19/20	13.1 to 13.7

Upstairs, in the roof, the lay-out was different from that normally found on bin floors. The gangway, which was raised above the bin floor by some 30 in. was L-shaped in plan, but its long arm was not below the ridge. The L-shaped gangway was caused by the T-shaped roof ridges. All of the bins had flat bottoms, and the three bins which abutted the water-wheel end of the mill had iron sheets lining their external walls. Part of the bin at the top of the stairs had been turned into a locked cupboard. Originally, this had been a pigeon loft, for there was a ledge and two pigeon holes with arched tops, which could be seen from outside the mill. Above the gangway, which had upstand edges to prevent the sack barrows from over-running, there was the sack hoist bollard. This was a horizontal wooden shaft, which still retained an old, rope-worked hand hoist drum made with beech rims and oak staves. The bollard was sheathed in iron, with the end link of the chain stapled into it. The clay-tiled roof was unlined and much of the tiling on the pond side was new. On the other flank of the roof, where the tiles were original, they had been bedded onto a layer of the old lime and sand mortar.

In 1902, Rudyard Kipling decided to remove the old water-wheel and install a turbine to provide electricity for his dwelling, Bateman's, nearby. He recorded this decision in his own inimitable writing in *Something of Myself:*

'The House (Batemans) was not of a type to present to servants by lamp or candle-light. Hence electricity, which in 1902 was a serious affair. We chanced, at a week-end visit, to meet Sir William Willcocks, who had designed the Asswan Dam – a trifling affair on the Nile. Not to be over-crowed, we told him of our project for declutching the water-wheel from an ancient mill at the end of our garden, and using its microscopical mill-pond to run a turbine . . . That Monday morn he came with us, explored the brook and the mill sluice, and foretold truly the exact amount of horse-power that we should get out of the turbine – 'Four and a half and no more'. But he called me Egyptian names for the state of my brook, which till then, I had deemed picturesque. 'It's all messed up with trees and bushes. Cut 'em down and slope the banks to one in three' . . . He said also: 'Don't run your light cable on poles. Bury it,' So we got a deep-sea cable which had failed under test at twelve hundred volts – our voltage being one hundred and ten – and laid him in a trench from the Mill to the house, a full furlong, where he worked for a quarter of a century. At the end of that time he was a little fatigued, and the turbine had worn as much as one-sixteenth of an inch on her bearings. So we gave them both honourable demission – and never again got anything so faithful.' (pp. 179–82).

When a London contractor came down to install a 15 in. diameter pipe through the mill-dam they came across a solid core of ancient brickwork. This work was apparently finished by local labour when the interesting discovery was made that the mill sat on a crib, or raft, of 2 ft. square elm logs.

The turbine was designed and built by Gilbert Gilkes and Co. Ltd. of Kendal, in 1903, and was installed by Christy Brothers and Middleton, Electrical Engineers of Chelmsford. It was served by a 14 in. diameter inclined cast-iron pipe (L) from the mill-dam, which provided an average 8 ft. head of water to the turbine (M). Discharge was through 10 in. diameter cast-iron pipes, one coming out each side of the turbine to discharge downwards. These outlets, which had to be submerged, were some $4\frac{1}{2}$ ft. below the horizontal turbine-axle, thus making a total head, delivery plus suction, of $12\frac{1}{2}$ ft. The turbine consumed 2,000 gallons of water per hour and generated about four horse-power when running at 280 rpm. The turbine case, which was some 4 ft. in diameter, received water from a single pipe which was aligned with the axis of the turbine, and was fitted internally with four fixed blades which caused the water to impinge on a 14 in. diameter 'runner' mounted on the horizontal shaft. This type of turbine was invented by James Thompson, who called it the 'Vortex Water Wheel'. The shaft passed into the brick-walled generator house (P) via a wall bearing and carried a 30 × 5 in. pulley. This had a wrought-iron rim and ten, circular-sectioned, steel, radial arms, and was split into two and bolted together on the shaft. The end of the shaft was carried by a bearing mounted on an 'A' standard. The belt-driven electric generator (N), or continuous current dynamo, was provided by Crompton and Co. of Manchester and was mounted on a high concrete plinth, probably to avoid the flooding of the tail-race that occurred on rare occasions. The generator pulley was 8 in. in diameter.

This generator could deliver a nominal 15 amps. and 110 volts d.c. at 1000 rpm. to fifty lead-acid storage batteries. These were connected in series and stood some 250 yds. away. When the batteries were charged, they could supply sufficient current to light ten 60-watt bulbs for about four hours.

The turbine, generator and switchboard had recently been refurbished to an immaculate condition by the instructors and pupils of the Mechanical Wing, Royal School of Military Engineering at Chatham.

POLE MILL, Boxley. TQ 774 553   Surveyed 1966.

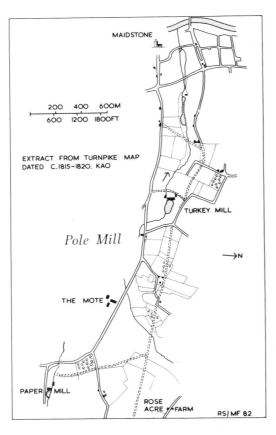

This was an unusual, perhaps unique, site, for it lay under the extensive waters of Mote Park lake. The mill was pulled down, probably in the late 1830s, and shortly afterwards the valley was flooded to make the beautiful lake which the public enjoys. Now the local sailing club course is above the old mill ponds.

Fig. 77.   Pole Mill

SLIP MILL, Hawkhurst. TQ 755 314   Surveyed April 1975.

This mill was L-shaped in plan, and was attached to a house, which had probably been the miller's quarters. Its lower elevations were of brick, with weatherboarding generally above first floor level, and it had a single-pitched clay-tile roof. Most of its windows were wooden-framed, with curved soffits in the brickwork. The water-wheel was still in place, though much decayed, but most of the mill machinery and fittings had been removed, and the rooms converted to domestic use.

Water was taken to the wheel via a concrete-based channel with converging brick walls, and then over a concrete cill lying beneath a débris grille composed of $\frac{1}{2}$ in. diameter vertical iron bars at 2 in. centres. Across the narrow end of this channel, between the apron and the grille, was a wooden footbridge complete with gate at one end. Water was carried to the wheel through

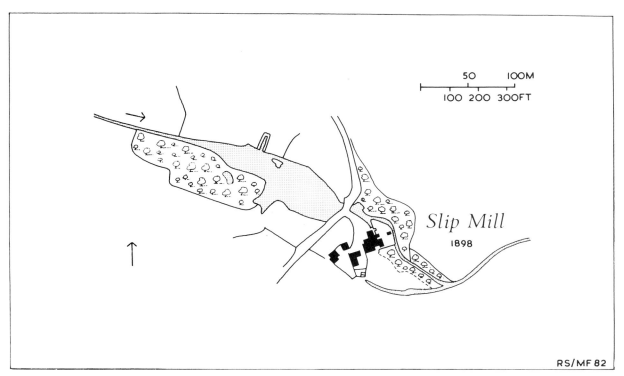

Fig. 78.   Slip Mill, Hawkhurst

a timber trough 5 ft. wide by 2 ft. deep held together by separate stay bolts passing through the bottom, and others through the side walls. At intervals, wooden struts braced the trough across the top. Near the end of the trough, above the wheel, were the remains of a vertical penstock. The mill-dam was held clear of the mill fabric by brick walls that created a deep culvert around the mill.

The wooden wheel-shaft, which had a decahedron section some 20 in. across the flats, was supported on the landside by a cross-wing gudgeon strengthened by four iron hoops. Its journal was 4 in. in diameter and was supported by the normal half-bearing in a cast-iron plummer block which, in turn, was supported by a large block of wood. The wheel was very rotted, so much so that each side-frame could be rocked independently, even though it was standing in 3 ft. of mud and water. The wheel was of a single bay, with each of the two side-frames consisting of ten, radial, cast-iron arms, of + section, bolted onto the cast-iron hub and wooden rim. Each cast hub had a decagonal bore with a casting section of about $6 \times 1\frac{1}{4}$ in., with cast boxes, at each angle, to receive the arm ends. The outer rim of the hub had a moulded profile. Each rim was in ten sections, each one being clasped by curved plates with bolts passing radially through the rims. Each wheel arm was bolted to a rim-section midway, and had a stay-bolt passing through the wheel to the other frame. The overall size of the wheel was 5 ft. by $20\frac{1}{2}$ ft., and it had fifty, iron, L-shaped, unventilated buckets, and a wooden sole-plate. Only some 20 per cent of the buckets and sole-boards remained.

Inside the mill, the only machinery remaining was the pit-wheel, the vertical shaft with three gears, and the hursting. The cast-iron pit-wheel, which was split into halves and bolted together at the hub and rim, was carried on a hub with an octagonal bore, and packed with wood off a

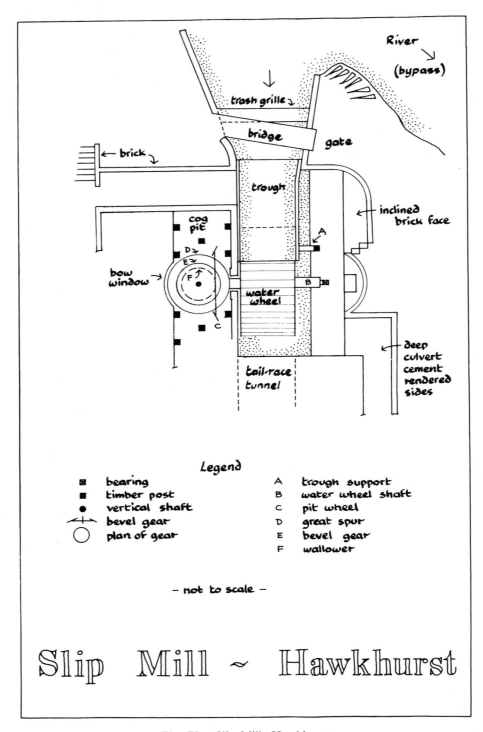

Fig. 79.   Slip Mill, Hawkhurst

wooden sleeve on the wheel-shaft. It had eight, radial, T-section, tapered arms, which supported a morticed rim carrying approximately eighty-five cogs nailed at the back on both flanks. This gear was roughly 10 ft. in diameter. The inner end of the wheel-shaft had a cross-winged gudgeon bound with four iron hoops, but it had sheared completely between the gudgeon and the pit-wheel. Both the wheel-shaft bearing and the footstep bearing of the vertical shaft were carried by a cast-iron arch with a flat plate devoid of any ribs or webs. This was supported by a large wooden block resting on timbers. On top of the cast arch was an integral box with the usual adjusting screws, one in each wall, for trimming the bearing. The vertical shaft was only 7 ft. high, and had a top bearing bolted to a first floor beam. For most of its length, it was 6 in. square, but it was tapered at the bottom; it had probably been shortened by being cut off at first floor level.

The wallower was a solid, cast-iron, bevel gear with a square-bored hub carried on two keys per face. Eight, radial, tapered, flat-sectioned arms sprang from the corners and mid-faces of the square hub, to support a rim with twenty-six teeth. Above the wallower was the great spur-wheel, which was 8 ft. 9 in. in diameter, with approximately one hundred and forty-eight cogs pinned at the back, on top. These showed a great many worm holes, and were soft to the touch, confirming advanced decay. The wheel had a single-piece, cast and morticed rim, bolted onto eight, radial, T-sectioned, tapered cast arms.

Above the great spur-wheel was another cast-iron bevel gear, with ninety-six cogs, which was split in halves and bolted together at the arms. What this used to drive could not be determined. It had eight, T-section, radial arms, tapered on the vertical flange that sprang from a square hub with eight keys, packed off the wheel-shaft by a square, cast-iron sleeve. Although all the millstones, vertical shafts and stone nuts were absent, this was probably a four-pair mill, although one bridge-tree was missing.

There were four millstones in the grounds, none of which were French burrs, suggesting perhaps that the mill had finished its days grinding animal feedstuffs. Two of the stones were 51 in. in diameter, one was 47 in. in diameter, but the other one, being difficult to examine, could not be measured.

SOUTH DARENTH MILL, South Darenth. TQ 563 698   Surveyed 1975.

This site was occupied by a firm, which was making furniture and took over the old mill in 1946 (Fig. 50). The water-wheel had gone when they moved in, so too had all the internal machinery, millstones, etc. The water-wheel was positioned under the west end of the north building. The top of the old arch which spanned the head-race could still be seen, but the pond had disappeared, apparently filled-in. In a ground-floor office, there were several photographs showing the old corn mill with a tall chimney and with a lucam at the gable end near the road. The manager, Mr Corbet, remembered finding a large oil-stained brick plinth in the southernmost building near to where the chimney stood. He suggested that it might have been for an oil engine. The lucam had disappeared because the building had been extended to the edge of the road. Where the stream passed the mill, it was bounded by brick walls and the position of the old bypass gate could be seen.

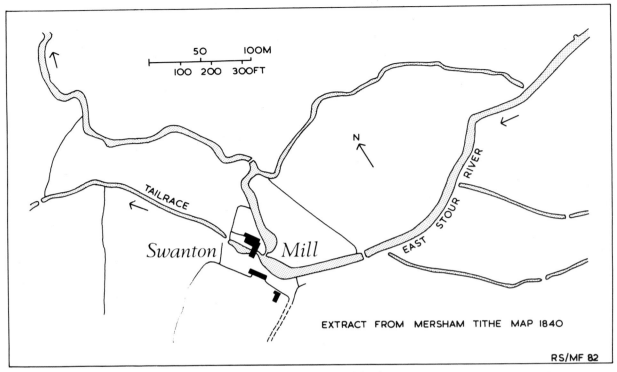

Fig. 80.   Swanton Mill, Mersham

SWANTON MILL, Mersham. TR 039 388   Surveyed 1973/74.

A cluster of red-tiled and white painted brick and weatherboarded buildings alone on a flat alluvial plain; a delightful situation but lonely in winter. In this region the East Stour had cut deep into the ground and allowed a head of water to be made without the need of embankments or mill-pond. When the boards of the water-gate were lowered at Swanton Mill, the river backed up a considerable distance due to the low gradient of the river-bed. There were three separate gates and a flood sill together beside the mill. Here, the waste water bypassed the wheel by the settings of the gates and, when the river was in flood, excess water automatically passed across the flood sill. This was slightly higher than the normal working level and yet not high enough to cause the river to overflow its banks upstream.

On the downstream face of the gate furthest from the mill was an eel-trap. Eels abounded in this river, running in the spring and at the fall of the leaf, and elvers had been noticed climbing the waterfall. Autumn eels were considered best, and the gates and the trap were set to catch the first big rain or thunderstorm when the river became muddy. The trap was designed to allow elvers to pass through and positioned so that the water did not buffet the eels, otherwise they would lose their skins. Live eels were much more valuable to a fishmonger.

The weatherboarded mill partly overhung the head water where it was supported by brick piers. Under here, in the darkness of the overhang, the water passed through a screen and penstock to the wheel. The tail-race passed through a tunnel under the garden and emerged some distance away from the mill. Mr Thomas, who regularly helped at the mill, remembered

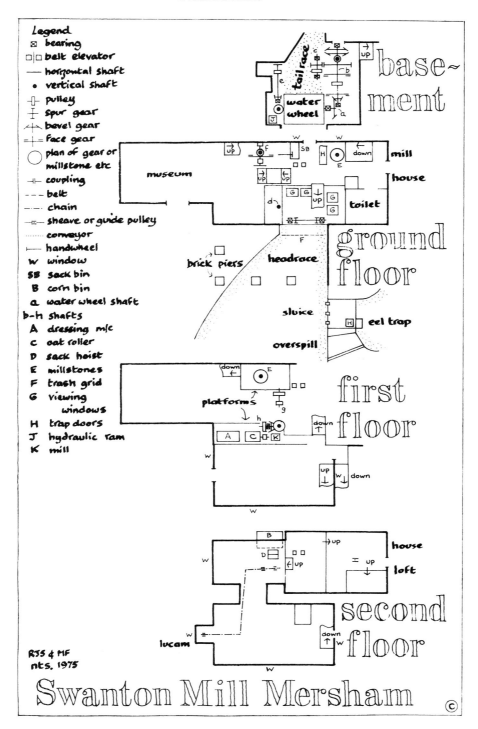

Fig. 81. Swanton Mill, Mersham

playing in the brick-lined tunnel when he was a boy. The water-wheel was an overshot one, 8 ft. 4 in. wide, 6 ft. 8 in. in diameter, and was divided into three bays. During 1973, the old corroded buckets were replaced by new steel ones welded *in situ* onto a new sole-plate, and the four shrouds were encased in sheet steel. There were fourteen, L-shaped, unventilated buckets, each nominally 10 in. long and 5 in. deep. The cast-iron shrouds were 10 in. deep and there were five horizontal iron tie-rods passing through all of them. Each of the shrouds was bolted onto six cast-iron, radial arms cast in one piece with a square hub. All of the arms, including the internal sets were + in section, and were tapered. On the shroud furthest from the mill-house there was bolted a cast-iron block – presumably a counter-weight, though whether it was added after the work on the wheel we do not know. Bolted onto the arms at this end of the wheel was a cast-iron ring gear having seventy-two teeth. It had been cast in six sections, each bolted onto the webs of the arms. The four cast-iron wheel hubs had square bores mounted onto the square, cast-iron wheel-shaft (*a*) with recessed faces. The shaft was 6 in. square, and inside each hub there were two steel keys per face. At the end furthest from the mill-house the shaft reduced to a 4 in. diameter journal carried in a cast-iron bearing block. This had a footstep bearing emplacement cast integrally into an arch passing over the wheel journal. The footstep bearing supported vertical shaft (*d*), which was driven from the ring gear. In this corner of the basement there was a hydraulic ram which had the words 'BLAKES HYDRAM' cast on it. The intake point for the ram could be seen from outside the mill, where a small trash grille rested against the bank of the head-race, under the first floor overhang. This ram used to pump water to the mill-house.

The basement housed three horizontal shafts, of which shafts (*e*) and (*b*) were driven from the water-wheel. Shaft (*e*) was 2½ in. in diameter and was driven by a solid cast-iron gear with six arms and twenty-five teeth meshing with the ring-gear. This end of the shaft was carried in a swing bearing that allowed the shaft to be moved off the ring gear to break the drive. This movement was achieved by a small hand-wheel mounted on a threaded spindle, which drew the bearing block along the paralled guides of a base-plate. Further along this shaft was a small pulley approximately 8 in. in diameter and 4 in. wide. At the end of the shaft was an overhung sprocket wheel having thirty-five teeth at 1½ in. pitch. Shaft (*b*) was driven via an overhung, cast-iron, bevel gear mounted on the wheel shaft (*a*). This gear had been cast as a single piece with a square bore having eight keys and six radial + section, tapered arms carrying a 56 in. diameter morticed rim. The fifty-four cogs had nails driven into their shanks on the water-wheel side of the rim. This gear engaged with a solid, cast-iron, bevel gear mounted on shaft (*b*). This shaft was 6 in. square with relieved faces, carried five other gears, all with square hubs and a single, solid, split wooden pulley approximately 16 in. in diameter with a convex face. The six gears are tabulated below in their order from the water-wheel end of the shaft.

There were originally four pairs of stones at Swanton Mill – two wheat stones and two for animal feedstuffs. Two of these were removed when the greater part of the old first floor was taken out. This floor used to run right through the mill on a level with the existing platforms. The mill extended into what became the sitting room of the house.

The ground-floor pair of mill-stones was driven from a 4 in. diameter vertical shaft via a cast-iron stone nut with approximately twenty teeth. This nut could be disengaged on the tapered square shaft by an iron forked arm. The shaft was carried by a cast-iron bridge-tree, which had a footstep bearing box with adjusting screws cast into its top surface. The bridge-tree was adjusted from a wooden brayer which was to view at the bottom of the basement steps. The adjusting hand-wheel was mounted close to the floor beside the tun case. The pair of stones were French burrs, approximately 40 in. in diameter, and were complete with a six-sided tun and a new horse and hopper. On these stones there was a bell alarm that was activated by a

	Teeth			Number of pieces	Arms			Method of holding shaft	Notes
Gear type	Type	Number	Holding		Number	Type	Section		
Cast-iron solid	Bevel	approx. 24	–	1	4	–	–	8 keys	Engaged the pit-wheel
Cast-iron morticed	Face	72	Nailed at back	2	4	Tapered Radial	+	–	Teeth missing, approximately 50 in. diameter
Cast-iron morticed	Face	48	Nailed at back, top and bottom	1	4	Tapered	T	8 keys	Approximately 46 in. diameter, hub had bolted side plates
Cast-iron morticed	Spur	72	Pinned front and back	2	6	Tapered	+	8 keys	48 in. diameter. drove shaft (c)
Cast-iron morticed	Bevel	approx. 64	Nailed top and bottom	1	4	Tapered	+		46 in. diameter. drove stone nut
Cast-iron morticed	Bevel	48	Nailed top and bottom	1	4	Tapered	+	–	

GEARING SCHEDULE – SHAFT (b)

suspended leather sheet – normally buried in the hopper of grain – whilst the alarm device was held off the damsel by a steel spring screwed onto the top of the tun.

Shaft (c) was currently being driven from shaft (b) but it had originally been driven by a large belt from the steam engine, which used to be positioned in the area that is now a museum. It was a twin-cylinder self-condensing beam engine made by Halls of Dartford, and had an 8 or 9 ft. diameter fly-wheel. A brass plate on the cylinder cover recorded that the engine was started in 1840. It was rated at a nominal five horse-power, and could operate two pairs of stones with the aid of the water-wheel. Mr Hancock recalled being excited, as a boy, when it was decided to start the engine in a dry period. It was a real joy to see the parallel motion slowly rising and falling, with the flashing brass and burnished rods. Early photographs of the mill show the large brick chimney that once existed. In the 1920s the engine was dismantled and passed to the Newcomen Society, intended for the Science Museum, but later it was purchased for Henry Ford's museum in America. Mr Nye could remember when Weeks of Maidstone came to remove the engine. They first photographed it from all angles, then every part was indexed with chalk or paint, and put into large wooden crates. In times of low water-power the engine was used to drive the stones, but the disadvantage of using the ground-floor pair of stones was that the water-wheel also had to be turned, as there were no means of readily disengaging the wheel-shaft and shaft (b). Shaft (c), however, could be disengaged, and this was best seen through the trap (H) in the ground floor. Each end of shaft (c) was carried in a bearing mounted in a vertical iron bar. The bottom of each bar was pivoted into a vertical wooden pillar, and the top was constrained by a wrought-iron strap bolted to the pillar and an additional bracket. This ironwork also supported a hand-wheel on a screwed spindle, which was the method of moving shaft (c), which carried a pinion and a pulley. There were two such hand-wheels, one at each end of the shaft, so that separate movements could be given to the pinion and the pulley. The one-piece, iron pinion had six cast-iron arms and hub, and carried a wooden rim faced with leather. It was some 24 in. in diameter, and was 10 in. wide, whilst the shaft was 3 in. in diameter. This pulley was, at one time, driven from the steam engine by a long leather belt.

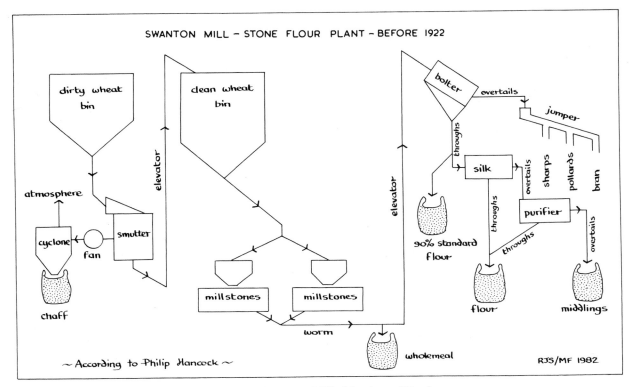

SWANTON MILL – STONE FLOUR PLANT – BEFORE 1922

~ According to Philip Hancock ~

RJS/MF 1982

Fig. 82.   Swanton Mill, Mersham (Flow)

From the small pulley on shaft (*e*) there was a vertical belt, with a counter-weight jockey, which drove a high-level, horizontal shaft (*g*) which was 2 in. in diameter. The belt drove a 26 in. diameter, double-flanged, 7 in. wide pulley. Further along the shaft was a flanged bollard, which powered the chain of the sack hoist above.

At the end of shaft (*e*) there was a sprocket that carried the 1½ in. pitch and 1 in. wide chain to the sprocket on shaft (*f*), both sprockets having thirty-five teeth. Shaft (*f*) was 2½ in. in diameter and was supported at each end by a plummer block and sole-plate. It carried approximately sixty teeth and engaged with a cast-iron stone nut with four arms and twenty teeth. This nut was keyed onto the shaft and did not appear to have any ready method of being lifted out of gear; thus the normal disengagement method was to pivot shaft (*e*) away from the ring gear on the water-wheel. Above the stone nut was a single-flanged, cast-iron pulley which carried a small leather belt across to a centrifugal governor driven by a leather faced, wooden-rimmed pulley having six cast-iron arms morticed into its rim. As the two cast-iron balls of the governor spun out with the increased speed, they lifted a collar which, via levers, lowered the bridge-tree fractionally thus causing the runner stone to bear upon the grain. Above the meal bin was a hand-wheel with five double-curved arms, which executed the same movement. The stone spindle was carried in a bridging-box with four equispaced adjusting screws. The pair of Peak stones was iron bound, and they were approximately 44 in. in diameter. Mr Nye recalled an attempt to drive this pair of stones from the steam engine – "they very soon found that they couldn't do it. It went so fast that the corn wouldn't come out of the stone; it filled up and came right over the top." Vertical shaft (*d*), which was 2 in. in diameter, was driven from the water-wheel ring gear by a morticed, cast-iron, bevel gear. This had five, radial, flat arms, and carried twenty-five cogs nailed at the back, but only on the tops. Cast into the rim of this wheel was COR 1897. Above this gear were two bracket bearings with stauffers, and a welded flange-coupling with four bolts. Higher up this shaft was a morticed crown wheel with approximately thirty-six teeth and four T arms. This gear drove horizontal shaft (*h*) via a cast-iron, single-piece, bevel gear with four arms. A short distance along this shaft was an iron pulley, with four curved arms, and this was approximately 12 in. in diameter. Below, on the platform, were three belt-driven machines.

MECHANICAL RATIOS			
	Element	No. of teeth	Revolutions per revolution of water-wheel
Ground-floor millstone	Morticed pit-wheel	54	1.0
	Bevel gear on lay shaft (*b*)	24	2.25
	Spur gear on shaft (*b*)	64	2.25
	Stone nut	20	7.2
First-floor millstone	Ring gear	72	1.0
	Bevel gear on lay shaft (*e*)	25	2.88
	Sprocket on shaft (*e*)	35	2.88
	Sprocket on shaft (*f*)	35	2.88
	Bevel on shaft (*f*)	60	2.88
	Stone nut	20	8.6

It was very difficult to see the penstock above the wheel, but it was operated by two cast-iron pinions mounted on a horizontal spindle. These engaged with two cast-iron racks bolted to the main timbers of the gate. The spindle was turned by a separate iron handle which fitted over the square shank projecting through the cladding. Behind this cladding could be seen the old curved operating lever which would have been set with a pin positioned in one of the series of holes.

From the ground floor a new set of wooden steps rose to the first floor, which was built over the head-race. This portion of the mill set above the water appeared to be of later construction than that which contained the machinery. There were two indications of this division between old and new; firstly, the old mill basement and ground floor were set against the original mill-dam and were at a level below that of the head-race. Furthermore, the later extension of the mill, taken out over the water, necessitated sinking brick piers into the banks and water without modification being made to the head-race. Secondly, the old and new mills had separate roofs, connected only by a narrow passage.

It seemed likely that, when the steam engine was installed in part of the old mill, new rooms had to be added for grain storage. The sacks of grain were brought up by the sack hoist under the lucam and were admitted through the two half-doors which overlook the yard. The rope controlling the hoist came through the floor above and was hanging down beside the doors. In the middle of the first floor was a pillar which appeared to be of wrought-iron, for it had a welded seam.

Upstairs, the owner had installed a visual display showing photographs, maps and literature on watermills, including material concerning Swanton mill. Above the old mill, the sack hoist

Fig. 83.   Swanton Mill, Mersham

chain and control rope pierced the floor and rose to a high level before running close to each
other through the connecting passage, over to the lucam. They were supported by numerous
iron and wooden sheaves, both single and double, and a wooden roller.

Up on the roof joists was a plain wooden chute and, nearby, was a single-thread, helical, iron
conveyor, about 12 ft. long. The wooden, unlined, grain bin with its sloping sides could be seen
on one side of the floor; but care had to be taken not to put too much weight on the old sack
hoist doors beside the bin, which may not be seen in the gloom of the loft. If the visitor went
down the short flight of steps, above the old mill, and moved towards the mill-house he would
have seen a delightful tiny dormer window, set high in the upstream side of the roof. There were
candle-holder holes in the cross beams. Also in the loft could be seen the apex of the
wooden-cased elevator, comprising an endless canvas belt with tiny buckets bolted onto it.

On the ground floor of the mill, where the old steam engine once stood, the owner had
established a museum of corn milling equipment. At the time of our survey the following items
were on display:
  1. A set of platform scales with ornate cast-iron brackets and fluted column;
  2. Wooden shovel with the initials TGC on the handle;
  3. A 3 ft. diameter, 6 in. thick, wood-rimmed pulley, with lapped and segmented rim. This
      has a cast-iron hub and six double-curved arms morticed into the rim;

4. A selection of mill bills without shafts;
5. A large beam scale;
6. A belt-driven grindstone with timber trestle frame;
7. A set of Victorian iron-bound corn measures, including 6 peck, 1 gallon, 1 quart, 1 pint, and ½ pint;
8. Two conveyors, (a) iron in a wooden case and (b) an octagonal wooden shaft with morticed wooden blades on each face;
9. An iron proof and a wooden staff for millstone dressing;
10. A pattern of a one-piece, morticed, bevel gear with six T-arms and a round hub and carrying seventy-three teeth;
11. A half pattern for a two-piece, morticed face gear with four T-arms and a square bore and carrying approximately seventy-four teeth;
12. Miscellaneous equipment generally mounted on the walls.

The second and final survey of the mill was undertaken by the authors during an October evening. When the work inside the mill was finished, the last task was to search the grounds for sunken millstones. The night sky was quite clear, with a bright moon high in the sky – bright enough to write by, out of the shadows, but for measuring and identification, a torch was necessary. A slow walk around the mill, searching the paths, revealed many millstones; on crossing the frost encrusted lawn, beside the rose garden near the river's edge another millstone was found under a sundial. Further on was the summer-house, where, inside, two much newer stones were leaning against the wall amid lumber and defunct machinery from the mill; one of these seemed strange until the light of the torch picked out tiny flint-like flecks embedded in the surface, as the torchlight was passed slowly across the face these sparkled and flashed. This was a composition stone, man-made with very hard small abrasive elements cast in a suitable matrix.

On finally turning back to the mill, the scene was enchanting and perhaps melodramatic. Below the mill-dam and sluice gates, mists were swirling between the river banks, perhaps generated by the tumbling water. A layer of mist was also forming above the meadows, stratifying a few feet above the ground, and upon this the moonlight shone, making it appear luminescent in contrast to the dark night sky. This scene was watched for a moment, but it was getting late and a search still had to be made of the yard behind the mill and round the old granary building. Although twelve stones were found there may have been one or two more about the grounds.

SWANTON MILL.

Fig. 84. Swanton Mill, Mersham

TABLE OF MILLSTONE DETAILS					
Type	Outside Diameter	Eye	Thickness inches	Features	Position
Composition	43	10 in. diameter	11	3 Bands	Summer-house
Peak	42	–	6	2 Bands	Summer-house
Peak	46	–	11	no bar marks	
Peak	39	–	–	–	
French	39	square	–	12 pieces outside, 4 inside	
Peak	36	9 in. diameter	–		
Peak	42	round	4		
French	40	–	–	11 elements hooped	Rose Garden Sundial.
French	46	square	–	bar marks	
Peak	41	11 in. diameter	–		
Peak	41 approx.	11 in. diameter	–		
Peak	42	10 in. diameter	3		

This group of buildings and their contents stood as a tribute to the spirit of endeavour and resource of the owner, Mrs. Gay Christiansen who preserved for us this good example of a rural watermill. Even some of the surrounding fields had been planted with wheat, which was processed in the mill to produce stone-ground flour for sale. Her satisfaction was fulfilled in the knowledge that Swanton mill was safely preserved, and one of her greatest pleasures was to meet people showing interest in the mill.

WANDLE MILL, Benenden. TQ 797 305   Surveyed June/July 1975.

Wandle Mill was sited where the southern boundary of Benenden parish, following the river Wandle, crossed the old Roman road, south of Iden Green. The present mill was built in 1828, (we are indebted to Miss Alice Reeves for this fact, and others concerning the history of this mill, which have been taken from memoirs written by her, and held by the owner of the mill). There were five floors, and the ground floor was encompassed by brick walls, with timber frame and weatherboarding above, topped by a slate roof with hipped gables. In 1856, a three-floor extension was built onto the south side of the mill, with matching fabric, i.e. brick and weatherboarding, under a slate roof. The extension contained a beam engine, boiler house, and tall brick chimney. Steam-power had to be installed because the water supply was often slack. This was a large mill, by rural standards, and must have been capable of a considerable output when powered by the beam engine and the water-wheel together, even though it was served by a relatively small pond.

The remains of this mill were most interesting; although in a state of bad decay on the upper floors, enough evidence remained to show the transition from water- to steam-power. The effect on the fabric could clearly be seen; the alterations to the drive and process machinery were less obvious but were, nonetheless, detectable to the skilled eye.

The mill was in a fine setting, amidst trees, and surrounded by pleasant meadows, while

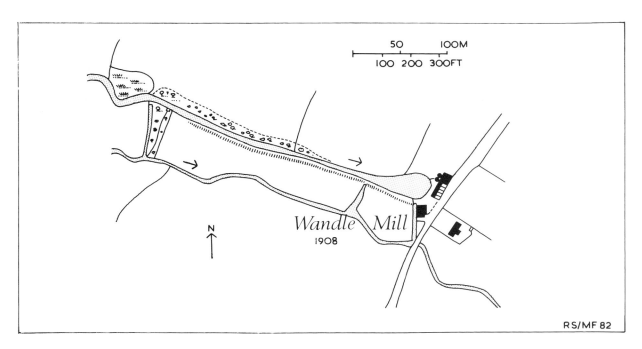

50   100M
100 200 300FT

Wandle Mill
1908

N

RS/MF 82

Fig. 85.   Wandle Mill, Benenden

opposite was a beautiful example of a Tudor, timber-framed, Wealden house. The grey
weatherboarding of the mill was in need of attention on most faces; all of the windows had lost
their glass, and many of the wooden window frames were badly rotted. On the east face of the
mill, against the road, there were double doors at ground level, and above them, on the first
floor, was another set of loading doors, with the top one divided down the middle, making two
small doors. Inside the mill, the wall which was on the south side of the earlier mill, was still in
place, serving as a division between the extension and the earlier building. An inspection of the
face of this wall revealed two, parallel, vertical, mortar joints, running from floor to ceiling. The
east one occured some 20 ft. from the east wall of the mill. Presumably, these marked the
position of the main entrance to the old mill, but when the extension was added, this was
bricked in, and a new doorway was cut into the road wall. This mill did not have a lucam, but an
external sack hoist served the road doors on the first floor.

For those with an engineering interest the ground floor was most intriguing. All of the
primary machinery was contained in the west end of the mill, furthest from the road. The
gearing was contained in a separate chamber within the mill, formed by a framed and boarded
division wall pierced with several doors and access hatches. This chamber really could be called
a 'cog-pit' because it was 6 to 7 ft. below the floor level, and contained the pit-wheel and step
bearing of the vertical shaft. The wooden ground floor of the mill had a considerable cavity
underneath, especially at the water-wheel end, where the machinery and hurst were supported
by massive brick foundations and buttresses.

The 8 in. diameter cast-iron wheel-shaft entered the mill through a large square hole in the
external brick wall. There was a bearing in the wall, but no vestige of a weather shield could be

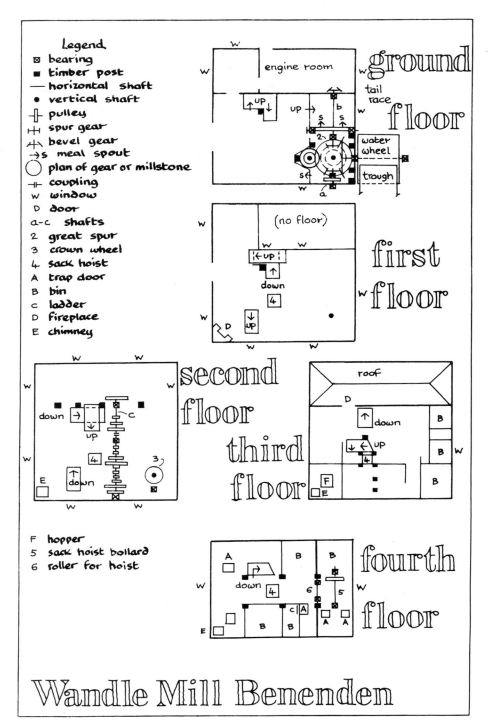

Fig. 86.   Wandle Mill, Benenden

seen and, not surprisingly, the pit was half full of water. There was another bearing at the end of the shaft, and the pit-wheel was hung between the two bearings. The cast-iron pit-wheel had eight radial ⊥-section arms, tapered on both the flange and the web, and supported a morticed rim carrying some eighty-eight teeth. The whole gear was split in halves between the arms, bolted together, and was mounted on an octagonal, cast-iron, packing sleeve with radial webs. Wooden packing had been used between the pit-wheel and the sleeve which, in turn, was hung on the square shaft with iron strips.

The wooden vertical shaft was octagonal, and measured 14 in. across the flats. It carried three hoops at the bottom, and was supported on a cast-iron arch. On top of the arch was the usual cast box with its adjusting screws in each side, and there were also long tapered wedges that had been driven through holes in the bottom of the side-walls. The arch had a long stay-bolt, presumably to stabilise the arch against any side thrust produced by the water-wheel and shaft. Mounted on the vertical shaft was a cast-iron morticed bevel gear, cogs uppermost, with + section tapered radial arms springing from an octagonal hub with moulded edges. This gear carried eighty-eight teeth and was cast as one piece, which meant that its replacement would involve either lowering it to the bottom of the shaft, or raising the shaft through it. Bolted to the underside of the arms was a cast-iron bevel ring-gear which acted as the wallower and had twenty-six teeth.

The upper, large bevel gear, drove two horizontal steel shafts, one on the north side and one on the south. The northern one was about 4 in. in diameter, and was driven via an overhung, cast-iron, single-piece, bevel gear with six arms, ⊥ in section, and tapered on flange and web. This gear carried some fifty-eight teeth, and was locked in position, probably against a shoulder, by a steel collar set-screwed to the shaft. At the other end of the shaft was a wall bearing. On this shaft was a cast-iron, single-piece rope pulley having three grooves on the rim, and measuring about 54 in. in diameter. Its round hub was probably keyed onto the shaft. Access was not possible at this end of the cog-pit to establish measurements or gear numbers with reasonable certainty. The southern horizontal shaft was 5 in. in diameter and passed from the cog-pit to the engine-room at low level, just above the floor. It used to transmit power from the beam engine to the primary driving gear in the cog-pit. This drive-shaft was supported by a bearing mounted in the wall between the mill and the engine-room while, at the other end, another bearing was positioned inside the cog-pit. This bearing was positioned below a cast-iron arch – the type more usually seen over a water-wheel shaft. The arch had a cast box on top, with a cover plate, and supported a timber column. At the end of the engine-shaft there was an overhung, cast-iron, single-piece, bevel gear having fifty-seven teeth and six + section tapered arms.

The vertical wooden shaft changed from octagonal to hexagonal at high level, and supported a large spur-gear – the great spur-gear. This had a single-piece, cast-iron hub, and arms which were morticed into a wooden rim. The hub had a hexagonal bore and was packed with wood off the faces of the vertical shaft, and was supported underneath by wedge-shaped pieces of wood mounted on each face. It carried six T-shaped tapered arms supporting a 7 in. × 8 in. rim which carried about one hundred and two cogs that were nailed on their shanks inside the rim.

On the east side of this chamber there was a triangular extension, containing a bridge-tree and vertical iron shaft. The extension was boarded out, and had a narrow access door. The cast-iron nut on the vertical shaft was the only gear driven by the great spur-gear. This shaft was $2\frac{1}{2}$ in. in diameter and carried a large pulley at high level. This had a round hub, and six curved arms that supported a curved face rim. The top of the shaft had a stauffer-fed bearing, and the lower end was supported in a cast-iron step-bearing box, with adjusting screws on each face. This box was integral with a curved cast-rion bridge-tree which was ⊥ in section, and had its fulcrum mounted on the face of a short wooden column positioned under the rim of the great spur-gear. The pulley on the vertical shaft probably drove a pulley high up under the first floor, above the sacking platform which was between the engine-room and the cog-pit. One side of this high level belt was boxed in; what it drove we do not know, for the machine had gone, leaving only a hole in the floor for its drive shaft.

The massive timber posts forming the hursting were worthy of scrutiny: these, and little else, told of the original millstone arrangement in this mill. There were signs that there had been three pairs of stones in the mill; the fulcrum and slots for the brayer could be seen for two of them; of the other one, only the circular trimming of the floor above remained, although the actual hole had been boarded in long ago. A fourth pair of stones may have existed – this would have provided symmetry around the great spur-wheel, but no evidence remained. The long, cranked, steelyards for two of the millstones could still be seen. When the beam engine was installed, its power was transmitted by the southern lay-shaft, and the northern one was put in to drive auxilliary machines on the floor above.

In 1856, the building was extended by 10 ft. on the southern side, and a small room – possibly the boiler room – was created next to the road. The remainder of the extension became the engine-room. This room probably had a wooden floor at one time, but this had disappeared to reveal two massive parallel brick piers or plinths running the length of the room. These would have supported the weight of the beam engine, and part of the floor was no doubt left open to act as a pit for the large fly-wheel that these engines usually had. Good top clearance was also necessary for such engines and this is why a first floor was omitted from the engine-room. An unusual feature of this room was the single-light lancet window, some 6 ft. high, built in the west wall of this room. There was no machinery on the first floor of the mill, and a great deal of lumber covered the floor where the stones once lay. A circular hole, boarded-in, could be seen marking the position of one of the millstones. The 12 in. diameter vertical wooden shaft had sixteen faces throughout its height on this floor, and was painted white. As there was no floor above the engine-room, the original walls of the old mill were intact, and two windows, which used to overlook the engine, were still in place. Above the first floor, the walls were timber-framed and weatherboarded, with the inside panels plastered on diagonal laths. In one corner there was a brick fireplace, and a brick chimney rose above; presumably this was within an office – perhaps the foreman's. All of the glazing was missing from the windows, and the frames were much decayed. Ivy had gained entry to the mill, forcing itself between the weatherboards, and great festoons had entered two of the windows, so that an evergreen mantle was steadily covering the plaster and laths.

The second floor was larger than the first because it extended over the engine-room. The main frame and much of the studwork remained as a division wall between the old and new sections. The floor over the engine-room had collapsed, some of it had fallen in, but much of it was still hanging, caught on one side by the built-in joists. Much of the flooring over the main mill was badly decayed, thereby making it necessary to walk on the main floor beams. The vertical shaft finished on this floor, terminating at high level in a crown wheel, which was made entirely of wood and had a quartered segmented rim. This was supported by four clasp arms, and had sixty well-worn cogs carried by the rim. The remains of a bearing axis existed close to the crown wheel showing where it had once driven a lay-shaft.

Running down the centre of the mill, from north to south, was a high-level lay-shaft and, judging by the number of pulleys remaining, there must once have been a great number of machines on this floor. The shaft was supported by three bearings, each sitting on a cast-iron drop-bracket.

The following table gives details of the pulleys on this shaft, taken from south to north.

Item	Details	Material	Diameter × face (in.)	Number of arms
Overhung pulley	Rim has internal web	Cast Iron	42 × 6	6, curved
Pulley	Solid, split and laminated	Wood	$7\frac{1}{2} \times 2\frac{3}{8}$	None
Pulley	Split with raised face	Cast Iron	$15 \times 3\frac{1}{2}$	4, curved
Coupling	With safety flanges and webs	Cast Iron	—	—
Collar		Cast Iron		
Pulley	Solid with raised face	Cast Iron	$5\frac{1}{2} \times 4\frac{1}{4}$	—
Pulley	Raised face	Cast Iron	26 × 5	4, double curved
Pulley	Rim had internal web split into halves and bolted	Cast Iron	$29 \times 5\frac{1}{2}$	6, double curved
Pulley	—	Cast Iron	14 × 4	4, curved
Pulley	Solid, split into two, laminated and bolted together	Wood	24 × 4	—
Pulley	Solid web	Cast Iron	$8 \times 4\frac{3}{4}$	—
Pulley	Solid and split	Wood	$7 \times 3\frac{1}{2}$	—
Pulley	Solid	Cast Iron	6 × 3	—
Pulley	Solid, split and laminated	Wood	$7 \times 3\frac{1}{4}$	—
Pulley	—	Cast Iron	25 × 7	6, curved
Pulley	—	Cast Iron	$21 \times 5\frac{1}{2}$	4, double curved

The third floor, which was limited to the area of the old mill, was sub-divided into chambers by wooden-framed and boarded walls. Some of the division walls showed signs of having been partly dismantled, areas of boards were missing and some frames had been cut out. There were various holes in the floor of the chambers which, with their cladding, suggested they had served as grain or meal bins. One area of the floor had sloping faces. Only one window existed on this floor, at high level in the west gable wall. In the south wall, there was a door leading onto the roof of the extension. On this floor there was an interesting wooden triangular truss rising through the floor on a north–south axis and almost touching the floor above at its highest point. It supported a vertical iron tie-rod, which passed down through the main beam under the floor below. Two other iron rods passed down through each inclined beam of the truss. The position and arrangements of this truss, lying parallel to and some 8 ft. from the west gable wall, suggested that it had been installed to take additional weights imposed on this floor. Further investigation is required to establish if it was installed some time after the mill was built. In the centre of the mill, the sack hoist was framed with posts and safety rails, suggesting that the sacks were not unloaded from the internal hoist at this floor.

The fourth floor had several grain bins on either side of a central walkway; some of the bins had been roofed over, with trap doors to provide access. Some areas of the floor had been taken up, leaving the joists to view. At the west end of this floor, at high level, was the sack hoist bollard which consisted of a 6 in. diameter horizontal shaft faced with longitudinal metal strips. In each end of the shaft was a gudgeon held by three hoops, one bearing was fixed, and the other, at the south end, was supported on a wooden pivoting beam which provided the necessary adjustment for the fast and loose pulley. At the end nearest to this adjustable bearing the shaft section was square and carried the belt-driven pulley, which was 42 in. in diameter and 4½ in. wide. It was made completely of wood, and had cross-halved clasp-arms that supported a laminated rim with staggered joints.

At a point a few feet away from the bollard, the sack hoist chain was supported by a wooden roller, smaller than the bollard, but carrying the same metal strips and a single hoop at each end. Above the hoist was a large, single-grooved, cast-iron pulley, but the sack hoist itself was missing. Each gable wall was hipped, had a central window and was rendered internally.

The mill-pond was quite dry, but the remains of the wooden trough could be seen, and the water-wheel was still in place. Part of the trough had been filled in with earth to form a vehicular track, but the end nearest to the wheel was still in place – though much decayed and partly collapsed. Both of the side walls and the bottom had been constructed of boards on a wooden frame supported on a horizontal steel beam. This was built into the gable wall of the mill and was carried on a vertical steel beam on the landside of the wheel. The decayed remains of a wooden gate were still lodged in the trough over the wheel, which was controlled by a 1½ in. diameter horizontal shaft carrying two cast-iron pinions. These engaged cast-iron racks bolted onto main timbers on the gate. On the end of the shaft next to the mill wall was an overhung cast-iron pulley with four + section arms carrying a 29 in. diameter and 4 in. wide rim.

The overshot water-wheel was made entirely of iron and steel, and carried the name of W. WEEKS & SON LTD. MAIDSTONE on the shrouds. It was 10 ft. 10 in. in diameter, and 9 ft. 8 in. in width, and consisted of two bays. Each of the three cast-iron frames was split in halves along one arm and bolted together. Each frame had eight radial arms, + in section, tapered both ways, and springing from a round hub with a square bore. The cast-iron wheel-shaft was 8 in. in diameter, and had square sections where each of the frames met it. Each of the outer cast-iron shrouds was 7½ in. deep and had a 2 in. wide flange on the inside, on which was supported the sole-plate. The centre shroud was an inverted T, and the steel sole-plate was bolted onto this and the outer shrouds at 3¼ in. intervals around the perimeter. Cast on the internal faces of the shrouds were inclined lugs some 10 in. long and ½ in. thick, onto which the L-shaped buckets had been bolted. The corroded remains of the buckets remained in the pit, which was partly filled with mud that reached nearly to the underside of the shaft, but enough remained to suggest that the buckets had been 13½ in. by about 3 in. in section. There were originally thirty-six buckets, and it is probable that they were of the unventilated type.

WARDEN MILL, Wateringbury. TQ 690 532   Surveyed 1975.

There were no definite remains to be found at this site, apart from the overgrown outline of the mill-pond along the bottom of which flowed the waters of the Wateringbury stream. It is known that the mill used to stand some little distance downstream from the head of the mill-pond, the waters from which were piped below the cart-track running between the nearby Bow Road, and Brattles Mill, the next mill upstream. A partly-hidden waterfall close to the track indicated that the head of water had been at least 8 ft. The mill was demolished in 1914, almost immediately after it had ground its last load of corn.

WHITE MILL, Sturry. TR 175 600   Surveyed February 1974.

White Mill stood on two islands formed by the bypass water, the mill-race, and a waste water-course. The Kent River Authority owned this site, and it was only with their help that

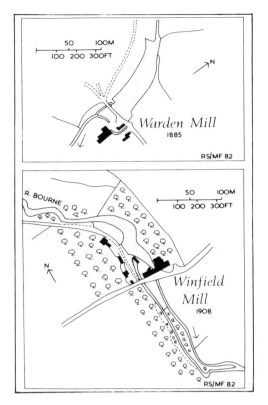

Fig. 87.   Warden Mill and Winfield Mill

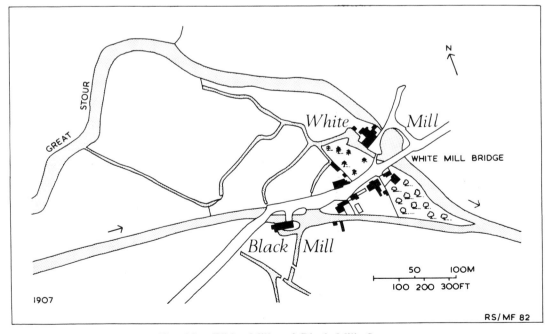

Fig. 88.   White Mill and Black Mill, Sturry

permission was given for a visit to be made to the islands so that the remains could be examined. To reach the island they provided a lorry loaded with ropes and long baulks of timber. The waterways which had to be crossed were both some 10–12 ft. wide, and it was difficult to see how two men could project a plank across, for they were $9 \times 2\frac{1}{2}$ in. in cross-section, and not much longer than the width of the waterways. However, the driver took hold of one of the baulks and casually threw it over to bridge the gap. It then became clear why a man of such heavy build had been sent to help with the operation. After firming up the end of the plank, he stepped aside and levelled an expectant look at the far from happy researcher. It was raining at the time and the wind came and went in squalls and, after looking at the wet, narrow plank and the water below rushing down the inclined bed into the raging tail pool, it was realised that it was no good . . . it could not be done! The driver was good-humoured about it, and quickly fetched a coil of heavy rope from the lorry. He tied one end of the rope to a nearby oak fence-post and sprang across the plank carrying the remainder of the coil. This answered well, and the first island was soon gained and the inspection of the turbine was under way. The same method was adopted later on to give access to the second and larger island.

Between the two islands were the remains of a water turbine, suspended from two, parallel, horizontal, steel I-joists, whose ends had been built into brick walls flanking each side of the water-course. The vertical turbine shaft passed through a bearing-block bolted to the steel beams and had a coupling just above the turbine casing. The turbine casing was approximately 4 ft. in diameter and some 2 ft. high. The outer casing comprised a set of fixed, angled, blades called 'guides' around the periphery, with a circular, cast-iron top with a hub and integral gland. On this top surface was cast the maker's name, but it was indecipherable, because of water weed caught on the hub, and inaccessible because of high water and bad weather conditions. The casing had a circular base flange, which was bolted to a timber floor which was supported, in turn, by steel joists spanning the water-course. At the time of inspection the water level was just above this decayed timber floor. The downstream side of the casing was open, and the curved turbine vanes – 'moving blades' – could be seen passing below the platform. This appeared to be an inward flow turbine, which discharged downwards. A closer inspection would no doubt have revealed more details of its working, but it appeared to have an adjustable cylindrical control plate between the fixed outer and moving inner blades. This was probably operated via a ring gear attached to its upper edge, which appeared to have been broken off together with part of the rim of the turbine housing cover. The drive to this ring gear was still *in situ* and consisted of a horizontal shaft that came through the mill wall and thence via a worm and cast-iron spur pinion, to a vertical shaft which connected to the control plate.

On top of the turbine shaft was a cast-iron, morticed, bevel wheel with eight T-arms and some fifty teeth. The horizontal shaft which this drove was missing, but a squat 'A' standard with machined top and shoulders sitting on the two main joists showed the site of its bearing. This aligned with a bearing wall-box set in the mill wall showing that the power-shaft and turbine control-shaft both passed into the mill through the same wall. It is likely that the turbine operated in a submerged state, with a head of water created by gates or a penstock just downstream of the turbine.

Some way from the turbine, across the larger island, stood the old water-wheel, which was hidden from public view by the remains of a brick wall. The head-race to the wheel had been filled in, but the wheel-pit and tail-race were open. The wheel was a low-breast wheel, although it may commonly be described as an undershot. It was a compass-armed wheel, with three sets of eight, tapered, cast-iron + arms, creating two bays. Each set of arms was cast in one piece and bolted onto the cast-iron rim, which consisted of two halves bolted together. The bolted

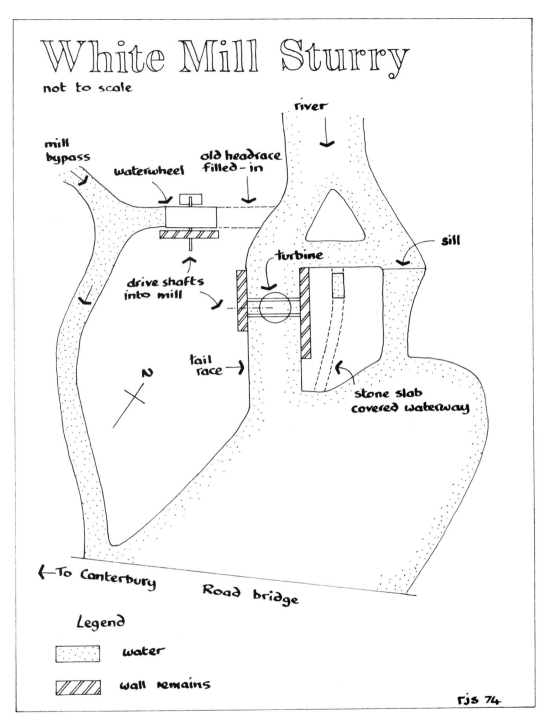

Fig. 89.   White Mill, Sturry

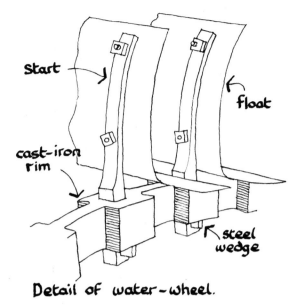

Detail of water-wheel.

Fig. 90.   White Mill, Sturry

joints of the two rims and centre piece were staggered, presumably to avoid an out-of-balance wheel. The cast-iron wheel-shaft was + in section, some 16 in. in diameter, and had been turned where the arm hubs occurred. Each hub had been bored to 18 in. diameter and packed with tapered steel keys on each of the four shaft projections. The width of the wheel was 7 ft. 2 in. and its diameter was 14 ft. 10 in. over the floats. There were forty-eight steel floats, essentially L-shaped, with 1½ in. vents, and each float was bolted to iron starts passing through the three cast rims, with tapered wedges inside. The floats were without sides and ran close to the walls of the wheel-pit. A curved breast probably existed under the wheel, but the decay and conditions of the pit did not allow an examination to prove its existence. About one-half of the floats remained in position but were badly corroded.

The wheel-shaft still had its outside bearing – away from the mill – with bottom brass and plummer block on a concrete plinth. The bearing was set on a cast-iron block with upstand walls and adjusting set screw. At the mill-end of the shaft the bearing was not in the wall aperture, the expected position, but inside the mill. Only the journal showed where its position was, for the bearing and pedestal had gone.

Nothing else remained on these islands, and when the water-wheel and turbine have corroded away there will be no evidence of man's industry on this site.

WINFIELD MILL, Basted. TQ 606 551   Surveyed 1980.

This mill used to stand beside the River Bourne but fell into disuse many years ago, and was marked as being 'in ruins' on the 1957 issue of the 1:25000 O.S. map (Fig. 87). When the site was examined in 1980, it was almost impossible to deduce anything from it, even with the advance information that a mill had once stood there. The area was heavily overgrown with scrub, reinforced at ground level with a dense carpet of stinging nettles, thus making close inspection somewhat impractical and painful. Large quantities of ragstone and dressed stone blocks were evident at a distance of some 50 ft. from the river's edge, and these were both tumbled about and in laid courses, but it could not be ascertained whether these were the remains of the mill or of some associated property.

Part of the river banks near these stones was lined in dressed-stone blocks, and a concrete and metal girder bridge crossed the river at this point, above a sloping spillway. The spillway had a fall of only 2–3 ft. and was not curved as it would have been had it formed the breast of a breast-shot wheel. Downstream of the spillway were two rebated, vertical, stone posts, set one into each bank, suggesting that they had been used to hold sluice boards. There was no sign of the overflow channel or sluices but, in view of the difficulties encountered in trying to define even the boundaries of the pond, they may have been hidden from view in the general ground cover.

II. THE WELLS COLLECTION

It may have been noticed that some of the illustrations in this book are based on works by a Mr A. Wells, so a few notes on this source may be of interest. The collection comprises 106 coloured sketches of watermills in Kent, and all are dated 1933. His source of information is not known, and in some cases it is known that the view depicted did not exist in that form in 1933. The authors have examined the sketches carefully, and are of the opinion that, despite the use of artistic licence, the general architectural details are essentially correct. The sketches have never been published, but we are fortunate that Mr Wells committed to paper his thoughts and his reasons for making the study. His notes are reproduced here in full. It was in 1933 that he collected all his data to make the sketches, and it may be coincidental, but William Coles Finch's classic work *Watermills and Windmills* was published in the same year. There is no evidence that the two knew each other, and it is not certain where Mr Wells lived. There are indications that he may have lived in or around the Medway towns.

The collection constitutes a most valuable source of information about the watermills of Kent in the period between the two World Wars.

"In compiling records of the Medway through the ages I thought I would include a few watermills on its streams and tributaries. But I got so interested in them, and thought it such a pity and neglect to let those old relics and links with the past pass away without any record of them. So I started out to snap and sketch all I could find on the Medway and its tributaries, with the result I found the remains of 81 watermills, and it was no easy task, as these mills are scattered all over the tributaries of the Medway, on roads and byeways that have long since fell into disuse – viz. mills wrecked and overgrown, ponds silted up and dangerous to attempt to walk upon to get snaps and sketches as the crust is hard, but underneath is pure bog, and you might easily sink out of sight.

Now each of these mills average 25 miles from here – out and home is 50 miles, and another 10 miles finding them makes 60 miles. That's approx five thousand miles, and several of these mills I visited several times, [so] that I must have travelled at the least six or seven thousand miles. Also [at] each mill I took at the least one film – viz. 6 or 8 exposures – that's approx at the least 500 snaps besides rough sketches. Had I time and inclination I could easily have written a book on this subject as each mill has an unique history of its own. As the youngest is 4 or 5 hundred years old, and the average 6 or 7, and the oldest a thousand years old. These are not artistic pictures but drawn as near as possible like the mills are or were from my snaps and sketches. I have made an album of the snaps so anyone can see for themselves. Anyone trying to find these mills will be disappointed as those that are still running are privately owned, and converted to make electric power. The greater part have fallen into decay or have been pulled down for the old timber and tiles for making modern houses etc. As I before mentioned these are not intended for artistic pictures, but records of the one time picturesque old water mill.

I might mention [that] the present inhabitants of the villages know absolutely nothing about the old water mills to direct or give you any information. But if I was fortunate to get hold of an old miller or old inhabitant they would go out of their way to direct or give all the information they could. Also, I was fortunate in getting all the snaps and sketches I did in 1933, as I found in visiting some of them this summer, 1935, some had been pulled down – burnt even – or otherwise destroyed or overgrown, except those that are converted for electric power.

Yours sincerely

A Wells. Oct 26/ 1935.

PS The pictures are drawn and painted in permanent inks."

III. MILLWRIGHTS' MEMORIES

ALF SPAIN   Recorded 1980.

As some mills prospered and grew, the old water-wheels could not keep up with the demand for power, and alternative sources appeared. First steam, then gas, oil and, finally, electricity spread to the towns and, later, to the remote valleys to meet this demand. It became common for the larger mills to employ their own engineers in order to reduce their dependence on external millwrights. It was quite natural that in some mills such men became known as millwrights. One such man was Alfred Spain, who for many years of his working life was Chief Engineer at Hayle paper mill, near Maidstone, where he was responsible for the maintenance of all electrical and mechanical engineering.

PLATE I

Alf Spain

'I worked at Lower Tovil Mill (Allnut's), and at Hayle Mill (Barcham Green's), from 1923. All the maintenance for both mills was done down at Lower Tovil Mill from some time in the 1850s until 1947. In 1935, I went to work at Reed's fairly new paper mill at Aylesford. Then, the war came along, and they started talking about shutting down the paper machines at Aylesford. They said, "If you chaps can find yourself a job, get one!" Temporarily I went to Short's – the flying-boat makers, and I had a year there as a turner. Then, there was a general call for people for heavier engineering – shipbuilding and what not. I thought that I would have a go at that, having been turned down for the RN, so I poked my nose in soon enough to have a choice of yards to go to, and I picked on John Samuel Whites at Cowes. A very nice little yard; a beautiful little shipyard that used to build very fine destroyers. Then I shifted down to Portland yard on emergency repairs, just before D-day. We didn't have a lot of repairs come in, funnily enough, not bad ones anyway. We got away very light on that landing really, as far as vessels were concerned.

I stayed there about eight or nine months, and then came back to Aylesford. After I had been there a couple or three years, Mr Jack Barcham Green came round to see me about starting at Hayle Mill. I thought, "Well, I don't know, it's better to be boss of your own small plant than be a nonentity in a big one." So I went back to Hayle Mill, where I was responsible for all electrical and mechanical services. I had two fitters, an apprentice, a carpenter and his apprentice, a handyman or pipe-fitter, and a bricklayer. George Spain, your great-grandfather, Bob, was the blacksmith at Allnut's, and a damn fine smith, too. "Old Fire Iron" they used to call him. I used to work with him a lot. When he used to rattle the old hammer on the anvil you'd have to go trotting out there; didn't matter who it was, you'd go dashing out there and pick up the sledge quick. Out of the fire would come the job, on to the anvil, tap, Bang, tap, Bang! And if you were a bit slow with it, he'd say "Where are you fetching them from?" Anybody had to act as striker for him. He only had to rattle the anvil and the nearest man would run. But he was a nice old boy, and the stuff he used to make, it was amazing! He used to make all his own tongs; that old forge at Allnut's was draped all round with tongs of all sorts; angle tongs, hollow tongs, bolt tongs. You never saw such an arrangement in your life – all for different jobs. And, of course, he had his big old hand-bellows. He was apprenticed with William Piper, the firm of iron founders and engineers that made the old pair of beaters that stand near the water-wheel at Hayle Mill. They went out of business in about 1870. George Spain died in about 1930, I think.

Lower Tovil had a water-wheel that was still running when I started work; it drove the agitators on the stuff chests. It was broken up and taken out before the war, in about 1928 or 1929, after I had been at work for some years. It was abandoned when we put in a 30-horse motor to run the new type of agitator. We had the bottom of the chests sculped, and vertical, propeller-type agitators put in, with a motor drive. It was a smaller wheel, smaller in diameter probably, and not as wide as the one at Hayle Mill.

The water of the River Loose was pretty foul at one time, by the time it got down to Allnut's, because in those days there was no restriction on what you could put into it. I've seen that river downstream from Straw Mill so loaded up with china clay that it looked like milk flowing through there, on its way to the River Medway. There was a bypass somewhere that used to allow clean water to come to us, and which we used for boiler feed-water and beater-floor water. The dirty water used to go down over the water-wheel and then out through Bridge Mill.

Lower Crisbrook Mill was pulled down because it had begun to get dangerous. We used to have constant trouble down there with boys getting into the mill and playing about. Well, old Smith, the scrap-iron merchant was the scrap-iron king at that time, and when the war broke out they were looking for scrap-iron, so he came along to do a deal with them over the old water-wheel in there, and he came over and smashed it up and took it out. It was all there but a bit lacey and holey. It was an overshot, with two bays, very much like the one at Hayle Mill, but not quite as big as the one at Crisbrook. The cast-iron gate is still there, and it's a fair width. Eventually, the mill got very dangerous, and it was decided to pull it down. We had some huge timbers out of it at the time – prime timbers about a foot square that we had by us for a long time, but slowly we used them up, one way or another. A firm came and pulled the mill down for the price of the tiles.

The old mill at Upper Crisbrook was used mainly for stores in my time, but it had its various ups and downs. Twice the big gear-wheel inside the wall got busted. Some mischievous boys got in there on a couple of occasions and stuck lumps of wood in between the teeth of the pit-wheel and the pinion. So twice I have been involved in putting a pit-wheel in there. The original was a very heavily-built spur-wheel, and we had another one built by Taylor and Bodley of Exeter, which more or less matched it. But the third one was made rather differently; it was made by the same firm, but by then either they'd lost the original pattern, or didn't make a pattern the same way, because this last one had big oval-section spokes instead of H-section ones. It was a cast-iron gear running against a cast-iron pinion which, as long as they were kept greased, lasted quite well. Finally, the water-wheel broke its shaft, in about 1929, and sat down against the wall, of course. We had to dig a couple of holes in the wall, underneath the arms, and pick the wheel up on a couple of girders that were put through the wall. Then, we jacked them up from the outer end until the wheel was high enough, just about at its working level, and suspended on the girders through the arms. We had got hold of a piece of six-inch-diameter steel shafting from an old mill at Dover – I think that it was Buckland Mill. Bearing in mind that the old cast-iron shaft was about nine inches square, we had to sling the wheel on that. We made up some cast-iron blocks, split in halves, and there was just enough room to get a three-quarter inch bolt through in four places to clamp the blocks onto the shaft. Luckily enough, the shaft had a keyway right along it, so previously we'd had only to plane keyway faces on the blocks – two on each face. We had to wedge the wheel on there with some temporary wedges on the blocks, swing it free, make sure that it was turning fairly true and was balanced, and then fit all the keys – a total of twenty-four keys – and then knock out all the temporary wedges.

The wheel itself had three sets of arms, cast in halves, with three bolts in each split arm, and it had some iron bands shrunk on round the centre hubs afterwards. That ran quite well for a number of years; I forget how many, but it was all finished by 1930. Then, the shaft was neglected, and it wore down to a very small diameter, about three inches, and collapsed again in about 1950. It wasn't repaired any more then, and we put in a gas-engine to take its place. In the meantime, as on previous occasions when it had broken down, we put in about a 5-horse electric motor and ran the place on that for the time being. The water-wheel drove a pump, an old six-inch bore, double-acting, plunger-pump with a massive valve box attached to the cylinder and with about six-inch diameter rubber valves on a grid seating. There was an inverted cup-shaped retainer against which the valves flapped up and down. The only trouble we ever had with that pump was the replacement of the rods periodically. The piston rods used to wear badly, until we had the bright idea of trying a bit of stainless steel in there, in about 1945 or 1946 say; and we never touched it again! We had to have one brass liner put in the pump barrel in that time – Tilling Stevens pushed that in for us. It pumped the water right up to Hayle Mill from the well which is in the garden of one of the Crisbrook cottages. On its course from the well the long suction pipe is buried in the stream – where it is covered against frost, then under the road, and up into the mill. From the pump, it runs right the way up across the other pond, and so into the tanks at Hayle Mill. The four-inch bore glass-lined pipe got broken one day when some small boys standing on the bridge dropped a boulder onto a section of it, and we had to replace it. We had just one length left in stock, funnily enough. We put that in, and in case it ever got broken again we bought a length of copper pipe, because we couldn't get glass-lined pipe then – nobody wanted to know anything about it! Since then we had a bit of trouble with dirty water getting into the system; a slight trace of mud was the trouble, so finally we decided to pressurise the whole system. Instead of having a suction pipe, that could suck up mud through any slight leaks, we put a motor pump in the well-house on the other side of the road, and pressurised the whole pipe-line up to the mill.

We didn't have to do much with the water-wheel itself. I remember they did have the old bricklayer and his mate down there once, scraping all the weed off the buckets and round the sides. Whether or not that did much good I don't know, because it probably exposed the metal to more corrosion than it was before, but it never went into holes, funnily enough. A man went down there one day in winter to oil it, without realising quite how cold it was outside. He stopped it to get some oil through the pit-wheel onto the bearing, but when he went to start it up again there was no start of course. The whole thing had just frozen solid onto the wall! It had been smearing itself round on the wall for a long time and, as soon as he stopped it, it stuck. So then there was an immediate panic – this was sometime in the morning, about 8 o'clock I think, and we all went rushing up there to start a fire. We had to make some heat in the wheel somewhere, right in the wheel itself. There was no chance of setting fire to the mill itself – a big, plain, wet brick wall was all there was there. There happened to be a lot of old timber inside, including some empty pitch barrels. We got a couple of lengths of iron fencing and put those in the bottom, settled them in, and piled some combustible stuff on the top, and then started chucking in those pitch barrels. Then we lit it, and the smoke and stink were glorious for hours. You couldn't see it! I suppose it took two or three hours cooking before it broke loose; it was already loaded with water where we'd tried to start it before, and all of a sudden away it went – whoosh! Then, of course, there were rails, firewood, smoke and a hell of a mess in there, so we had to stop it then and ash up the gate a bit decently to make sure we could get inside it to chuck all this tackle out. When it happened again, this freezing up business, we had the same procedure but, as we hadn't got as much wood-fuel this time, it took rather longer getting it free.

On one occasion I got caught in the wheel, running, after some boys had chucked an oil-drum in there, and of course the noise was terrific. It went on all night, and the people over the road were crying their eyes out in the morning! So we stopped the wheel, and we did ash it up, but probably didn't make too good a job of it. I hopped in there, and got the drum out – I was always careful to go in on the upgoing side of the wheel anyway, and the same coming out but all of a sudden, I felt the whole thing starting to move, and I thought "Hello, here we go!!" Of course there's plenty of height there, a sixteen-foot wheel, I think, room for me to stand up under the shaft. So I just toddled round in the middle like a dog in a cage until it stopped again and I nipped out smartly. Of course, there was someone there to give me a hand out a bit quick; he got hold of the top end of me, and out I came, like the cork from a bottle!

The pond supply is very constant, and there's always been ample there for what we wanted, although when they used to have a rag cutter in the mill as well, that used to take maximum power off it. This took round about another six or seven horse-power on top of what it usually did, so I suppose the total was about twenty horse-power. They used to keep the wheel shut for about an hour to build up the pond, and then let the water go full spate over the wheel to drive the rag cutter, and do about half an hour's cutting. By that time the pond was down again, but they had probably done enough by then. There was only need to use it just occasionally, for

WATERMILLS   145

preparing rough stuff – bagging and stuff like that. Then, of course, they had to let the pond recover, for fifteen or twenty minutes perhaps. They let the wheel trickle away at its usual rate, which was an output of about five horse-power, I suppose, driving the pump.

In 1928, I put in and wired all the motors at Hayle Mill when they put in the electric services, and some of those motors are still there, I know. We took out the old steam-engine, and we had the job of putting a new boiler in, but first we had to take out the little old Galloway boiler, on the roadside of the boiler-house. Then, we put in the larger one – a coal-fired Lancashire boiler. After that the boiler sank once, after quite a few years, and the boiler inspector said that it was down at the back, and that she'd got to come up. How far? About three or four inches, he said, to judge by the amount of water lying in there at the back. I looked at all the pipes up on the top of it and thought "I wonder what'll happen? We'll try it." We got underneath there and put in some thumping great lumps of girder in the bottom of the flue, and a 50-ton jack, with a nice bit of wood packing under the boiler shell itself. We took the covering down blocks off first, of course, to give a clear lift, and then we pushed it straight up, settled it on the seating blocks, and when we looked around afterwards there wasn't a single leak.

We had to cut the Galloway tubes out of the other boiler some years later, and have the holes plated over. These are the cross tubes that go through the ordinary furnace tubes. One of them started to leak one day; the stoker came round and said "Something's the matter round there; there's water in the fire, and it keeps making steam out of the fire door." I went and had a look, and I could see this black in the fire, with steam coming off it, and, sure enough, there was a little hole in the top radius of one of the Galloway tubes. We got the inspector down there; "The boiler's finished," he said, "you'll have to have a new boiler." Dear! Dear! Then we looked out in the yard, and he said "I can't drive home in this fog" – he was a chap getting on, in his fifties I suppose – "Where can I find a lodge for the night?" "I don't know", I said, "you'd better come home with me, I can fit you up all right with a bed for the night." So he came home with me, and my wife, Grace, fitted him up with a decent supper. We got to talking about this and that, and then the boiler problem. "I don't see why you shouldn't have that plated over", he said, "I'll go for that. As long as you get in the right people." So this was done, and he passed it, and it ran for several years after that until they decided to have an oil-fired boiler which, for a start, was not quite fool-proof. I remember one time when I had to go down to the mill on Christmas Day – I was there until half-way through Christmas night, and then I had to go down there on Boxing Day to see if it was still alright.

I was called out on one particular Sunday morning when I had been set to go fishing, but it was raining so damned hard that I couldn't get across to the garage without getting wet through. So I decided to stay at home. About half past eight it was, when Bang! Bang! on the door, bell ringing, and what not – "Come down at once, the mill's under water!" Off I went, in such a hurry that I forgot to take my boots with me. I was in three feet of water for about two or three hours. The yard was full of water. There was about two feet of water in the bottom of the yard in front of the offices, and all the offices were flooded. The beater-floor steps were just like a waterfall. The salle had three feet of water in it, and the vat-house was full. The water couldn't get away over the wheel and the bypass, and it was building up until it came in over the floor. Also, above the mill, it was sweeping down the road after bursting through a wooden fence up the road – or what there was of it at the time – and pouring into the yard that way. That was quite nasty, but it was the only time that anybdy had known the pond to flood.

We had two sources of spring water at the mill. One was from the high ground on the right-hand bank, going downstream; the other one was from the high bank on the other side of the stream, upstream from the mill, and about half-way up to the cottages. That one feeds into a long narrow tank, then it is piped down to a two-inch pump just inside the mill-head. Above the mill there is a narrow tank that is about sixty or seventy feet long and about ten feet deep. It has a perforated wall on the side towards the high bank, and water trickles in through little holes in this wall. A copper pipe then takes the water all the way down to the mill. It's a hell of length, about a hundred and fifty yards long I suppose. There used to be an old plunger-pump of some sort there, and the air vessel is still there, half-buried in the wall.

It was possible only at the best of times to use more than about nine inches, I suppose, of the top of the pond at Hayle Mill. After that the water was down to the level of the ingoing leat on the wheel. The wheel could provide power all day and night, but, of course, we never got the power from the Hayle Mill wheel that we did from the Crisbrook one. I suppose that we got about four or five horse-power all the time, but we never really knew. The Crisbrook wheel was much more powerful, and we could get anything up to twelve horse-power from that for a limited period, and probably somewhere about eight horse-power continuously. The pond had an area that acted as a bit of a cushion, so that you didn't drop the water-level going into the wheel quite so quickly. Rather like the air vessel in a pump line that allows the water to bounce up and down, and keep the flow constant.

One of the owners further upstream had his pond cleared out once and he let all the mud come down the river, and of course it filled our pond up. That caused a lot of trouble! If we let our pond go a bit suddenly through the bypass gates – there's a terrific build-up of soft mud in that corner – it all goes away in a rush and blocks the ponds and the stream. The lower ponds go black as far down as Reed's top pond at Tovil Mill; and they don't like it! But normally we had two ponds to settle out in, and then we didn't have to worry quite so much because they're both under our control. It would be hell if all the mill-owners let it go all together, and it would go right the way down to the River Medway. Of course, at one time when labour was cheap, they used to mud out these ponds by getting navvies up there to clear them out.

We only ever had one bother with the wheel at Hayle Mill, and that was with a bearing replacement, The pitwheel-side bearing went down a few years ago and we had to replace the brass liner. Luckily this was of brass; the other one – down at the flour mill (Lower Crisbrook), used to be of white metal. We got the old brass out, made a pattern of it and got another one cast. We didn't do the machining out, just scurfed out the face with a file so that it hadn't got any sand left in it, put it on the wheel and let it rub itself in.

The Hayle Mill water-wheel used to drive geared-in with the steam-engine, via the cog-pit. After the engine was taken out, in about 1929, the drives were left on one side of the water-wheel, out towards the size house, and it was used to drive the felt washer, the sizing machines, and one or two other odds and bobs. It was doing that until fairly recently; I think we took off the drives to the sizing machine only a few years before the change of ownership in 1972. The engine was a tandem compound. The high-pressure cylinder was about twelve inches in diameter, and the low-pressure one was about twenty inches in diameter, and it was a rather peculiarly-built engine. You usually have the low-pressure cylinder in front, at the crank end, with the rod extending through, or keyed onto, the rod of the high-pressure piston, and then through to the jet condenser after that. This one had two rods into the low-pressure piston, outside of the high-pressure piston, which was in the middle. So she had a long cross-head pin, with one rod up the centre to the high-pressure cylinder that was in front. An awkward looking thing, but she was a pretty old engine all the same. There are some photographs of it somewhere.

The Hayle Mill wheel had got a gate on both sides of the wheel. There was an overshot gate, and a breast-shot gate which had a plate to direct the flow down into the buckets. I don't know that it was any good, because you could always fill the buckets from the first gate without putting any extra on. Once they were full up and that first gate was wide open, there was no use putting water on from the back gate. I can't remember whether it was used much, because the control of both gates was left in the hands of the beaterman. The water-wheel was connected to the beaters up until the time the steam-engine was taken out; and the whole lot was geared together. That cog-pit was like the inside of an old alarm clock! The steam-engine had a shaft that went through the wall, not the crank-shaft, of course, and the three-foot wheel on this drove into the eight-foot intermediate wheel. Then, on the eight-foot wooden-toothed intermediate, there were two beater pinions and another biggish wheel driving back into the salle and vat-house. There was also another wheel, that was connected across to the other side of the pit, to gear in with the pit-wheel of the water-wheel, so that they all drove together.

The big pit-wheel on the engine-side was a cast-iron, morticed, wooden-toothed wheel, and twice I was involved in the job of toothing that darn thing. That was a busy old job – a proper old millwrighting job. The first time we did it they wanted it done in a week. We worked a day, and a night, and a day, I think it was: of course, we had a little nap. Then, we had a break the following night, and came in to finish the day and night after that. The teeth had already been rough-cut by the two carpenters there on the job. We tapped the teeth into the mortices, and then tapped them out again, and they planed off the rub marks until they went down fairly snugly within half an inch of driving home all the way round. They were somewhere about two and a half, or three inches pitch I suppose. They were pretty hefty lumps of wood those apple-wood teeth, about six inches wide – the tooth heads practically touched each other when they were fitted for a start. Well then, when that was done, we set up a tool post, and uncoupled the engine and ran the pit-wheel from the water-wheel side. We skimmed the cogs off, and their sides down, and then the wheel had to be pitched out, and that was a busy old job. We had to go round it three or four times to make sure that we got it right – six point pitching, or something like that, we put on it for a start, and got that exactly right, and then we subdivided from there. We had all the centres marked on a pitch line of course, dotted on, and we had two or three teeth on a sector of wood that just fitted on the ouside of the turned teeth, with a hole in one of them. We got the dot on a tooth lined-up with the hole, and scribed round that one and the next two. Then, we went round a bit further and did the same until we'd got it all the way round. When that was all marked out they had to be sawn down by hand. There was a carpenter on one side, with a decent hand-saw; we then, the fitters, were on the other side, just keeping the tip straight. They'd go down those teeth within a sixteenth of an inch of that mark, and then the whole lot had to be pared down with chisels. All of us used to do that, one on each side, carpenter on one side and a fitter on the other, and we'd shape the teeth right down until they were just about right. Then, we'd wind the other gears back into mesh with it – they had all had to be lifted previously, of course – then we ran them round, if they would. There might be a bit of a rumble, and a bump here and there, and then it would make it. Then, we found the high, rough places, and chiselled them off, until she was running very smoothly. It used to run with a low rumble when it had been done properly. [He produced a low inimitable running cog noise from the back of his throat – most realistic.] They used to run those for about seven years before they needed attention again.

I don't know where the apple-wood for the cogs came from – there are plenty of orchards in Kent, of course! I believe that Balston's (at Springfield Mill, Maidstone) used hickory or greenheart. The cogs were pinned underneath with horseshoe-like nails. After the cogs had been driven in, we drove a nail in underneath the rim, on each side, just to retain them. The nails were about two and a half inches long, and the heads about three-eights of an inch square.

It went at a sharp taper, and then a slower taper down the shank of the nail – much like a cut nail with a big head – and the head was all on one side so that the top was completely flat for going under the rim.

The wheel at Hayle Mill was always just dancing about in the water, but it was too much of a job to try and clear the tail-race because it was all under the floor of the mill. The bypass went down by the side of the feed-water tanks of the boilers and under the side of the boiler nearest to the road. Somebody got a small drum jammed down there once, and we had to get at it. We had to dig into the wall alongside the economisers to get down to it and get it hooked out. As far as I can remember that was about three to four feet down from the boiler-house floor-level.

The best of all our patterns got lost many years ago. There was a pattern of a half water-wheel – I think it was for the one at Crisbrook – hung up in the woodshed down at Allnut's. A beautiful pattern it was, and still as sound as a bell. Of course, when the war came along a lot of 'orrible things happened; all that sort of thing was taken out and burnt, or just stripped out, as they were after scrap-iron. They took away our manual fire-pump, with its leather hoses, that was under the Crisbrook flour mill. It was worked by four people on each side. That was really a museum piece, because I know of only one other like it, and that's up at All Souls, Oxford. We had a beautiful old oscillating engine on top of the boiler at Hayle Mill. It was put up there many years ago to operate the scrapers on the economiser tubes. It was only a little engine, with a four- or five-inch bore, oscillating with a most peculiar slide valve operation. It had a long tongue, hinged on the end of the cylinder, going down through a pair of rollers on the front of the bed so that, as the cylinder oscillated, this engine worked the slide valve on the top. Steam was fed in onto one side of the slide valve, and the exhaust went out the other side. It had a fly-wheel with a cast-iron rim, about two inches square in section and about five feet in diameter, I suppose, with beautifully moulded wrought-iron spokes cast into it. I remember that I took it out a long time before the war, when the economisers were taken out, and set it up on a little brick pillar somewhere near where the coal-shed is now. That would have been back in about 1933. It was there until the war and then, of course, I was away. That went with a lot of other things.

The gates on the water-wheel at Hayle Mill were no trouble, but they are pretty well done in now. One of them we just jog open, and we let the wheel just trickle round to keep the water clear, so that it doesn't get smelly. The wheel was never affected by ice. I can remember J.B. Green going up there figure-skating on that pond years ago; twice I think, it's been fit to skate and slide on. He went out there, put his skates on, and was cutting figures of eight, twirligigs and all sorts of things out there on the ice. This would have been in about 1926 or 27, I suppose.

Of course, they reckon that was thumping good pike fishing at one time, and there have been pike there in my time; I remember seeing one about two feet six inches long sitting up there in the rushes by the tank waiting to pounce on something that came by . . . beautiful! There were a few bream and roach about, but all we see there now are trout. There are no pike there now, of course.

The only other watermill I've had a look around to take an interest in was the one upstream at Great Ivy, where there's a turbine installed. I think it was a Francis type – a vertical radial turbine with a draught tube on it so that it kept a vacuum in it. It wasn't running then, but the owner talked about getting it running. He had a most interesting old dynamo there, a big old bi-polar machine with a couple of thumping great fat coils. Two shoe ends coming up round the armature – an old gramme ring armature – one of the wasteful ones with copper wound round and round the ring on the outside. The commutator had big bundles of gauze wire for brushes, one of the early types, round about – I don't know – 1880, 1890 or something like that, before they got down to carbon brushes.'

Although Hayle Mill did cease operations under the direct control of the Barcham Green family during the years 1973 to 1975 – as mentioned by Alf Spain – it should be put on record here that the situation has changed since that time. The mill is once again controlled entirely by the Barcham Green family, and continues to make hand-made paper, under the chairmanship of Simon Barcham Green.

PHILIP HANCOCK   Recorded December 1974.

The material for this section was taken from information related by Mr Philip Hancock, of Mersham, Ashford, a very experienced miller and mill-owner, and a wonderful person to talk to about milling. There is such a wealth and diversity of information that, to preserve the informal nature of the conversation, it has been left in the order in which it was discussed.

PLATE II

Philip Hancock

'My father rented Swanton Mill in 1902, and Hanover Mill in 1910, and in 1918 and 1921, respectively, he purchased both mills. Hanover Mill has its wheel and machinery, but a few buckets need repairing, and this work is to be done by Elvines of Faversham. It has three pairs of stones – originally there were two pairs of French stones and one pair of Peak stones, and they were all 3 ft. 10 in. in diameter, and made flour until the drop in flour milling at the time of the First World War when mills came under Government control and flour making was stopped. Hanover was quite a modern little mill for its time, with its silks and purifiers, and it used nearly all English wheat apart from the latter days when father introduced foreign flour, by a mixer, in order to get the strength – that is, a high gluten content. Whatever he did, though, he could not compete with the highly refined flour made by the roller-mills. He always hoped for a revival in country mills, and sent me on a three-year apprenticeship in roller-milling in 1912 because he thought that small mills would rise again. An engineer called Tattersall brought out a small roller-mill for the country miller, but it lasted for only a very short time. The country miller was swamped by competition from the big port mills, who imported foreign wheat to make a strong white baker's loaf that could take a lot of water. English wheat was unbeatable for scaling flour – for cakes and biscuits, and for flavour, and I still use it myself.

Red wheats were stronger than white wheats and, before 1914, a very strong wheat, called Atle, was imported from Sweden. It was a spring wheat, that was almost as strong as Manitoba. Yeoman was another good wheat, strong and quite a good yielder, but the Canadian Manitobas were so strong that no English wheat could compete from a baking point of view.

When the mills came under the control of the Ministry of Food, because of rationing, all the millers had to send in to the Ministry returns of the flour they had made, and they were then paid a form of subsidy to keep the price regulated. Thus, all the millers got a certain price per sack of flour produced, and I can remember my father receiving a small cheque, as we were millers in only a small way, but some of the larger mills did very well out of it as this payment was on top of the selling price. I can remember when, as a boy, I used to cycle to the bank in Canterbury to deposit the week's takings. I always went alone, and took the gold, silver, and cheques in a leather bag, but I had no fear of being robbed on my journey.

Grain was supplied mostly from local farmers, and the miller dealt mostly with the farmers that bought their feeding-stuffs from him as this gave a form of two-way traffic. They submitted samples and, if necessary, the bulk of the material was inspected at the farm, but, apart from that, the grain was bought on the Corn Exchange at Ashford. My father and I went there every Tuesday, and farmers would submit samples, and a bid was made, based on the market price, according to the appearance of the sample, and its moisture content. There were no moisture meters in those days, so we went by the feel of the teeth and fingers to tell if it was dry. We looked for a nice white grain for pastry flour and, for bread, we looked for a red wheat with as high a gluten content as it was possible to judge. If it was high, the flour took so much more water than the soft flours and thereby made a strong loaf. We could have bought Manitoba from the Corn Exchange, but transport charges were so high as to make it unrealistic. It came by rail to the nearest station, from where it was hauled to the mill, but even then we couldn't buy it in such quantities as the port millers and, thus, we were handicapped in competition right from the start. Port millers discharged by suction pipe straight into their bins, as, when roller-mills were introduced, it was realised that waterborne grain would be a great advantage. It was estimated that there were 20,000 mills in this country prior to the introduction of roller-mills. Country flour-milling started to decline in about 1870 on the introduction of the first, Austrian, roller-mills. Prior to 1900, flour-milling was clearly declining in the stone-mills, which then switched over to producing feeding-stuffs, but Swanton and Hanover were still making flour in

1921. Swanton's purifier and silks made it quite modern for its time and this permitted the production of the very nice white flour that was in such demand then. Of course, people now realise that white flour is not as wholesome as flours containing a higher percentage of bran, and we made flour down to about 72 per cent extraction, which was pretty good for those days. The purifier took out the flour adhering to the middlings, and sent it back to be re-dressed, but the modern purifier cleans the semolina after the bran has been extracted – the semolina is the white part of the wheat – the starch, and that is sent back over smooth rolls and reduced to flour. Roller-mills have break rolls which run at different speeds, and these take off the bran before it can, so called, contaminate the flour.

There was a revival of country stone flour-milling during the campaign for Standard bread (90 per cent extraction) round about 1910–18. The demand suddenly sprang up from articles appearing in the press suggesting that the health of the nation would be greatly improved if bread made from Standard flour 90 per cent was eaten. We were very busy at Swanton at this time producing this flour, and we worked long hours into the night. The stone-ground 100 per cent wholemeal was dressed over a bolter – with inclined revolving beaters and clothed in a coarse cloth, which took out only bran. As the machine revolved, the loose cloth beat on fixed wooden bars to knock the flour through whilst the bran passed over the tail of the machine and was taken to a jumper to extract any middlings or pollards that might have adhered to the bran. The older mills were excited about this development, but the demand for Standard flour lasted only a year or so as people reverted to using white flour again. An old miller told me of a dream he had had one night where he was walking through a churchyard in which a large notice was displayed that stated:

> "These people would not now be dead
> If they had eaten Standard bread"

We had heavy Shire horses for long-distance work, and for retail work we had Welsh cobs because they could be loaded up and still trot home, and my father bred Welsh cobs especially for this purpose. They were a recognised animal for this work as they were sturdy little creatures, and two of them could easily pull one and a half, or two tons of corn about the countryside. When they had finished unloading, five or six miles from home, they would trot back just as easy as not, whereas the old shire horses were always plodding along at the same old rate. At one time, we had five horses that served both mills – two of these were Shires, but then we had a trace horse to help get up the hills in bad weather. Especially in frosty weather, they all had to have frost nails to keep them from slipping. We changed to a motor lorry in 1921, and we were one of the first to have a lorry round about here, but we had to sell the horses, and the poor old waggoner was in tears. He used to take such a pride in his horses, and he felt it so when we had an auction sale of the horses and vans, but he learnt to drive the lorry, although when he wanted it to stop he called out "Whoa"! The men took such a great pride in their animals, but could not show them because they were always at work, except on Sundays.

Hours of work depended on the work-load and the available power, but when I started work I did a seventy-two hour week – six days of twelve hours, and this was the usual thing. When I went to Hooker's, at Canterbury, the hours were 6.00 a.m. to 6.00 p.m., and we counted ourselves very lucky when the governor reduced the weekly hours to 70, as we then knocked off at 4.00 p.m. on Saturdays. A good labourer received twenty shillings per week, a foreman received twenty-five shillings, and thirty shillings was considered a truly wonderful wage.

When my father first took the mill, it was operated by one man, but, when business increased, they got a boy, and added to this work-force as trade increased. We preferred boys straight from school, and who were keen on their work, and several lads came and asked for work at the mill.

They were given jobs, and turned out to be first-class men. They were most reliable, and were skilled craftsmen who did their work loyally and conscientiously, and if anything was wrong they came to me, and everything was settled in a family way. There were no specialised functions; each man had to be a craftsman, and dress stones and look after the mill properly and correctly, but when we became compounders of animal foodstuffs the work was divided up. We then had a crude departmental system, in that one man was responsible for milling, another for compounding, another for the stores and loading and unloading, etc., but certain of the men were interchangeable even then. The compounder had to mix up the full range of balanced rations which we made after the flour-milling stopped – these were for poultry, pigs, horses, lambs and sheep, and, in the latter days, minute amounts of medication were added. Minerals and vitamins were also added, but only ounces per ton were involved, and the operation was really quite delicate. These were introduced in the 1920s and early 1930s, and the formulae were devised from nutritional angles, but farmers also specified their own recipes. The basic ingredients were middlings, maize meal, barley meal, cod-liver oil, and Sussex ground oats, and additions were distributed by means of Fountain mixers – we had two or three of these. The additives were also pre-mixed, and fifteen or twenty minutes were required for the final blending.

Swanton Mill was sold in 1969, but I had had over sixty years there, after having been brought up as a boy there, and I felt that I did not want to return. I have a great sentimental attachment to the place, as my most impressionable days were spent there, and my parents brought up six children at the mill.

The output from the two wheat stones fed a bolter that threw out the flour, whilst the bran extracted from the back of it went over a jumper which separated bran, pollards, and middlings. The middlings from the purifier were first-class middlings, and these fetched a higher price than ordinary bran, sharps, or pollards, and we could not sell enough of these, but we were flour-millers then, not middlings-millers. Hanover had a more primitive arrangement that was not modernised because the trade was declining when the mill was taken over in 1910. There was a very unusual machine at Hanover Mill – a very long silk that extended from one end of the mill to the other. It was fed from mill-stones at its head, and was clothed with different types of silk – coarse, medium, and fine, whilst divisions underneath allowed us to take out the very best household flour, and then seconds, and a cheaper grade altogether at the end. The bran and middlings came over the tail, and went over a bran duster.

Linseed cake and cotton cake were delivered in large slabs, which were broken up into lumps by spikes on the spindles of the cake breakers, and these had large funnel-shaped mouths that accepted a slab on end. All of the cake breaking was done at Swanton Mill. The bran duster at Hanover was used to remove husks from Sussex ground oats, and the husks were put back into the stones: the grinding of these oats was a very fine operation, and a special dress had to be used for the stones. If the mill ran a little faster, or the feed was increased in some way, it would pass through some husks, but the poultry people who crammed their birds in those days wouldn't have any husk in their meal. Although the husk was returned to the stones, "the stones don't want to see it again once they have seen it. They don't like grinding empty husks."

We used to make up a 1 : 1 mixture of Canadian and Plate oats for Sussex ground oats – the Plate oats came from Argentina. The Canadian oats were always dry whereas English oats were inclined to be full of moisture, and the Sussex ground oats needed low moisture oats. The oats were mixed in a bin, and they ground very well together – the Plates were very sweet but husky, whereas the Canadians were rather soft. There was an oat roller and a maize kibbler at Hanover; the kibbler had two grooved steel plates that broke up the grain, but this was succeeded by a maize cutter that actually cut the maize in half. The poultry farmers in those days used to demand a pretty-looking maize and ours went over a reciprocating sieve that graded it into coarse, medium, and fine, and that is still there and operational.

Barley stones took twice as much power as wheat stones and, if there was a great pressure of work in hand, we used to cram the water and feed on as hard as we could and get the work done as quickly as possible – provided that the quality still remained high. The wheat stones could not be rushed, so a certain speed and grain feed had to be maintained. We had three pairs of stones, but no more than two were used at once usually, but, if they were on animal feeds, we could not even use two stones at once because of the amount of power needed. We once ran a pair of barley stones, the kibbler, and a pair of rollers together, but that was when we were on Derbyshire Peak stones. We later used composition stones that contained emery, and these were sharper and were also self-sharpening, and therefore did not need dressing so often as the natural stones. We installed nearly all composition stones at the finish, and the use of Peak stones on what was called hog corn was not a patch on the composition stones. Runners fresh from the quarry weighed about a ton apiece and, with normal use and careful dressing, they would run for about three or four years before being put down as bedstones. The dress of the stones then had to be altered, and the lands and furrows were replaced with a circular dress for use in vertical mills. The one we had ran rather fast – at about 500 r.p.m., whilst the horizontals ran at about 120 r.p.m. for wheat, and 150 r.p.m. for oats. The speeds were altered by varying the amount of water applied and, although the wheat stones had a pair of governors, they were not really reliable, as they swung out only when the mill was running at top speed. They dropped when the wheel stopped, and therefore raised the stones, and the advantage of this was that the stones did not need re-setting when the mill started up again.

Hanover had an elevator from the wheat stones to the silks, and another from the smutter to the wheat bins. The smutter had a system of beaters running against a wire sieve, and this knocked the smuts and small seeds away from the grain, and the dust, etc., fell through the sieve and dropped into the tail-race below.

Grain was bought from the farmer in whatever quantities he had, but usually measured in quarters – one quarter equals four and a half hundredweights of wheat. If, say, twenty quarters were bought, they could be delivered in five or ten quarters at a time and this was shot up in a dirty wheat bin before being fed to the smutter, cleaning equipment, and millstones. Grain was often stored in sacks, if it was dry enough, and we often bought it in against a rise in the market prices. Hanover Mill could hold about sixty tons of wheat, and the grinding bin held about twenty tons, which could last about a week to ten days on normal output. A pair of stones produced about five to seven hundredweights per hour from barley, but oats could be treated at only something like two hundredweights per hour. Sometimes, we ran into the night on overtime if we were frightfully busy, especially just before Christmas when bullocks and poultry were being fattened-up. A lot of farmers sent their own corn to be ground at so much per bushel – perhaps 3d. or 6d., and this was called grist work. It was often collected when the foodstuffs were delivered, and then taken back next week. Orders for grist varied a lot, but smallholders might order only a bushel or two – enough to keep the pig going.

After the wheat had been smutted, it was delivered to a clean wheat bin ready for the stones. Foreign oats were very dry, and we had a machine which used to moisten them via a drip feed on a tank of water, and a semi-vertical worm that fed this water into the top of the oats, which were then set aside to condition. Then, they rolled out most beautifully, flattened out like half-crowns, and they were better for the horses, too, as dusty oats could lead to broken wind. The conditioning disposed of the dust, but an imported oat was required because English oats could not take the moisture.

We also produced, through the stones, pea meal, bean meal, cracked peas, and cracked beans for lambs, and these went through the barley stone. Grey peas were good for pigs, and were included in the pig meal whenever possible. Rations were prepared for sows, weaners, fattening pigs, and bacon pigs. Layers mash, chick mash, and growers mash were produced for poultry, and also high protein breeders mash. It was very complicated, with so much to look after, and run the business, do the buying, do the office work, look after the men and lorries, and run the mill. It was a full-time job, and I was never done, as we used to work all the hours created in order to get a living, and my wife saw very little of me in those days. But I enjoyed my business and was very happy; we had good men, built up a nice trade – we never advertised, we went by recommendation, and had some nice customers, most of whom were fairly loyal.

When we first took Hanover there were several dry summers, and the breast-wheel was almost useless, so we had to take all the stuff to Swanton to have it ground, and then we had to fetch it all back again. When we could afford it, we put in a crude-oil engine that was coupled up to the mill, and we could then run in times of water shortage. The spring-fed mill was badly affected in drought as it had virtually no pond, and we could not afford the money to buy the land to make one. The springs are disappearing now because of the borings made by the water companies. The water was O.K. until the end of May but, if there was no rain, then the mill was short of water until after harvest time. The early autumn rains came in September or October, but a lot of rain then produced tail-watering, and this also prevented the mill operating. The miller used to be able to maintain a really good head of water but, when the River Board took over the river system, they provided marks for each mill, above which the water level should not be allowed to remain.

Hanover Mill was oiled up every Monday morning – the stauffers were filled, oil rings were checked, and all bearings were examined for the week. The work stopped at 11 a.m. on Saturdays, so that the mill could be swept out and be left neat and tidy for Monday morning. We very seldom had hot bearings, and all new machinery was fitted with ring-bearings and, latterly, ball-bearings. The old bearings were oiled with Russian tallow, as was the water-wheel – this ran very slowly – a nice gentlemanly speed!

The oil engine was a 20 h.p. engine and could drive two pairs of stones very nicely but, as it would have been too difficult for one man to have controlled three pairs of stones, it was never called on to try and do this extra work. It could be disconnected from the water-wheel by means of a rawhide sliding pinion that engaged a machine-cut gear, and this could also be done at Swanton where the drive was disconnected by means of levers acting on the belt drive. In the summer-time, the wheel was run with only about half a gate but, in winter, when there was plenty of water to deal with the work that day, then more water was put on the wheel. The oil engine was used both in drought and flood conditions. It was a 2-stroke Clayton and Shuttleworth that ran all day long and gave no trouble at all but then "anything from Lincoln is well made, isn't it?" We started it by pumping oil into the hot box, and swinging the fly-wheel against the compression. It was a very quiet engine as we had had double exhausts fitted, because of the neighbours, and it gave out a deep chuffing noise.

The noisiest job in the mill was rolling oats, and then you couldn't hear yourself speak, but when millstones were correctly set they were pretty quiet, and the gearing gave out only a sizzling noise, that sounded very sweet. One of my old millers, a Sussex man, used to say, "Ah, she does run sooent." The water-wheel gave out a plop, plop, plop, noise as each bucket came round filled; it was like a little clockwork thing going – very pleasant. I had an old miller was with me for very many years, called Frank Oliver. He was a first-class miller, trained our head miller that's just recently retired, first-class stone dresser and a very nice man, and a very straight man. Got great bushy eyebrows, and he could look through a man almost to his back buttons. Upright and downright, he wanted everything just right. All those sacks must be put up just right, not a cleval of wheat on the floor, he used to say. He was taken ill with bronchitis, and was very ill. He lived in the little mill cottage close to the mill. The doctor said, "Well, you are getting better, a little bit better, now I suggest you have a holiday. Where would you like to go?" He said, "Doctor, all I want to do is to go round the mill and hear that wheel chucker. I do love that wheel chuckering." A wonderful old man, a very, very dear old man, and I was very fond of him indeed. When he died, it felt like losing a son.

There was an eel-trap at Hanover Mill, right across the river, and the eels were sent sometimes to Billingsgate fish market. Eels run at the spring of the year and the fall of the leaf, but the autumn eels are best. They are up the river, and they put on their silver wedding-dress to go down to the sea, and that is when they are caught, but the salmon is quite the opposite. Although I saw elvers climbing up the waterfall to get into the top stream, where their parents had lived, I cannot recall any provisions being made for salmon. There was a trash grille above the mill, but this did not affect the progress of the eels. The eel traps were set by ensuring that certain water-gates were open to strain off the eels as the first flush of water came along, but they could not be used at all, if the water-level was too high as they could have impeded the flow. The best time of all was just after the first big rain or thunderstorm in autumn, when the river became muddy, and I can remember a hundredweight of eels being caught at Hanover in one night. Quite a lot were caught at Swanton Mill, but these were bought by Mr Hogben, the Ashford fishmonger, and as soon as it had rained he used to ask me if there were any eels for sale. As the water rose up the grating, the gate was set to sweep the eels into a box where they could be recovered without lowering the gate. Live eels were much more valuable to a fishmonger, and they were kept alive by the water flowing through the box, but a closed box would kill many of them through the water buffeting the skins off them.

Our millwrighting was done by Holman's of Canterbury, and, when they did a job, it was done properly – they didn't have to come back again. The stones were put down, they were faced, set out, and dressed, the bearings were repacked – including the neck, and the stones were bridged, but we considered these only as running repairs. Packing the neck involved packing the spindle, via the adjusting screws in the toe brass, so that a jack stick carrying a quill ran parallel to the face of the stone, and touched it all the way round. Wood was not provided for the millwrights, and although we saved an apple-tree once, it was considered unsuitable as they preferred beech or hornbeam. The millwrights were always called for any gear work but, treated with care, cogs could last for years and might eventually wear down very thin, but then there was the chance of stripping a gear. To repair this might take three or four days even though the wright and his assistant worked from very early until very late, and even be given board and lodging by the miller. Hence, charges for wrighting work were always high. Early warning of gear trouble could often be heard, and prompt attention such as trimming an ill-fitting cog could extend the working life by months. Cogs could be heard to run more sweetly after the occasional lubrication with graphite in linseed oil or grease, and this was prepared at the mill. Once when a piece of metal got into the stones through a scry missing from above the hopper, some cogs were stripped out from the gear. This suddenly pulled up the mill, and away went the weakest point. The cogs were cut out roughly in the block form and were sawn back to within half an inch of the final size, then they were set out carefully by compass, and each cog was chiselled to its final shape. I always wanted to design a machine-cut counter gear, with a rawhide pinion for the stone, for then there would never be any trouble in stripping them. Leather was preferred for belts, if we could afford it, but the composite ones which we used did not last as long as leather, as the fibres parted, if the belt was not run true. Good cotton belts would last a long time with care, but leather ones lasted almost indefinitely. The water-wheel bearing had to be renewed about ten or twelve years ago [1962–64], through gritty water falling onto it, and although we scraped and scraped the old one the wheel eventually started to foul its breast. The present iron wheel is about one hundred years old, but the old one was made from wood.

Ratting cats were kept in the mill, and vermin were not really much of a problem, but the little terrier that we once had was unfortunately killed when he got caught in the gearing one day. The mill was originally lit by candles stuck in carriers fixed into holes in the walls but, in the thirties, lighting was installed when electricity was brought to the village. Electric motors were also installed in the mill at the same time, and many farmers were then able to run small roller-mills, thus depriving us of quite a lot of grist work, but we were not unduly worried, as the work didn't make a lot of money anyway. It was more of an obliging job than a remunerative one, but it was a service that we offered.

The river froze right over in hard winters, and the wheel became frozen right in, but no attempts were made to free the wheel as this would have been a vast operation, and even then it would freeze in again if there was an easterly wind blowing through it. I used to skate from Swanton Mill to Hanover Mill in times like this, after being taught to skate by a neighbour who had been in Canada. We went skating on any suitable winter's night on any little pond, or on the river, but taking care to keep well away from any trees where the ice could have been thin. The farmer here was very keen on skating and sliding, so he used to flood the meadow near the mill and let it freeze, and then all the village used to turn out, light it up with lamps, and enjoy themselves: he used to complain though, if the meadow became flooded without him doing it!

I don't know much about the interior of Evegate Mill (the next one upstream) because the miller and I had a healthy and normal respect for each other as competitors, although I would have shown him around Hanover Mill had he asked me to do so. The mill is presently owned by Mr Child, who has restored the wheel, and he makes poultry food there, although his main interest lies in the restoration of antique furniture. The small overshot water-wheel was made by Hills, of Ashford, and they built Hoddiford Mill at Sellindge, and this was a beautiful little mill, a model of a place. It had an unusual pit-gearing in that there was an idle gear between the wheel and the pit-wheel so that the cog-pit was set up on a higher level, clear of all floods.

Hanover Mill didn't have funnel bins because the height of the mill was insufficient to allow this; so, instead, the bins were flat-bottomed, and had to be trimmed towards the outlet by using a wooden shovel until all the grain had been fed to the stones. The stone floor was built in line with the mill-house and is, therefore, too low for comfort for tall people, but it should really have been level with the top of the water-wheel. Now that the water-wheel is covered in with a wooden box, this sticks up into the room by about 2 or 3 ft.

The mill is situated on a branch of the East Stour and was one of the six mills that this river used to turn. It was rebuilt by Messrs. Holman Bros. in 1879 to replace an all-wooden structure with a wooden water-wheel. The present wheel is a low breast-shot one that measures 12 ft. in diameter by 6 ft. in width, and it has fifty-six ventilated buckets. The pit-wheel is 7 ft. in diameter, and the gearing driving the millstones is called the counter gear. Flour milling ceased in 1921 when a pair of stones was replaced with a high speed Barron Vertical Grinder that had emery composition stones. A hammer-mill was installed when electricity was put in, and another one was installed recently to provide the main method of grinding wheat, barley, oats, and maize for use in compound rations for animal foods. Flour from Hanover went to several surrounding bakers, and there was a good trade in Ashford, Hythe, and at Brook where there was a nice bakehouse and bakery, and where my father once had the mill. There wasn't a bakehouse at Hanover, but we brought the milling trade connected with Brook when we moved from there. Household sales of flour for pastries and bread – perhaps one-gallon lots, or so, were commonly made at Hanover Mill, and we had a set of beam scales on every floor, and an Avery's platform scale, and these were all tested annually for accuracy.

I did quite a lot of grist work in flour for the farmers and big houses, when they might have sent a bushel of their very best wheat to be ground and dressed. The flour, sharps, and bran were all returned to them, for the two latter grades to be fed to the pigs. When I was a boy, it was quite a feature of our business that grist work was done very cheaply, even too cheaply, and we charged only a shilling or so, but then it didn't take us very long. The wheat was weighed in, and the product was weighed, but it sometimes overlapped with somebody else's to get the weight right. We didn't use the bins for grist work, the hopper was fed directly from the sack, nor did we use the cleaning machines. Hanover had Derby Peaks, and then French burrs and, later, composition stones made from emery and silica run into a mould and allowed to harden. Some millers made their own – Mr Hicks, at Egerton Mill made his stones, rather than go to a milling engineer. First of all, they broke up the Burrs and Peaks, and then they set these in a mould and added the silica and emery. A composition stone could last up to four times longer than a Peak. A hard, black stone, with very fine dressings found at Swanton Mill was not a composition stone, and may have been a malt stone from a malt mill that used to be in Mersham, at the top of Swanton Lane.'

GORDON CLEMENTSON   Recorded *c.* 1969.

The material for this section was taken from the transcript of a tape-recording made by Julian Hippisley of Gordon Clementson talking about his memories of Hope Mill in the early part of this century.

'As we approach the Seventies, it may be of interest to recall what it was like at Hope Mill a little more than a half-century ago. Both my father and myself were born there, but my grandfather moved here, when he was four, in 1841. In those days, it must have been a very peaceful and quiet place because there was no railway here then; that came in my father's boyhood, and the only houses here would have been the Lodge gate leading to the Scotney estate. All the houses in and around were not here then and it was all open countryside. The next house up the road going towards Goudhurst would have been the Forge, at the foot of Blacksmith's Hill. I'm not sure if that is the name under which this little hill goes by now, but it was just before the turning leading off to Bedgebury. There was another Lodge gate for the Scotney estate that went in at the top entrance, and above that there were four cottages, and a pair of cottages on the left-hand side which, in those days, were known as Hope Mill Cottages. It was there that our two millers, the carmen, and the stockmen lived, and they came down daily to work at the mill, or to go on up the hill towards Bell Farm, which was another parcel of land that we farmed in those days. As a boy in my teens, just before the First World War, I knew the mill very well indeed, and, of course, it was my great ambition to be left alone in charge of it and, indeed, often I was; it was a great honour for a small boy to run the mill and look after it. I was also taught how to dress, or sharpen, the stones.

The older and senior of our two millers was George Reeves; he was a wonderful old character really, and the most irritable old man, although I used to get on with him exceedingly well. As I look back at his figure, he was absolutely doubled up with back trouble, or hernias, or something of that nature, because he used to have to wear a special truss. This was so very common, and I think it was often brought on by the enormous weights they were always heaving and lifting about, because it was nothing for them to carry these sacks about on their backs on and off all day long; they weighed about two hundredweights and a half, and were a great tussle for an old man of seventy.

The working-day started with the loading of the delivery vans with sack barrows, and the commodities – the corn, the flour, the feeding-stuffs, were loaded in the reverse order in which they were to be delivered, so that it would be easier for the carman to off-load it when he arrived at the various farms and estates to which he had to deliver. The loads were usually two-horse loads, but the vans needed additional pulling up the hills. That was one of the problems of a watermill, as opposed to a windmill, because the loads from a windmill were usually going downhill, but with a watermill, which is usually right at the bottom of the hill, there is the problem of pulling the full loads up the hill. It was for this purpose that we had a chain horse, or cock horse, that was used to assist the vans away. It was always the house-boy's duty to go out with the first van-load, either up to the top of Goudhurst Hill, or up to Spelmonden Hill, and bring back the horse afterwards in readiness for the second van-load. He would go away with the second van and then he would bring back the horse, unharness it, and resume his house-boy's duties.

The passageway up from the Mill House and the mill itself was, in those days, very much narrower than it is today, because in recent years there has been removed from the house itself one room, both downstairs and upstairs, and a lot of store-room. The downstairs room was in the front, with the office, and it was over this office that my bedroom was situated, so I was very close to the mill all the time and used to hear all the various goings on when I was a young boy. When I became a schoolboy, and came up from boarding school, it used to be one of my duties to go out and help superintend the loading and booking of the various items as they were loaded onto the vehicles, and to see that they were correctly allocated, and placed in the vans, and that the right orders were put up. As the goods were loaded into the van, the miller or the vanman would shout out what he'd got, and I would tick it off from the list. I well remember how extremely cold it was out there in the winter mornings with a frost going on outside and, as there was no heat at all in the mill, one sat in overcoats and mufflers at the desk. Even so, it was absolutely perishingly cold, and of course it was pitch dark at that time of a winter's day and, even on a Saturday, loading used to start at half-past five. The only light we had came from candles, but at the desk we did have a double-burnered paraffin-lamp with a circular tin-reflector above it which threw down a measure of light onto the work.

The routine of the mill was that both millers used to turn up at six o'clock and work through until three o'clock, with a dinner hour from twelve to one during which time they used to walk home. Then, one of them would go home for a half-hour tea and he would then return to the mill and relieve the other miller, who then had the evening off. The one who had come back would then carry out stone-dressing from about six o'clock until half-past eight, with the mill still running. Saturdays were a half-day off, but the men made it up a little bit by turning up at half-past five on these days. There was usually a van to go out on a local load, perhaps up into the village, or round to Horsmonden, or to some of the other neighbouring villages, with some special loading. These were loaded on at half-past five, and the mill closed down at noon. So, you see, every other day was a thirteen-hour day, and then Saturday was a half-day. The senior miller earned twenty-five shillings per week, whilst the junior was paid twenty-two shillings per week.

Now, I think I should say more about the mill itself. It would be natural really to start with the water-wheel and, in this respect, Hope Mill was particularly interesting because it had two water-wheels, which ran in opposite directions. The wooden breast-shot wheel was the more powerful and was $16\frac{1}{2}$ ft. in diameter by 6 or 7 ft. in width, whereas the iron overshot wheel was only 8 ft. in diameter, but it was some 10 ft. wide. Because of this rather unusual arrangement, I always felt disappointed that some means could not have been found to preserve this unique old mill.

The iron overshot-wheel remains much the less deteriorated at the present time, whereas the arms and rim of the larger wooden wheel are completely disintegrated. These arms and rims were renewed in the early part of this century. In fact, I can just remember – I should imagine I was seven- or eight-years-old which would have made it in about 1907, going with my father and grandfather in a pony and trap up into Horsmonden Park to where they were selecting oak-trees that would be suitable for felling for this renewal. I think it was in the following year that these oak-trees were brought down to Hope Mill, and permission was obtained to set up the sawing arrangement in the railway property opposite. A traction-engine lent by my uncle, William Lambert, came over from Horsmonden and the whole of the gear was set up there and the oak-trees were sawn up on the spot for the rim and the arms, but the rims had to be done in segments and the necessary curvature had to be put in them. The buckets or paddles on this wheel were set at right-angles to the rim and I should imagine they were about 9 or 10 in. in depth. I am very familiar with them because it was in the 1920s, whilst I was an apprentice at Messrs. William Weeks, at Maidstone, that I took a few weeks unpaid leave with two of my workmates who came over, and we spent the time fitting on a new set of buckets. When the arms were taken out in 1907, Dad had them put by, and later on he had them made into two tables, one of which I have at my home here at Groombridge, and the other one of which is with an aunt of mine at Whitstable. These were not in any way valuable types of table – they had turned legs and, because of the narrowness of the arms of the wheel, the tops were made up in a pattern resembling a dart-board. Although they were only knocked up by a local carpenter, they have sentimental value from my point of view, of course.

Each of the water-wheels drove a crown wheel on upright shafts that went right up into the mill. The upright shafts were used to drive lay-shafts, which carried pulleys for driving the various pieces of equipment in the mill, including the hoist. At two places on each of the crown wheels were two spur-gears, set on upright shafts, which drove the stones.

Because the water-wheels were of different diameters, they entered the mill at different levels, and each one drove its own system of gears. On the end of each wheel-shaft there was a pit-wheel carrying oak-cogs set in a bevel, and these in turn powered a vertical shaft via another bevel gear with which it meshed. The upright shafts passed right up into the mill and, in the cog-pit, they carried a crown gear set about 2 ft. below the stone floor, that is, the first floor. The crown gears carried applewood cogs and each gear drove two stone nuts, or small spur-gears, that were mounted on upright shafts, which terminated on the first floor and carried the runner stones, thus numbering four. The two main vertical shafts terminated in crown gears that turned lay-shafts carrying pulleys for driving various pieces of ancillary equipment throughout the mill.

Since the mill-pit has been filled in, I think I should explain how the gearing was rigged. I mentioned previously that there were two small spur-gears called stone nuts – if I describe one of the stones and its bearings, that will suffice, but it was repeated four times, of course. There was a heavy beam, known as a bridge-tree, that ran in an east–west direction right across the pit. This supported the short, upright shaft that carried the upper millstone, and was pivoted at the back and could be raised or lowered slightly at the front end through a set of worm gears adjustable by a wheel that was positioned on the wall at the back of the trow into which the meal fell. By turning the wheel, it was possible to raise or lower the bridge-tree and thus raise or lower the upper millstone and bring it closer to, or farther away from, the bedstone. In this way, we were able to get the correct height of stone so as to yield the degree of fineness which was wanted for the meal. After this fine manual adjustment had been made, it was automatically maintained by ball governors, which regulated it according to the speed of the water-wheel and the flow of material into the stones. This slight movement of the bridge-tree was called tentering. It should be realised that the stone shaft had to be very accurately aligned and, to achieve this, its lower end sat in a step-brass fitted into an iron box on the bridge-tree. The step-brass could be moved within its iron box by means of four set-screws.

Apart from the four sets of stones there were some additional items of machinery on the stone floor – in the centre of the floor was a steel roller-mill for rolling oats, but we never separated the husk from the kernel of the oats and so the oats that we rolled were for horse-feed principally. Also, there was a very small pair of stones, which were used purely for cracking maize and beans, and behind them, on the south side, in the centre of the mill, was what we called the silk machine.

By the time I was old enough to take an interest in the mill, the whole organisation had turned over to feeding-stuffs, but there was a 3 ft. diameter pair of French burr-stones driven by the small wheel and these were used to grind wheat. The bigger breast-shot wheel drove a 4 ft. diameter pair of Derbyshire Peak stones that were used to grind mixed corn for hog feed and chicken feed. We also ground oats, and these were a very tough consignment that always required a very sharp and newly-dressed pair of stones. After we had been running a day or two with oats, it was usually necessary to go over to grinding some sort of cattle food, or hog corn, because the stones just wouldn't cut the oats.

A little way back in from the front entrance of the mill were the hatchways which went right up through the mill to its upper storeys. There was a chain hoist that also went right up through and then went over a pulley at the top, and then back over a windlass at the water-wheel end of the mill. This was operated by a slack belt on a revolving pulley that was driven by the water-wheel: when it was wanted to hoist anything, a rope was pulled that activated a lever at the back of the mill. This tightened the belt, and the hoist started to draw up, and it would lift anything up to about three hundredweight – a sack of wheat weighed about two hundredweights and a half, and it was about the same for maize.

Where the hatchways passed through the various floors there were flaps that were opened by the sack as it came up through from one floor to the next. The two flaps then dropped back after the sack had gone through, and the floor was then intact again, but they could be flapped right over when it was wanted to let stuff down at any time. This then called for careful adjustment of the leverage so that it slipped the belt and allowed the load to go downwards instead of upwards.

I remember one very dark morning when George Reeves, the senior miller, was staggering about upstairs, one floor up, and on this particular morning he came walking along there with his old candle, and I expect the light was in his eyes and he didn't realise that the hatchway was open. He stepped straight into the hole in the floor to come down, but fortunately he managed to grab hold of the chain and he sort of slithered to the bottom. He had some awfully funny sayings; such a curious way of expressing himself, and I so well remember his words on that morning when he said "Bigger and blast, I was upstairs just now". You see, he was a very religious and very conscientious old man who wouldn't think of using a swear word, but at times he came very close to it.

The hoist was controlled by an old bell-rope so arranged that the red-and-white hold was on the first floor where most of the hoisting was done. It probably came to be there because my grandfather used to be the vicar's churchwarden.

The flow of materials in the mill was something like this; the corn came in and was taken up to the top floor by means of the sack hoist, and then the various sorts of grain – whether it was corn, oats, maize, or mixed corn, were shot over into the bins. The grain then came down from the bins by means of a chute, and thence into the hopper, then through the eye of the stones, and the meal then fell down into the wooden trow below, where it was handled again to clear the trow. The mill ran fairly well on its own and didn't need a lot of attention; one had occasionally to go and see that the general fineness of the meal was as required but, apart from that, the mill would go on quite comfortably without very much attention.

The sacks of corn or maize were taken to the top of the mill and shot over into the storage bins from where it could be drawn out into sacks, if a small amount was needed. This was done through sleeves of bagging that hung down through the ceiling of the floor below. The sleeves were tied into a knot when they weren't required and we used to undo them by holding the bag or sack underneath the arm-pit and extending the other end out with the arm. We then put the sleeve down into the sack and drew out the amount required.

Considerable power was required to drive the stones which, in the case of the large wheel, were 4 ft. in diameter, but only 3 ft. diameter for the smaller wheel. Only one pair of stones was used at a time and this enabled the other pair to be 'up for dressing.' To enable part of the mill to be shut down for this purpose it was arranged that the stone nuts could be wound up off a keyed taper on the shaft so that they were clear of the spur-wheel and thus were not able to be turned. I suppose it took about six or seven evenings to dress a pair of stones, but if the millers had any odd moments during the days, they always used to buckle in on to stone dressing.

If we now consider the stone, or second, floor perhaps the most obvious things were the casings, or tuns, which surrounded the stones for protection and kept the meal within bounds. Above each tun was what was known as a horse, and this went right across the structure and supported a hopper into which the corn fell from the bins on the floor above. Within the hopper was a leather strap, and a string that was attached to it came out through the side of the hopper and was attached to a bell. All the time there was corn in the hopper the weight of it held the string taut and kept the bell up away from a rapper, but if the corn got low the bell dropped down onto the rapper which rang it and attracted the miller's attention. This was a real necessity because of the great risk of sparks, if there was no corn between the stones. Underneath the hopper there was what was known as a shoe into which the corn fell and the flow from which was controlled by a sliding gate, and in addition it was possible to raise or lower the bottom end of the shoe by means of a cord that went downstairs. The cord could be adjusted from the back of the trow in much the same way as the tentering was controlled. The lower end of the shoe had a horizontal cord tied onto a steel spring which in turn held the shoe tight back against what was called a damsel. This was a three-pronged metal upright that was set in the centre of, and was driven by, the runner stone and it rapped against a brass rapper-bar fixed into the end of the shoe. The continuous vibrations set up by the damsel striking the rapper-bar shook the corn down into the eye of the stone in an even flow. The damsel was so called because it was considered that it made more noise than anything else in the mill. After falling into the eye, the corn circulated round between the stones, being cut and ground all the time, until the meal found its way out between the outer rims of the stones.

On each side of the doorway entering the pit, there were two wooden boxes called trows, and it was into these that the meal fell having come down a chute from the stones on the floor above where it had been ground. The trows were kept clear by use of a short-handled shovel, but the meal didn't come down very fast and one could leave them for half an hour or so before they needed emptying into sacks. These were held open by means of a piece of wood with three hooks fixed in it and which, for fairly obvious reasons, was known as 'the boy.'

On the wall behind, the trows there were two controls for each pair of stones. One was a spoked wheel which controlled the height of the stone and thus regulated the fineness of the meal being ground, whilst the other control was a little wooden knob that could be used to wind up a piece of cord that adjusted the flow of corn into the eye of the stone by raising or lowering the shoe so as to allow more or less corn to flow to the stones.

After the corn had been ground into wholemeal, it had to be separated into its constituents. This was done with a bolter and silk machine. The silk machine was an inclined cylinder clothed in different sizes of silk mesh, and the wheatmeal was fed into the upper end and soft rotating brushes helped the various products through the different meshes as the meal passed down the cylinder. The material that passed right through the cylinder and fell out of the end of it was called offal. It fell into elevator buckets and was taken by this up to the top of the mill to then come down and be processed through the bran jumper, or bolter. This was an inclined, tray-like affair, about 15 ft. long by about 1 ft. wide, that was pivoted about a third of the way along and made to oscillate by means of a snatching arrangement. It contained three or four different gauge wire meshes set in layers one above the other, and the bran was dropped onto the top gauze and jumped its way down to the lower end where it was directed into a sack. The finer offals fell through to the various layers of mesh which sorted out the bran from the pollards, and the pollards from the sharps, and the sharps from the middlings, each one emerging from the end of the machine on its own tray to fall into its own sack on the floor below via sausage-like sacking tubes known as sleeves.

Of all the various kinds of grain that a miller had to contend with the most exacting was probably oats. These were ground in the Peak stones, but they blunted them very considerably and, to get a good fine oatmeal, it was necessary to dress the stones once about every ten days.

When the mill fell into disuse in the 1930s some of the flooring was in remarkably fine condition, particularly that part just inside the mill entrance. Some of the woodwork on the first floor was deal and wasn't very attractive, but on the ground floor and the second floor it was good oak that was absolutely black. It was very slippery, and had become highly polished through the combined effects of continual use and the flour dust that was always present.

The two millers came down to the mill at six o'clock in the morning and, after oiling and greasing through the mill, and the outside bearings of the water-wheel, and greasing the cogs with tallow, which I remember being kept in an old tin at one end of the ground floor, the mill started up at half-past six so regularly that one could almost set one's watch indoors by it.

I have here, in my garden, a Derbywhire Peak stone that I have actually dressed myself. Before the stones could be dressed, they had to be separated and this necessitated lifting the runner stone with pulleys and slings before it was turned over. To George Reeves, our senior miller, went the privilege of dressing the runner stone; that was the one that had been turned over. The bedstone was down on the floor, and it was more awkward for the man dressing this one because he had to lay on the floor to do his work. The runner was the easier because, with it up on wooden wedges, it was possible to sit on the edge of it and lean the left elbow on a sort of cushion. This was just a sack with some bran in it, to soften it a little, and then you held the mill-bill with the left hand as a fulcrum and tapped away with it. You could hear the tap-tap-tap-tap-tap-tap-tap of the mill-bills working on the stones all evening long, summer and winter, whenever you showed your nose outside the door.

It was a perishing cold job in winter, when it was a common procedure to get two thick corn sacks and put one inside the other, and then to get inside that and lie or sit with the feet and body in the sacks so as to try and keep your feet reasonably warm and out of the draughts. Remember that all this work had to be done by candlelight, and that it was quite an accurate job to do the stone dressing properly because, if everything was not absolutely level, we got a very poor cut on the corn. You had just a candle in front of you – a flickering, guttering candle, and it depended on how the wind was blowing whether the candles guttered very much and whether they lasted very long. Once a week, or twice a week, the men came to the house to get a new supply – about half-a-dozen or eight at a time, and these they took back into the mill for their use. Each candle was forced down into a triangle of three nails hammered into a little block of wood or, alternatively, it was just a little piece of tin, with a point at one end. However, it was not carried by the pointed end but by the thick end and, all around the mill, in various places into the beams and walls, holes were bored about $\frac{3}{4} - 1$ in. in diameter, and we used to push the pointed end of the holder into one of the holes and it just used to stay there. It was absolutely precarious, really, because after the candle had been pushed into the hole the cobwebs all around it would catch fire, and then fizzle out above it, and I often wonder that the place was not burnt down time and time again.'

Dr. W. URRY   Recorded April 1975.

Some recollections from a millwrighting family

The material for this chapter has been used with the kind permission of Mr Glyn Jones, who recorded the information during an interview with the late Dr W. Urry – Mr George Urry's son.

George Urry was born in 1867 and was a millwright by profession, as had been his father, Richard, before him. Richard Urry was born in 1822, and died in 1910. He was a convivial, well-known character, who owned his own millwrighting business in Chichester, as had William, his father. Richard carried out work on many mills in West Sussex and Hampshire; Kipson Bank and Hainaker windmills in particular, and numerous watermills - one of which, in West Wittering, was frequently being mentioned in conversation.

George had a rich West Sussex dialect, and was a brilliant anecdotist who made many of his endless fund of milling tales sound very amusing, or even outright funny. Although he talked rather little about his daily work, he was intensely proud of it and, if he had been carrying out major repairs to a mill, the family would walk out to that particular mill on Sunday to inspect his work. His devotion to his craft was such that he would even cut firewood square so as to make a "proper job" of it. Should anyone be unfortunate enough to refer to him as a carpenter he would give a snarl of rage and contempt – he was not a carpenter; he was a millwright!!!

After moving to Godalming to work with an engineering firm, George Urry took employment in 1910 with Messrs. Holman, the well-known Canterbury firm of millwrights. The premises were in Dover Street, and the large workshop had great windows all along one side. A bell, which was rung at seven o'clock to indicate the start of the working day, was also used as a waking bell by households within hearing distance. Before the First World War, it was usual to start work at six o'clock, and any workman arriving after this time found the gates shut and, consequently, he lost an hour's wages.

As might be expected from a millwright working in a particular area, George carried out his work in almost all of the working mills in east Kent at that time. Amongst the many routine jobs that he did were some notable major ones – he made and installed the sweeps for Barham Mill near Canterbury; he installed the water-wheel at Wickhambreaux; he is believed to have fitted the breast-shot water-wheel at Chilham Mill. He made many visits to Black Mill and White Mill at Sturry to attend to their problems and regular needs; Denne's Mill, and Hooker's Mill in Canterbury also called on his time extensively.

One evening, after he had returned from working at Littlebourne Mill, near Wickhambreaux, he was having a smoke whilst soaking his feet in some special brew, when he thought that he would read his newspaper. His plan was foiled when he was unable to locate his spectacles. A detailed search of the house failed to reveal them, and it was realised that he had mislaid them – possibly back at the mill; a failing that had not been entirely unknown to have happened before. His son, William Urry, was despatched post haste by bicycle to the mill, the keys to which he collected from the house opposite, after successfully beating off a determined attack by a flock of vociferous geese. Luckily, he found the missing spectacles where his father had last been working and, after returning home with them safely, peace again returned to the household.

When Black Mill, Sturry, was demolished in 1938/9 its millstones were left in an adjoining meadow. It was whilst photographing and measuring them that Dr William Urry was noticed by a passerby, and taken to be a spy or saboteur. The situation was a delicate one that took considerable explanation before his good intentions could be established.

George Urry was called to Denne's Mill, near Blackfriars in Canterbury, to attend to the breast-shot water-wheel which was rubbing on the base of the runway. The wheel was jacked up, and fillets were hammered in, but within a few minutes of running, the wheel was rubbing again as badly as before. It was decided that the best solution was to install a new shaft, the pattern for which was made at Holman's workshop, prior to its being cast at Messrs. Biggleston's nearby. The same mill had a steam-engine, sited across the yard, well away from the mill, and one day the great shaft connecting the mill and the engine buckled badly. George made the pattern, which was finally painted a bright blue, for some special brackets designed to prevent the shaft from buckling again. After they had been in position for a few weeks, he was distressed to find that it was no longer possible to sight through a series of holes in the brackets that previously had lined up perfectly. After much investigation and head-scratching, it was realised that the brackets were fine, the problem was that the mill was slowly sinking, the effect being magnified by the length of the shaft and the number of brackets supporting it!

When Billy Holman directed one of his workmen to undertake a rather tricky job he asked the man how he was going to do it. He replied 'Oh, it will be a bit difficult, but I will wangle it', whereupon Billy Holman shouted out at the top of his voice, making everybody in the workshop jump, 'I do not want my work wangled!'

William Urry could remember going, as a child, for a walk with his mother, when their steps took them beside a watermill. His mother lifted him up so that he could look over the parapet at the water-gates, and he was convinced that the jet of water was made of glass, it looked so green and bright and solid as the sunlight shone upon it.

In 1933, the owners of Denne's Mill bought up some old secondhand electric motors, hoping to use them in the mill, and George Urry was instructed to install them. Although he did as he had been asked, he advised the owners not to use them until they had been thoroughly cleaned because they were full of dust and cobwebs, and had given out a great arc of fire when they had been run up. At 8.30 one morning he went to catch a train to go to work in Faversham, but as he opened his front door he called to his wife to come and take a look at a great column of smoke in the distance. He later heard that Denne's Mill had caught fire and become gutted. Some of the corn that fell from the bins in the roof was taken downstream by the river, and was later found to have germinated along the river bank.

Mr Nye started work in 1920 at the age of fourteen, when he assisted the miller, Mr Shrubshole, at Swanton Mill. For this he was paid 14s. (70p.) per week. Although Mr Nye did not serve an official apprenticeship, it was at Swanton Mill that he learnt his trade through working for Mr Hancock, the owner's son, who had served his apprenticeship at Hooker's Mill at Canterbury. Mr Nye worked for two other millers and one of them, Mr Moon, impressed him as being an extraordinarily good miller, although he was a hard task-master. Lessons were learnt the hard way, and there was no formal training, so the trainee learnt by doing exactly what he was told, and doing the work thoroughly and correctly.

Mr Nye worked at Swanton Mill for twenty-one years as a stone dresser before spending thirty-two years at Ashford Mill, which was rather larger and more modern than Swanton Mill. He also dressed the stones in Willesborough windmill.

PLATE III

Wally Nye

The three millers most closely associated with Mr Nye had continued milling until they were nearly eighty years of age, yet he could not recall that any of them suffered from the respiratory diseases so often associated with this trade. He placed great faith in the filters built into the machines and believed that, as long as they were properly in place, the dust could not cause any great damage.

The first indication that the stones needed attention was a gradual loss of production, which eventually could fall to less than one-half of the normal output. Other symptons were a loss of quality and an increase in the temperature of the meal which should be warm, not hot. It was the miller's responsibility to decide when the stones should be dressed and, once he had decided this, he helped the stone dresser lift off the runner stone with a set of rope blocks and lay it face upwards on the floor. Chain blocks were better than rope blocks because they locked when the pulling stopped, whereas rope blocks needed unceasing maximum effort until the stone was down on the floor. The stones were first marked off with a wooden staff, carrying red ochre on the face. The staff was held square and turned round on the stone to mark the highest spots with red ochre. Half the width of the stone should have been coloured and the remainder should have been clear. The grinding of animal feedstuffs often wore the edge away so that the eye of the stone came right up and this had to be knocked away until the staff cleared a penny laid next to the eye. Mr Nye's first job as a boy was to knock these spots down and he found it very aggravating to think that he had finished the job and then have his governor sweep the staff and reveal more high spots. After a while he found that he could knock off high spots not revealed by the staff and thus reduce the number of times that the staff had to be applied to the stone. Following this, the quarters were marked out, and there were nine or ten quarters depending on the size of the stone. Separate marking sticks were used to set out the lands and the furrows, to maintain regularity and reduce any wander. The main furrows were cut tangential to a circle (drawn around the eye of the stone) to produce a 'draught', which carried the meal out of the stones. As a general rule the displacement was 1 in. per foot diameter; for example, the displacement was 4 in. out of square on a stone that was 4 ft. in diameter. After the dressing was complete the stones were cleaned and dried and reassembled with the upper stone lifted well clear of the bedstone. Deep work was put into barley stones so as to get a good draught, but if a wheat stone was treated similarly it would have been almost impossible to get fine flour from it.

It was essential that the stones were taken up for re-dressing at the right moment, but they normally ran for two or three weeks between dressings. Mr Nye used to take up the stones at 7.30 in the morning and the dressing was finished by 4 o'clock in the afternoon so as to have them ready for work next day. The miller might assist by dressing one of the stones whilst continuing to run the mill, but some mills carried a spare dressed stone which meant that only one stone had to be dressed at a time, making the operation much shorter.

The only light came from the nearest window and from candles fixed onto spikes carried on pegs, which were plugged into holes bored into the timbers. Mr Nye could not recall any fires caused this way and felt that the light was quite sufficient to cut ten cracks to the inch provided the tools were sharp. There was no heat in the mill and, in cold weather, he climbed inside a corn sack, but even then it was bitterly cold. Gloves could not be worn because of the loss of sensitivity and this allowed the steel fragments to drive straight into the hands to such an extent that Mr Nye's hands were sometimes raw and bleeding when he went home at night. At home, his wife would pick out as much steel as he could stand, but much of it remains in his hands to this day.

The grain should not have had a moisture content greater than 15 per cent or else the meal particles were inclined to stick together rather than remain free-flowing. Under the right conditions, a pair of 3 ft. 6 in. wheat stones would produce about one and a half hundredweights per hour, but the same stones would produce two hundredweights per hour, if they were grinding animal foodstuff. This was usually Sussex oats, which were ground up quite small and demanded stones in first class condition, but, even so, this work wore the stones away quite fast.

Barley stones were called pig stones by Mr Nye, and he believed that this term simply reflected their uses for the production of pig feed. He had a poor opinion of composition or emery stones which, on their introduction, were alleged to need less frequent sharpening but which, in fact, required almost as much attention as a conventional stone.

A normal stone would turn at about 90 r.p.m., and the speed did not usually fall below 80 r.p.m., whilst speeds above 100 r.p.m. could cause the bed stone to start moving. As the runner stone wore down, there occasionally came times when the bar had to be reset into the stone, as the limit of the tentering adjustment had been reached. The point was eventually reached where it would have unduly weakened the stone to set the bar in again, and the runner stone was then put down as a bedstone. The bedstone was also adjustable, either by means of wooden wedges inserted between the base of the stone and the floor timbers, or, in more modern mills, by means of adjustable iron plates set under the stone. A runner stone was put down as a bed stone when it was about 9 in. thick, and bedstones were taken up and discarded when they were about 2 in. thick.

Although bakers collected their own flour from the mill the miller also sold smaller quantities of flour to locals buying direct from the mill. These were 7 lb., or one gallon, bags of flour.

Mr Nye felt that although Yeoman wheat produced the finest flour, it was not a good cropper and, for this reason, was not sown very much by farmers. It was a strong wheat and contained plenty of starch, rather than the sugar contained by most English flours and which prevented them producing good flour. It was Yeoman wheat that made the English loaf that many old people say it is not possible to get today. The old loaf kept very well, but it was definitely 'puddeny', and Mr Nye remembered his mother would only buy stale bread from the baker as it could be made to last longer. Yeoman wheat was last used in any significant quantity during the period between the First and Second World Wars. Although Yeoman was the best wheat, Mr Nye considered that there were several other good ones, such as Red wheat.

The only cleaning needed for wheat that had been threshed out was a fan to blow out the chaff. Combine harvesters do not clean the wheat as well as a threshing drum did and therefore combine-wheat needs a little extra cleaning. Wheat contaminated with smuts (a fungus) was washed and scrubbed and then had to be dried or conditioned, although not all mills had this equipment. The drying units often consisted of steam radiators distributed through a multi-floor building. The moist air was extracted at the top floor, and the lower sections were often used as cooling or conditioning units.

There was considerable variation in the amount of grain that mills could hold in their bins, but Swanton held about forty tons. This was taken in immediately after harvest time, and any extra amounts were stored in two and a half hundredweight sacks in the top of the mill. Sufficient grain was taken in at this time to last for the complete year.

Peas and beans were also ground at the mill. The peas were grey peas grown on local farms for animal feed and were considered to have no superior for the final fattening of pigs. They tended to clog the stones but were much less trouble than beans in this respect. The peas and beans were mixed on the floor with oats, wheat and barley and then were loaded into a hopper for grinding into pig feed. If the stones clogged up with beans, the miller had to react promptly and throw a gallon of maize into the eye of the stone and, with luck, this got them off the stones. The most obvious sign of blocked stones was a lack of meal flowing from the spout and, if this was ignored, or not noticed, the runner stone would slowly rise up on the solid bed of peas and could sometimes even lift itself out of gear.

Nearly all types of bean were ground at Swanton Mill, except for locus beans, which gave considerable trouble in the stones, as did mazagan beans if they were not completely dry. If in good condition, mazagans ground up to give a meal that was sand-like in texture and this was used for cattle and sheep feed. Damp beans would stick to the surface of the stones and pack so solidly that the runner had to be lifted for them to be chipped off.

Oats were considered one of the best animal feeds, and the local owners of hunters were careful to specify their use in animal feeds. These oats were twice as long as the modern white oat and they were grown on large areas around Swanton. Maize took most wear out of the stones, followed by Sussex oats, which had to be ground hard so as to break up the huk [husk] because there was no dresser to remove them afterwards. Even if the huk could have been removed, it would have been very difficult to find a buyer for it. In Mr Nye's time, barley was considered to be of very low quality although the same fields produce good barley nowadays. The straw was of so little use that it was burned. Wheat and oat straw were both held in high esteem for animal feed, but oat straw is of comparatively low quality now.

Eighty per cent of the mill's trade was devoted to animal feeds, and this percentage increased as flour production fell. The last flour was produced in about 1935–40. If there was plenty of water in the mill-pond, it was the custom to operate a wheat stone whether the flour was required or not, and the meal thus produced was elevated to a large cold bin. If flour was then required whilst the mill was producing animal feeds, it was possible to use this flour meal to boost the output of the pair of stones producing flour meal. The two flows went through a mixing unit that also regulated the varying proportions of each meal before delivering it to an elevator discharging into the dressers.

Nearly all the material ground at the mill was supplied by local farmers who fetched it to be ground, the miller very rarely went out to collect material from the farmers. The sacks of grain weighed $2\frac{1}{4}$ hundredweight, but sacks of flour weighed $4\frac{1}{2}$ hundredweight, and mill outputs were expressed in sacks per hour until quite recently. If maize was unobtainable locally, it could be collected from Faversham at £3 15s. 0d. per ton. Cereals could not be weighed in the field but this was done at the mill, with the farmers closely watching the weighing to ensure that it was accurate.

The mill was normally staffed by two people but, occasionally, an extra person was employed. The governor would pop in every day to give his orders, although there was nearly always an order book ensuring continual work. The mill used to do a lot of grist work and this normally consisted of various small orders from any number of farmers. Grist work was considered to be the miller's bread and cheese.

Grist work was not normally loaded into the bins in the roof, but was put into a small bin on the floor above the stones. Small quantities, such as a few bushels, were bagged up and loaded straight into the hopper which was kept topped up manually. When doing grist work in small lots, it was usual to run out as much of each order as possible, which meant that the bell alarm was operating for a minute or two – as Mr Nye said, 'You put up with a bit of music for a little while.' When the mill stopped for the day, the stones were raised before the water was shut off – the water was never stopped when the stones were hard down.

The two-mile long tail-race was cleaned out twice a year by a gang of men who were paid £5 for working through a weekend. The cogs were treated occasionally with linseed oil in the summer-time as they were inclined to shrink a little. The working day began at 7.30 with an all-round oil-up, starting with the water-wheel bearing on which was slapped some Russian tallow with a padded stick. Belting was normally made of leather, and Stockholm tar was used to make them grip better. The belts were all fastened with strips of raw thong which, at one time, were made from the skins of eels caught in the eel trap set into the mill-dam. The eel trap was used after Mr Nye left the mill but only to catch eels for selling, and other fish which were caught in the trap were usually thrown back.

Holman of Canterbury did most of the re-cogging at Swanton Mill. When cogs were fitted properly they gave out a singing note whilst they were running. Sometimes a cog became loose and gave out a rattle instead of singing, and it was then packed with a piece of paper or board. If a gear had to be re-cogged, it was usual for the millwright to fix the cog in position with a clout nail to guard against any shrinkage loosening the fit. A badly fitting cog never wore in, and, at the worst, it could cause a pinion to rise up out of gear and then fall back and smash out cogs.

Cogs were made of apple or hornbeam and, if a miller came across any hornbeam he would often store it, sometimes for many years, in order to have a supply in case of emergency. In the case of a gear-wheel which was likely to get wet, it was the practice to use oak cogs. Mr Nye knew of some fibre cogs which had been fitted to a gear-wheel at Hanover Mill and he considered that they worked very well.

The meal was put through two revolving dressers that operated in series. The first one had a loose, rather coarse, white cloth through which the middlings were brushed, whilst the rejects came over the end of the silk to go onto a jogger which separated them into bran and pollards. The middlings then passed into another dresser, fitted with a fine silk cloth that rubbed against longitudinal wooden beater bars. Flour, or fine middlings, passed through this silk whilst the middlings passed over the end. The silks were mended or changed by the miller, and a silk that sagged or bellied soon needed attention – they had to be drum tight for the best performance and a lengthy life.

Flour was tested by being spread onto a board and then wetted with water, whereupon any grey particles immediately showed as dark specks, indicating a fault with the silks. A particularly trying period came during the war when the government ordered that barley was to be mixed with the wheat as an economy move. The silks had to be removed each week-end and the numerous small flakes of barley then had to be laboriously picked out of the silks because it was impossible to remove them by brushing. The grain supply was also extended by the inclusion of other materials such as potato flour or milk powder, which came from Canada in big barrels.

The mill-dam at Swanton consisted of three sluice gates (the height of which can be increased by loose boards), and a tumbling bay (or overspill). When the mill was in full production, the mill-pond was full to the top of the flood boards and the surplus water escaped via the tumbling bay. This amount of water was necessary to ensure the correct water-wheel speed but it was not unusual for the miller to put an extra three boards in the tumbling bay to further increase the head.

The water supply was no trouble in winter, but in summer-time it was not uncommon to find less water in the pond in the morning than there had been when the mill had been stopped the day before. The mill-pond was quite often badly flooded in winter but the mill buildings were normally unaffected, although the water sometimes backed up the tail-race and affected the operation of the water-wheel. It was not possible to use the steam-engine under these circumstances because it was coupled up to the water-wheel. During a particularly severe spell of weather the wheel froze completely solid and not even the prolonged application of a blowlamp would free it. Freezing of the river surface had no effect on the water-wheel as the water continued to flow beneath the ice.

The steam-engine was connected into the wheel system, but when it was in operation the engineer did not welcome anyone in the engine-house and therefore Mr Nye knew very little about it. The boiler was coal-fired, and one of Mr Nye's jobs was to pour in the two hundred buckets of river water that it held. Maintenance was carried out by a local man who was a fitter in the Ashford railway works.

When Mr Nye first worked at the mill, rats and mice were quite a problem, but his governor paid him the then grand sum of 3d. per rat's tail and gradually the numbers decreased. Mr Nye set dam traps below the floorboards, and also used box traps to catch the rats alive so that a neighbour's dog could kill them. It was known that vermin sometimes got into the top of the stones overnight, to feed on the meal inside the tuns. Mr Nye used to creep into the mill in the morning and give the stones a quick turn before oiling up. The result of this was that the rats or mice fell down the spouts with 'their jackets off', as Mr Nye delicately phrased it.

The last job of the day before going home was to push a piece of sacking into the shoe so that corn could not roll into the eye of the stone overnight. If this was not done, it was possible for the corn to fill the stone, thus making it very difficult to start them up in the morning because of the increased load and static friction.

There was a three-beat and a four-beat damsel fitted to the stones in the mill, but Mr Nye preferred the three-beat one because it gave out a more steady plodding noise that could be heard nearly all over the building. He once had to shut the water off as quickly as possible after an iron bolt accidentally got in between the stones and caused the stones, tuns and fittings to go whirling round. However, before he could stop the mill, the runner stone, which was on the thin side for a runner, had jumped off the mace.

Between the house and the mill there was a passageway that was matchboarded, and a previous miller had made his notes here. Mr Nye went in there many, many times with a candle, reading with fascination the jottings that this miller had made – the weather, the trivial round, freak weather, special occurrences and occasions – the boarding was literally covered with his notes. Unfortunately, this has since been taken out.

There were no bad accidents in the mill, but Mr Nye recalled the day that he had had to move a stone from one floor to another using rope blocks. He had taken one turn round a post to hold the stone, but this failed to hold it and it rolled away down the stairs. Eventually, he had to let go of the rope, but luckily no one was hurt, and the stone did not do the damage that he feared. He recalled another occasion, whilst he was working in East Mill, when a smell of burning steadily increased during the day, but a series of searches failed to reveal the cause. During the final search, at the end of the day, he took the lid off the elevator in the top mill and was met with a tongue of flame. It was a double elevator, in one casing, but one of the bands had stopped turning and the opening of the lid caused a spontaneous combustion of the overheated materials. It was not usual to keep buckets of water in the mill, and Mr Nye had to go down five floors to get some water to dampen the band and wooden casing. The only concession to fire precautions was the spreading of limestone flour on the mill floors during the war to reduce the risk of a secondary dust explosion should the mill be bombed.

Records of input and output were kept in ledgers, and the owner paid the miller a bonus of a shilling per ton of material ground to keep everything working as efficiently as possible. Regulations required that the mill was decorated internally with lime wash every other year to keep down insect life.

Pledge's Mill, Ashford

Mr Nye was able to recall some information from his experiences gained whilst working at this watermill which, sadly, was burned down a few years ago. It was quite a large mill, rated as being a ten-sack plant, and was latterly a roller mill. Before the refining process was modernised, one floor was almost completely filled with silk machines arranged one above another, three units high.

There was a private swimming-pool close beside the mill and the mill-stream was used to clean and refill the pool once a year, but permission to use the water was sought from the miller, even though he may not have been using it at that time. The water rights belonged to the miller and could not be treated lightly. This is rather an interesting modern twist to the popular examples of barges and other river traffic awaiting flashes of water, by courtesy of the millers, to float them over shallows in the navigation.

The re-cogging of a gear gives rise to a cautionary tale. The work was carried out by a firm of engineers from Rye who were employed to do all of the engineering work at the mill. The millwright and his assistant worked right through the weekend to complete the job and the mill was duly started up at 7.30 on Monday morning. Mr Nye telephoned his governor as soon as possible to report an unusual and unpleasant harsh sound coming from the gearing and asked whether or not the mill should be shut down. His governor decided that the mill should continue to run to let the gearing run itself in but by 10 o'clock that morning nearly all of the cogs had been smashed out of the gear. This is another example of the risks involved in ignoring the old-established maxim that a badly meshing cog will only get worse and worse; it will never get better without skilled attention.

TED UREN   Recorded May 1980.

'I started in the milling industry in 1954, but I've recently retired from it. I came into the trade via the animal feeding-stuffs industry. I started by selling feed for a large firm which covered the whole of the country. They had a system of commission agents selling the animal feed in designated areas, and there were some 400 of them, up and down the country. As the thing expanded, and competition caused more and more amalgamation, they became part of a much larger concern. The pattern of the trade over the last twenty-five years as I've known it has altered, and inflation has taken its toll, of course.

PLATE IV

Ted Uren

I then went to work as a poultry adviser for a very old family firm of millers who were acquainted with the Hancock family – the Dann family at Hellingly in Sussex. Grandfather started his working life going round on his bike peddling seeds as a commission agent, and, hand in hand with this, he used to sell a bit of cattle cake and pig meal. In 1896, he got the tenancy of Michelham Mill, and there he set up business. In 1901, he took up the tenancy, and eventually bought, Coldharbour Mill at Hellingly, which was in the next parish. I eventually finished up working from Union Mill, Cranbrook, managing their affairs in the eastern part of the territory over here in Kent.

At Cranbrook Mill they gave me the fancy title of curator, a bit of oil on the fantail once a week and dust off the cogs, but then the Kent County Council, who own Union Mill, decided they wanted to pass the job over to a millwright, which they did. There used to be a big old gas-oil engine sited just outside and, until the mill was painted two years ago, you could actually see where the shed that housed the engine had been tacked on the side of the windmill. The drive used to come into the side of the mill to power the corn cleaners, plate crushers and other bits of milling equipment.

It was quite an eye-opener to us, the questions that people would come with, and there's nothing like questions to set you searching for answers, from selling the stuff through to making it and managing it. It was a fairly close-knit sort of community, as are most craft trades, such as the local builders, bakers and butchers. And so those in the milling industry would meet at market or the corn exchange, and this camaraderie and brotherhood stretched quite a way. These people at Hellingly were farming out their sons to the other side of Ashford to do their apprenticeships. There's always been this family element in milling, and you can trace it back a long way. The Russells at Union Mill [Cranbrook] go back at least three generations – and further.

We knew we were coming to Chegworth in the summer of 1961, and we used to make a practice of coming over to learn the ropes with the retiring miller – Harold Potter. He was very helpful, and was anxious that whoever came after should look after his friends and all the people he'd been looking after for donkeys' years. He retired in the October and they bought a cottage in Boxley, and I believe it was during Christmas week that he fell asleep in his armchair and never woke up. We only knew him from June to Christmas, so there were certain things, by virtue of the seasons of the year, that we never got into, and one of them was these blessed field beans that people kept bringing – "Harold used to make lovely feed with these." I was presented with these things and they said that he used to crush them. I rather fancy he must have soaked them and made them wet, because I never did get the hang of crushing them with the equipment we had got up there. We had a Hungarian crusher, and the Hungarians were very advanced with their milling techniques in the late 1800s. They produced some very good machinery, and this was one of the prototypes – one of eight imported into this country. But the field beans were too fat to go between the rollers, but we had an old hammer-mill, and I used this to make them up into some sort of meal after grinding them through a coarse screen.

He was a character, Mr Potter, and about the first week or month I was here an old chap came round to the door selling bags. This fella had a great big pile of "Seemeal" bags, which were bags that had contained fish meal – very heavy stuff, so small that they were no good for bagging mixed corn. This fella told me they were wonderful bags, and how Harold Potter gave him sixpence each for them. I told him, "Well, really, they're not much good for me," – they were too big for half hundredweights but you couldn't get a hundredweight in 'em. Adopting the salesman's selling technique, he said "Oo, he could get a hundredweight of mixed corn in 'em, *and* tie 'em round the middle."

One of my friends recalled the day we came to see Harold during the summer. As we came in through the door of the mill, he waved us to be quiet, and put his finger up to his lips to let us know something was on, so we stopped still. We noticed that in one hand he'd got a piece of string, and he was sitting on a sack at the bottom of the stairs, and was watching over by the hammer-mill. Well, all of a sudden, he sprang into life, pulled the bit of string and rushed across the mill and jumped on this bit of flat wood he'd got over there! He'd caught a rat which had been baited by some meal under the piece of wood, which was held up by a peg tripped by the long string. Another of his techniques, if he found a hole in the floor where they'd been coming up, was to put a box over the hole, and he would listen until he could hear them coming up through the hole. Then, he would creep across and quickly move the box away. He'd got a pretty good old mouser – an old grey tom cat which was around here for years, but you couldn't get friendly with it as it was a real old misery – and he'd call the old tom cat, and it knew what Harold wanted. The cat would sniff, and he'd know there was a rat under there, then up 'd come the box and that was that!

There was one place on the other side of Ulcombe that he used to go to every other Monday, and because I took over the milling round from him I had to do the same. You were all day getting rid of about a ton of bits and pieces. Going round the back doors of cottages delivering fourteen pounds of layers' mash and seven pounds of mixed corn – it wasn't worth me doing it, so I told them I wouldn't be coming any more. From Chegworth he'd go out one week along the main road to Harrietsham, and then he would take the road out to Sandway where he had several people that he would supply. There were a lot of little cottages and smallholdings out there, and he would run down towards Lenham Heath and Charing Heath, and then backtrack with his Austin three-tonner with its bald tyres and cranking handle, along the top of the hill. Then he would come back towards Fairbourne, and up towards the White Swan, and then down Liverton Hill, as far as the "Who'd a thought it." That's where he used to have his lunch, which consisted of a couple or three games of darts, a cheese sandwich, and a pint. Then, he'd gradually work his way back through from there along to Pye Corner at Ulcombe. He did this once a fortnight, and Monday was his delivery day, but the following Monday he would do another run which went out through Leeds and Langley towards Sutton Valence and this one was much meatier as you weren't calling at every door. He'd been doing it for years – he came here in 1909 and was still doing it in 1961, and nothing much had changed. He had one or two decent accounts, and he used to do a bit of contracting for a firm in Maidstone – used to kibble all their maize. He used to grind quite a lot of barley for one or two local pig farmers who used a lot of barley meal. They would bring in their barley which was hauled upstairs, tipped in, and ground. He would get 110 lbs. out of a hundredweight of barley, and the rest was called 'steamage', which he kept. He would take a toll now and then in lieu of payments. Perhaps, somebody would come down with a ton of barley to be ground or crushed, in the winter, for sheep and cattle, and that was not unprofitable, and we continued doing that for quite a long time. Because we used the loaded power of the wheel for that – we weren't using TVO or Diesel, it was a slow process which didn't interfere with anything, and you could change the bags – it took an average thirty-five minutes to fill a bag.

Folks would very often say, "If we bring you down 25 hundredweights of something we would want to take back 'so much'" – a given quantity – crushed or rolled or whatever, and that was an acceptable practice. And any surplus would, of course, be put into the mill stock and subsequently be sold for cash, and this paid for the processing.

During that winter we were grinding quite a lot. People were coming to us and asking us to take a bit more because, obviously, with the very cold weather the animals were eating more, and so we were working quite long hours. At that time we were using the water-power for crushing oats and barley. The most you could do was fifteen hundredweight in an evening and at the end of the night you'd earned yourself anywhere between 14 bob and 17s. 6d. But it was really, as much as anything, that you'd got the corn to mill, and you knew people's situation; they'd got sheep and cattle to feed and they were wanting the stuff.

In those days we would have oats brought in for crushing, for sheep, and we would sometimes mix in flaked maize and bran, groundnuts, and locust beans, which were very popular for sheep. The other thing that several people round here used to grow were those field beans I've already mentioned.

A practice that I wasn't very struck on late in the summer, when grain was getting expensive and short and very dry, was for one or two of Harold's cronies to come round and say that 'Arold would always let them have five hundredweight of wheat for their laying hens until harvest. The first year I sort of acquiesced, and several of these fellows went off with five hundredweight of blooming expensive dry wheat. In about the first week of September, when it had been raining, these fellows would turn up with about five hundredweight of soggy old wet wheat when it was worth five bob-a-hundredweight less!

When barley came in during the summer months, with a fairly low moisture content, – but Harold wouldn't use that term, he would say it was a bit gritty, – he would boil a kettle, and take it over and open up the neck of the sacks, and go along and put a bit of boiling water into the tops. The following morning that moisture had permeated through the sacks, and the barley used to crush that much easier. I can remember, when I was a young man down in Devon, that grain would be stood in a barn if it was very wet, and one of the things they would do there was to put an old dry stake down into the middle of a bag of corn, and the stake would take up a lot of the moisture. They never used to throw away old fencing stakes!

Harold Potter had three major customers and they used to provide him with the bulk of his work – crushing, rolling and grinding barley and maize, kibbling maize, and mixing up various rations for the poultry. Perhaps 60 per cent of his work came from between the three of them, and then he had five or six tons a month of various corn to grind again for resale. We might have been shifting between twenty and thirty tons of corn during the month. The five or six tons he would buy from a merchant – he might contract to take so much a month, or he might put some on contract and buy some – playing the market. He considered himself a craftsman rather than trader, but it was the craftsmen who went under in this business, and the traders that are in the ascendency all the time.'

We sat in the kitchen of the mill-house listening to Mr Uren recounting his experiences with apparent ease and confidence. Few questions were necessary; his story unfolded itself in a very natural way. Outside, the late May sun had set and the light in the kitchen had become gloomy. His talk now turned to Chegworth Mill, and was full of essential and valuable memories and observations. Interruption was to be avoided, and we were content to sit and listen. From one corner of the kitchen came a peculiar intermittent sound threatening to break our concentration. We later learnt that it was the family hampster who had begun his nocturnal displays. During the rest of our stay he alternated between taking runs in his squeaky wheel, and furiously grinding the chrome bars of his cage. By now it was difficult to see the face of Mr Uren – such was the darkness within the kitchen, and only the hampster was making observation on the narrative. Eventually, light was requested to ensure that the tape recorder was behaving itself. Later, when we interrupted our work for a cup of tea and some delightful home-made biscuits, we saw the sandy-coloured hampster still furiously gnashing his cage bars, quite oblivious to his owner's invaluable contribution to the history of Kent watermills.

'When the water was scarce, through the summer time, people would bring stuff down, but you couldn't work, and there the grist would stand with their different names on it. Some would ask if we could grind their little bit, and we would be working hand to mouth to keep them going. Then, when we got a bit of rain the river would swell. Neighbours have told me that they had seen old Harold out there working sometimes two or three days and nights on the trot, with candles, after a drought had broken – there was no electricty in the mill in those days.

We were often short of water during the summer, and Harold would always try and stop up the cracks in the flush gates to hold back as much water as he could. He would never throw ash away; there was always a pile of ash which, during the summer, he would go and sprinkle near leaks and it used to drop down and seal the flushes and gates and help retain the water. It was normal practice to hold back the water overnight. When you had got the wheel spinning, and it was running on a good even rhythm, you could conserve your water as much as possible by extracting only as much energy as was required. They used to put no end of grease and oil on the ends of the shaft to make sure they were well lubricated. They would go and scrape the pond, to get a greater depth, and take the slurry out, and Harold reckoned it was wonderful stuff for the garden. I suspect that it has been done over the years, for there are certain parts of the farm where it has been thrown out and spread around. There's one particular place – up by the two greenhouses – which is a really beautiful bit of soil, and it is so much different from the rest. They cleaned out the mill-race every year because that was very important, but I don't know how frequently they did the pond. Harold told me that the last time that he did it was in 1957, when he used one of these dredging machines, a crane on crawler tracks, with a long boom and a bucket on the end of it. That was the first time it had been done since before the war. I would imagine that one would clean the pond more frequently – the idea is really to raise the bank, because there is no advantage in having a greater depth than the cill of the apron.

We only ever get a few moorhens and duck on the pond, but I've got a picture of my son pulling out a sizeable trout. The small fish seem to have gone in late years. When we first came here, our children were always pulling out sticklebacks, but you won't find many of them in there now. I've never seen eels up here, but I understand that they're not unknown.

One thing we've had for several years is a kingfisher, and year after year we find him in the reeds. Sometimes I come home along over the top of the flushes when he's in that area, and I stop in the car. He'll stay there hovering until something disturbs him, then he goes under the willow trees, upstream, towards the wood.

I suggest that the normal working output of the mill wasn't much more than a ton per day. You had to physically take in a ton a day, send out a ton, and process a ton of food, in some way or the other. The output was about a ton a day from either the crusher or the stones, and so about every half-hour or so you would have to change a bag. In between this, you did a bit of oiling or sweeping up, but really your 'spare' time was spent sitting there and dressing the stones. By the time you had got them up, turned them, dressed them, levelled them, and put them back in again I suppose this occupied as high a percentage of your time as any other function as a miller.

I think that when the thing was running as a full-time affair, they got very little trouble with cogs and gears simply because they were under constant scrutiny. The gear at the top has got pear-wood cogs, and Harold had that one re-cogged in 1933 – they would remember such things as that as being milestones.

They hadn't ground flour here, well I'm almost sure, since 1909. The Wicks were the last bakers and flour millers here, and I believe they finished baking in 1896. The mill was built in such a way, with a bakehouse on the side of it and a faggot store next to it, that from the mill a chute ran into the bakehouse. I don't think their trade extended as far as Harrietsham, where I think the villagers must have had their own baker. At one time they must have had quite a substantial business, because they had two bread vans here.

Each of the five storage bins in the mill would take three tons. There's a flat area at the end where you would put a couple of tons in sacks but, as well as that, the chute that served the crusher would cope with another thirty hundredweight. The mixed corn chute or corn cleaner was used for making mixed corn, and into it we would tip wheat, barley and kibbled maize in various proportions, according to which was most expensive. They liked a lot of maize in their mixed corn, but they didn't always get it. They didn't like the price to fluctuate, twenty-five bob was the price for mixed corn. The mixed corn chute could hold another ton and a half so that, if you were full up, you could say there were about twenty tons in the top. But this could vary a lot; sometimes, you'd have virtually nothing, if you were busy, at other times you wouldn't really want twenty tons to come in one go. This was because it involved so much work, as it all had to go up by the hoist, be lugged around with the sack barrow, and then be tipped over. A pretty old gut-tearing job! The snag with leaving it in the sack, in those days, was that there were a lot of charges on sacks. There were always more quarrels over sack hire charges than anything else – short-weight? No, nothing to worry about; or delivery at the wrong time, or anything of this nature – no problem; but these blessed sacks! So, if you could, you got it out of the sacks, bundled them up, sent them off and got your credits of 1s. 6d. or two shillings a sack, or whatever it was. Sometimes you would need to keep them if your bins were full up. There were sack hire companies in those days that would hire out very heavy sacks – two hundredweight sacks some of them – and the grain was shunted around from merchant to merchant – of course there was quite a lot of string trading done over the years (buying corn speculatively to sell it on, and sometimes you didn't even take delivery, if you sold it on quickly, so that only a bit of paper changed hands). If a lot of corn was stored in hired sacks, and the market went against you, you could run into considerable debt over them so you really wanted them gone as quickly as you could. I wouldn't accept corn in hired sacks as it was always more nuisance than it was worth.

It would keep quite well; of course, through the winter you would have a busy throughput. We were having it come in all the time and so it was being topped up as gravity fed it out, and so presumably you weren't leaving the same stuff up there all the time. They're all flat-bottomed bins, and you would empty one and fill the next – use them in sequence.

The hammer-mill used to deliver via the screens into a cyclone fan arrangement, which blew it up from the side into a holding bin at the top where there was a bagging-off point and a two-way chute. Out of the top of this bin was a 'chimney' of five-gallon drums that Harold had rigged-up, so that the heavy stuff fell into the bagging-off chute whilst the dust would float up the 'chimney', and at the top he used to have a bag.

Oats don't go through the stones very well. First year we were here there was a fellow up at Sutton Valence/Langley way that did quite a lot of Christmas poultry, and much prized for this trade was the Sussex ground oats. They used to mix these with milk or whey, and one thing and another, to fatten these birds. He used to bring these oats down to have them ground very finely, and this stuff used to ball up like cotton wool – terrible stuff to try and grind. It was taking ages, so I put it through the hammer-mill, but it was so light, and there was a fair bit of wind in the cyclone of the hammer-mill that most it of got blown away somewhere. He brought down eight hundredweight of oats, but the next day when he came to collect it I'd only got four and a half hundredweight of this stuff left for him! I never did see him again – I think he thought I was a crook.

We would grind wheat finely for one chap who used to particularly use in in pig meal. Why he had it fine ground I don't know because, normally, if one is incorporating wheat into pig ration, you wouldn't put in more than 20 or 30 percent for choice. If you did, you put it in as a fairly coarse grist because finely ground wheat tends to paste up and is not very palatable to pigs, or chickens for that matter. What we used to sell quite a bit of was very coarse ground wheat for growing chicken – almost kibbled – and this we would sieve over a scrier. This was a fairly coarse sieve which was erected underneath the meal spout and which took off the very fine ground stuff and retained only the coarse grounds. We had quite a nice mixture of coarse ground wheat, which was prized for young growing stock, and we used to sell quite a lot of that to these people. The sievings which would be left in a heap on the floor underneath was run off into a bagging-off box. The floury portion of the grist would be mixed with the layers mash.

We used to crack or kibble maize on the very hard Derbyshire Peak stones and we used to have them set fairly well apart so that they didn't grind it up too much. The whole maize used to come in about the size of your finger nail. Again, we would pass it over the scrier, and the maize meal used to fall into a heap. That's pretty good stuff to mix in with layers' rations. There was no science in the way this was done. I used to have a foot in both worlds – on the one hand, I was selling what was probably the most advanced and technically nutritious animal feed on the market, but on the other end of the scale, when I came home at night, I was mixing this stuff up with a shovel. It was what you had, and how much you could afford to put in, that determined the formula.

If you had plenty of water and had the mill running about right, and the stones were fairly well dressed, you could put about a ton a day through them. You could also, with plenty of water, have the crusher going and get a ton through that with both running off the wheel. I can't remember having two pairs of stones going at once, because of the limited space to take it off.

As far as the speeds of the stones were concerned I feel that this is where much of the craft and technique came in and, to be honest, I don't think I ever really mastered it. I can remember Harold coming out to me and saying "Cor! you are wasting that water." But we'd got plenty and I didn't think anything of it. He said, "You can cut back on that", but I said, "Then you'd have to cut back on the feed!" "That's all right", he'd say, and then he would talk about ratios. He knew you could get more grain through the mill for the same amount of water. The limiting factor wasn't time, it was water. The speed was important as there were so many adjustments you would make – a combination of many things, but of course what we have never used was the governor. In those days, there were many different grades of miller's offals which were separated, yet in late years you can't buy really broad bran for love nor money, because the milling technique is not taking so much out. What does come out, comes out as plain middlings which is pelleted because it is easier to handle. In those days, they would have been quite fortunate to get perhaps fourteen hundredweights of flour out of a ton of wheat, whereas today we might be looking for perhaps seventeen or eighteen hundredweight out of a ton of wheat, but of course they are using different wheats nowadays.

I can remember two or three occasions when ice formed on the wheel to such an extent that eventually it froze the wheel to the wall of the mill. It came to a halt and welded itself onto the ice. We went out with buckets of hot water trying to free it, but it was a question of sledge-hammers and crow-bars, bit and pieces, and chipping the ice away until the wheel had been freed. Then off we would go again.

In 1963, we had a big freeze. We could see the pond freezing over one evening, so we broke up the ice and kept it free round the flush gates, but we were fighting a losing battle. The cold weather had been going on for a couple or three weeks, and there were big lumps of ice getting stuck in the gates, and then the whole of the pond was completely frozen. When the ice froze completely all round the flushes, no water was getting away by the wheel, so the level of the ice floated. We suddenly noticed, late at night, that the whole thing was rising and, when the ice rose above the level of the bank, suddenly all the water underneath it came right across the yard under pressure and gave us one of the biggest floods we've ever had. We went out there, but didn't really know what to do. We tried using picks and sledge-hammers to break the ice up and allow the water to get away. At two o'clock on a cold February morning I was up to my thighs in icy water. Underneath the mill there are two or three drains, which run into the mill-race, and these are a foot or eighteen inches in diameter so we always expected a lot of water to come from somewhere, but gradually these drains were icing up. We built a bonfire on the ice, but the heat just went up and we were making no impact at all on the ice underneath. So my brother-in-law got down in the culvert underneath the road and we lit a bonfire there with old tyres. We nearly choked ourselves out with them, but it had the desired effect of melting the ice, and eventually the water receded to its normal level. Once it started to come through in any quantity, it put the fire out. We were frozen stiff – the miller's life is not always a happy one!'

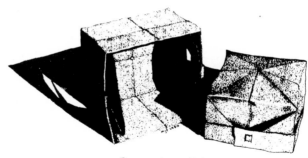

Papermakers' Hats.

IV. GLOSSARY

Glossary of terms occurring in this study, and others which can be associated with watermills. In a few cases, the names of mills in which an example may be found are given in square brackets. (Arch.) = Archaic. Syn. = synonymous; but it should be noted that some terms may be – (i) peculiar to localities and counties, and, (ii) imperfect or partial synonyms. These are words that in *some* contexts or in *some* of their senses, may be substituted for another without affecting the meaning.

Whilst the origins of a few terms are known, the geographical extent of their use is unknown; for this reason the origins have not been specified. Where more than one meaning of a term is known, they are numbered.

'A'-BRACKET
: [Hope] 'A'-shaped iron frame used for supporting a bearing. Syn. 'A'-STANDARD.

ALARM
: See BELL ALARM

APRON
: Flat plate at the end of the trough delivering water to the water-wheel.

ARCHIMEDEAN SCREW
: (1) [Chilham, Hythe] Horizontal hollow tube in which a spiral screw or an arrangement of spiral blades rotates to convey meal, etc. Syn. AUGER, CONVEYOR, CREEPER, SCREW, WORM.
: (2) The same principle is used, but here an inclined tube raises water from a lower to a higher level. Usually for drainage or irrigation purposes.

ARTIFICIAL STONE
: See COMPOSITION STONE.

ASPIRATOR
: A machine used for separating grains through differences in their specific weights.

AUGER
: See ARCHIMEDEAN SCREW (1).

BACKING
: See SOLE.

BACKLASH
: Free movement between two sets of gear-teeth or cogs. Sometimes two staggered rows of teeth are used to avoid backlash.

BACKWATER
: Water in the tail-race touching the water-wheel and impeding its movement. Syn. TAIL-WATER.

BALANCE BOXES, BALANCER BOXES
: Cavities in the back (top) of the runner stone. For holding lead weights to ensure the correct balance of the stone. Later, adjustable weights in recessed iron boxes were used.

BAR
: See BRIDGE.

BARLEY MILL
: Machine for removing the hulls and tough bran or skin to leave the kernel clean and white. The product is called pearl or pot barley.

BARLEY STONES
: Millstones made of Derbyshire millstone grit. Used for grinding barley, oats, and beans, etc. Syn. PEAK STONES, PIG STONES.

BARREL VAULT
: Hole in the millwall through which the wheel-shaft passes, sometimes with an iron shield or plate to keep out the spray and weather. [Field]

BASEPLATE
: See BEDPLATE.

BAY
: (1) Dam built of wood, caulked and made watertight.
: (2) Dam or embankment of mill-pond. Syn. DAM, MILL BAY, MILL-DAM, POND-BAY, STAGNUM (Arch.)
: (3) The division between the frames of a water-wheel, i.e. two frames = one bay.

BEADING
: Continuous projecting lip or raised feature, usually convex, found on castings.

BEARING — Element supporting a journal. Usually made of brass, or gunmetal, but sometimes of hardwood or stone. Syn. BRASS, HALF-BRASS.

BEARING-BOX — See WALL BOX.

BEATER —
(1) The wooden bars in a CENTRIFUGAL which throw the meal against the silks.
(2) Machine for cutting and/or fibrillating a water suspension of fibres in preparation for the paper-making process.

BEDPLATE — A cast-iron plate which acts as a foundation for machinery. Syn. BASEPLATE.

BEDSTONE — The lower, stationary, stone in a pair of millstones. Syn. DEAD STONE, DEADMAN, LIGGER, LOWER MILLSTONE, LYER (Arch.), NETHER STONE.

BEHR-STONE — (Arch.) See BURR STONE.

BELL ALARM — A bell which is struck mechanically when the feeding hopper above the millstones runs empty. Syn. ALARM, FEED ALARM, WARBLER.

BELT —
(1) An endless loop of material (India rubber, canvas, cotton webbing, etc.) for transmitting power from one pulley to another.
(2) See DOG-IRON.

BEVEL GEAR, BEVIL — A gear having teeth set an angle to the face of the gear. Used to connect shafts meeting at any angle. See GEAR also.

BEVEL WHEEL — A wheel having its cogs oblique to its axis.

BILL — See MILL-BILL.

BIN-FLOOR — Top floor of a mill, where the storage bins are housed. Syn. GARNER FLOOR.

BI-POLAR MACHINE — Believed to be an early type of simple electric motor.

BIST — Small bag of bran. Used to lean on when dressing a millstone.

BIT — See MILL-BILL

BLACK-GREASE — A dark grease, made from powdered black lead (graphite, plumbago) mixed with lard.

BLOCK — One or more pulleys, called sheaves, mounted in a wooden shell or cheek piece, used for moving heavy weights.

BLUE STONE — [Chapel] Millstone made from stone of volcanic origin. Quarried from the Andernach and Koblenz areas of West Germany. Syn. CULLIN STONE, DUTCH BLUE STONE. See MILLSTONES also.

BOLLARD — A short, large-diameter, wooden shaft, around which the sack hoist chain or rope is wound. Usually horizontal, but rarely vertical [Maplehurst]. The bollard, which can be flanged [Swanton], often has additional material on its face to provide grip and reduce wear. It may also be wrapped with iron sheeting [Hammer, Park], or sacking [Ashbourne], or canvas [Chegworth], cloth and leather [Chilham], or be provided with wooden slats [Groombridge], or metal strips [Wandle]. Syn. SACK BOLLARD, WINCH BARREL, WINDLASS.

BOLTER/BOULTER — An inclined, wooden-framed machine in which a rotating cylindrical frame covered with a sleeve of cloth, later calico or silk, rubbed against stationary external bars. Syn. BOLTING MACHINE, PASTRY, SILK MACHINE.

BOLTING CLOTH — The revolving sleeve, made of wool, calico or silk, in a bolter. Syn. SILKS.

BOOT — The bottom of an elevator.

BOSOM — See SWALLOW.

BOX SECTION RIM — A hollow rim of square or rectangular section.

BOY — See SACK BOY.

BRAN — Husks of grain separated from flour after grinding. It is the covering that encloses and protects the germ and endosperm in a grain of wheat.

BRAN DUSTER — A machine which removes any flour adhering to the bran; or separates, for example, husks from Sussex ground oats.

BRAN JUMPER — See JOG-SCRY.

BRASS — See BEARING.

BRAYER — Pivoted beam supporting one end of the bridge-tree; intermediate lever between the bridge-tree and the steelyard. Used for tentering. Syn. BRAY.

BREAK ROLLS — See ROLLER MILL.

BREAST, BREST —
(1) The curved face of the wheel-pit.
(2) The middle third of the millstone's radius, on the grinding face.

BREAST-WHEEL	Type of water-wheel where the water is applied at roughly the level of the wheel-shaft. Syn. BREAST-SHOT, HIGH-BREAST, LOW-BREAST.
BRESSUMER, BREASTSUMMER	Horizontal wooden beam across an opening. Used to support joists on an upper wall, etc.
BRIDGE	Curved iron bar transferring the weight of the runner stone to the stone-spindle. Usually set in cavities, lead-filled, on the underside of the runner stone. Syn. BAR, BRIDGE-RYND, GIMBAL BAR, GYMBALS.
BRIDGE-TREE	The pivoted beam, of iron or wood, supporting the stone-spindle, and forming part of the hursting. Syn. LIGHTER-BAR.
BRIDGING-BOX	Housing for a thrust bearing. Usually set on the bridge-tree, to accommodate the stone spindle. It is normally an open-topped cast-iron box with adjusting screws in each side. See also FOOTSTEP BEARING.
BRIGGING	The process of adjusting the set screws in the bridging-box so that the stone spindle is truly vertical. Syn. TRUING.
BROAD BRAN	Large-flaked bran.
BRUSH MACHINE	Machine for brushing and polishing wheat. Used after the smutter, but before the magnetic separator and wheat grader.
BRUSH SIFTER	A machine, sometimes suspended, for sifting meal. It consists of a fixed, horizontal, cylindrical wire screen, from 4–6 ft. long, in which angled brushes rotate thus driving the meal along the screen. Syn. ROTARY SIFTER, SIFTER, SUSPENDED ROTARY SIFTER.
BUCKET	Receptacles around the water-wheel, whereby the water is retained. Can be curved (U- or J-shaped) or straight (V- or L-shaped), and may be ventilated or unventilated.
BULL'S EYE	Circular opening in a brick wall.
BURR	A selected piece of hard quartz found in France, in the vicinity of La-Ferté-sous-Jouare and Épernon. Used for making millstones.
BURR-STONES	A millstone made from siliceous burrs, the best having a roseate hue, cemented together with plaster of Paris, and bound around the circumference with iron hoops. The best stone for grinding wheat; it is also suitable for beans, oats, and maize. Syn. FRENCH BEHR (Arch.) FRENCH BURR, FRENCH STONE. See also MILLSTONES.
BUSHEL	A measure of volume for corn; the avoirdupois weight of a bushel of wheat is 63 lbs. One sack equals four bushels, or one coomb.
BYPASS	Channel taking the water which is excess to the mill's requirements. Syn. WASTE.
CAKE BREAKER	Machine for breaking up animal cake, such as linseed or cotton cake. Syn. CAKE CRUSHER.
CANAILLE (Arch.)	See MIDDLINGS.
CANTS	Wooden elements built into the rim, or bolted onto the arms and rim of a gear so as to strengthen it. Cants, which can have straight [Ashbourne, Groombridge] or curved [Dunster] inside edges, can partly or totally fill the face of a gear – 'planked solid'.
CAPSTAN HEAD AND BAR	Rack and pinion arrangement for lifting a sluice gate whereby the iron pinion is attached to a capstan head thus allowing an iron bar to be used.
CARBORUNDUM STONE	Trade name for a compound of silicon and carbon. Sometimes used for making artificial millstones. Syn. ARTIFICIAL STONE, COMPOSITE STONE.
CARMAN	Horse-van driver.
CASING	See VAT.
CENTRIFUGAL	An improved type of separator for dressing meal and flour. It relied on the beaters inside the reel rotating very fast, so that the meal was thrown against the whole sieve area by virtue of centrifugal force. Syn. CENTRIFUGAL BOLTER, CENTRIFUGAL DRESSER, CENTRIFUGAL SILKS.
CENTRIFUGAL GOVERNOR	See GOVERNOR.
CHAIN CONVEYOR	A device for the horizontal transport of material. It consists of flat scrapers,

	mounted on parallel chains, moving within a long wooden or metal box. Syn. CHAIN CREEPER.
CHAIN HOIST	See SACK HOIST.
CHAIN HORSE	See COCK HORSE.
CHAIN PURCHASE WHEEL	See 'Y' WHEEL.
CLAMS	See FOLDING WEDGES.
CLAPPER	An obsolete device, fitted to the top stone, for shaking the shoe.
CLASP-ARMED	Crossed double arms gripping a hub or shaft; similar to a noughts-and-crosses design. Syn. GRIPED ARMS.
CLEWERS	See PENSTOCK.
CLICK	See PAWL.
CLOSED BUCKET	See BUCKET.
CLOUGH/CLOW	See PENSTOCK.
COCK-HEAD	The top of a stone spindle.
COCK HORSE	Horse added in front of another, often ridden, to help draw a heavy load using trace chains. Syn. CHAIN HORSE.
COCK-PIT	See COG-PIT.
COG BLANKS	Cogs, roughly sawn to shape, ready for mounting and final shaping.
COG-BOX/COG-HOLE	See COG-PIT.
COG-PIT	(1) An area, usually enclosed, with access doors and hatches, containing the main gears, i.e. pit-wheel, wallower, great spur, and stone nuts. Syn. COCK-PIT, COG-BOX, COG-HOLE. (2) The floor cavity containing the pit-wheel.
COGS	Removable wooden teeth, usually pinned or wedged into the morticed iron or wooden rim of a wheel. Resilient and close-grained wood in best. In Kent, apple [Hope, Hayle], beech, pear [Chegworth] hickory, hornbeam, lignum vitae, and English Spine oak were popular, the last two often used for wet work. Other woods used include acacia, hawthorn, holly, ash, and elm; fibre cogs also occur [Swanton].
COLOGNE STONES	See BLUE STONES.
COMBINATION PULLEY	[Ashbourne, Lovehurst] A pulley made of iron and wood; usually an iron hub and arms, with a wooden rim.
COMPASS ARMS	·Arms that radiate from a hub or shaft. Syn. RADIAL ARMS, SPOKE ARMS.
COMPOSITION STONE	Artificial millstone made from carborundum, emery or particles of French burr embedded in a strong cement. Syn. ARTIFICIAL STONE. See also MILLSTONES.
COMPOUND BEAM ENGINE	Beam engine utilising the exhaust steam from its high pressure cylinder to feed a low pressure cylinder. The HP cylinder is sited nearest to the beam trunnion, the LP one is further away.
CONICAL PENDULUM (Arch.)	An old name for a governor.
CONVEYOR	A mechanical device for the horizontal transport of grain, meal, etc. It consists either of a rotating auger or screw, or moving flat scrapers, working within a long wooden or metal box. Syn. CREEPER. See ARCHIMEDEAN SCREW, CHAIN CONVEYOR, SCREW CONVEYOR.
COOMB	Four bushels of grain. See also BUSHEL.
CORN CLEANER AND WINNOWER	See WINNOWER.
CORN CUTTER AND GRADER	A combination of two machines; one for cutting wheat or maize into grits, and a sieve for grading it according to the various particle sizes.
COTTER PIN	An iron pin or bolt retained in place by a flat, L-shaped cotter.
COUNTER SHAFT	A shaft driving another one parallel to it.
COW POP GEAR	See TRUNDLE.
CRACKING	(1) The process of cutting fine grooves in the 'lands' on the face of the millstone. Syn. SCRATCHING. (2) The process of breaking maize, beans, etc., through millstones or rollers.
CRADLE	See HORSE.
CRANE	See MILLSTONE CRANE.

CREEPER	See CONVEYOR.
CROOK STRING	A string or cord used to regulate the opening from the hopper to the shoe.
CROSS-HALVED	A timber joint, whereby two pieces of wood that cross each other are let into one another. Syn. HALF-HOUSED.
CROSS-HEAD GUDGEON	[Burnt, Ashbourne]. Iron journal or bearing pin with four wings let into the end of a wooden shaft, which is often bound with iron hoops to prevent it splitting. Syn. CROSS-TAILED, CROSS-WINGED.
CROSS RIBS	See FEATHERS.
CROSS-STAYED	Diagonal iron stays set between the frames of a water-wheel so as to strengthen it.
CROTCH	The forked lower end of a quant that engages the mace or rynd of overdriven stones.
CROWN WHEEL	A gear, usually cogged, at the top of the main vertical shaft. Usually, it drives pinions on a lay shaft for ancillary machinery. Syn. FLY (Arch.)
CROWNED FACE	The curved face of a pulley.
CRUSHER	[Chegworth] A machine for crushing oats, barley, etc.
CRUTCH	
CRUTCH POLE	See QUANT
CRUTCH SPINDLE	
CULLIN STONE	See BLUE STONE.
CULVERT	An underground water channel.
CURVILINEAR BUCKET	A carefully designed curved bucket, associated with the Poncelot water-wheel, which causes the minimum of shock and disturbance to water entering and leaving it.
DAM	See BAY.
DAMPER	See SPATTLE.
DAMSEL	An iron device projecting through the eye of an underdriven stone for jogging the shoe to keep the grain flowing. They can be three-beat [Hope], or four-beat [Hythe]. Syn. DANDELION, DANSIL (Arch.).
DEADMAN	See BEDSTONE.
DEADSTONE	See BEDSTONE.
DÉBRIS GRILLE	A grille, usually of vertical iron bars, sometimes covered with a wire screen, set in the head-race or in the entrance to the trough to prevent débris, leaves, twigs, etc., from entering the water-wheel. Syn. TRASH GRID, TRASH GRILLE.
DECORTICATOR	A machine for removing the husks from certain seeds.
DERBY PEAK	See PEAK STONE.
DISC SEPARATOR	A machine consisting of rotating, vertical discs designed for trapping unwanted cereals; a grain cleaner, introduced in the 1920s.
DOG-IRON	A hooked iron strap for holding timbers together. Syn. BELT, STRAP.
DONKEY ENGINE	[Hothfield] An engine used for hauling or hoisting; usually with two cranks at right angles, and without a flywheel, to facilitate stopping and starting in any position.
DOUBLE-FEED CENTRIFUGAL	A centrifugal machine fed independently at opposite ends, which can be used for treating two separate streams of material.
DRAFT	The radius of the circle in the centre of a millstone face to which the furrows are tangential. Syn. LEAD.
DRESSER	See WIRE MACHINE.
DRESSING	(1) The operation of cutting, on the grinding face of the millstones, the furrows and fine grooves.
	(2) The style or pattern of furrows and grooves on a millstone face, e.g. circular or 'sickle'; two-furrow or two quarter; three quarter; straight or union dressing, etc. Syn. DRESS.
	(3) The process of separating or sifting flour from the rest of the meal.
DRIFTING	See FURROWING.
DRILLS	See STITCHING.

DRIVEN — A wheel-gear or shaft, etc., which is powered directly from another element called the driver.

DUTCH BLUE STONE — See BLUE STONE.

ECONOMISER — A series of heated tubes through which the feed-water of a boiler passes. They are arranged so that they are heated by the waste gases. Their sooty surfaces have to be constantly scraped. Syn. FEED-WATER HEATER, FEED-WATER ECONOMISER.

EEL-TRAP — A 'cage' of iron bars in which eels are caught. It is usually found immersed in the bypass channel. When a trap is well arranged, the eels are kept in it alive and undamaged until wanted. Earlier traps were made of wood or wickerwork.

EFFECTIVE PURIFIER — A machine for separating particles, where the product drops through a horizontal air-stream and is graded according to the densities of the various products.

ELEVATOR — A vertical, or near-vertical, device for conveying material upwards. It consists of an endless belt of containers (boxes, cups, or buckets) running over top and bottom pulleys. The belt is usually enclosed in a wooden case.

EMERY STONE — See COMPOSITION STONE.

ENDOSPERM — The starchy substance forming the main body of a wheat grain which yields flour when broken.

ESCAPE HATCH — See FLOODGATE.

EYE — (1) The central hole in the runner or upper millstone into which the grain is fed; the term also applies to the bedstone.
(2) The area covered by the inner third radius of the grinding face. Syn. SWALLOW (upper stone only), WAIST.

EYE STAFF — Short staff for proving the eye of the dressed face.

EYE TIN — See NECK BOX.

FACE-GEAR/COG-WHEEL — One in which the cogs or teeth not only lie on the face or flat of the gear, but are not bevelled, i.e. the edge or tops of the teeth lay in a flat, single plane. See also GEAR. PIN-GEAR.

FAGGOT STORE — A store for bundles of sticks or twigs kept for fuel; sometimes found in association with bakeries.

FALL TROUGH — See TROUGH.

FALSE BOARD — The upper 'door' of a hatch controlling water serving an undershot water-wheel.

FALSE HOOP — An iron hoop used for holding a balance weight on the rim of a millstone.

FANTAIL — The fan that turns a windmill automatically into the wind. Syn. FLY.

FARROWING HOUSE — A room or building where pigs are born.

FAST-AND-LOOSE PULLEY — An arrangement of two pulleys, mounted side by side on a common shaft, where one is free to spin and the other is fixed or keyed to drive the shaft. Power is transmitted when the belt is pushed onto the fixed (fast) pulley by an iron fork or striker.

FEATHER — (1) Vertical back edge and sloping bottom of a furrow where it meets the 'land' on a millstone.
(2) Ribs introduced for strengthening purposes on cast arms, etc. Syn. CROSS RIBS.

FEATHERING. — See STITCHING.

FEED-ALARM — See BELL-ALARM.

FEED SHOE — See SHOE.

FEED WATER HEATER — See ECONOMISER

FELLOES, FELLIES — The sections of the rim of a wooden wheel.

FELT WASHER — A machine for washing the woollen felts used in paper-making.

FILLET — (1) Narrow flat band separating two mouldings.
(2) Small curved internal corner of a casting.

FINEST FLOUR — The best grade flour. Syn. FIRST GRADE FLOUR. PATENT FLOUR.

FISHBELLIED	A term applied to a wheel-shaft which is thicker in the middle than at the ends.
FLANGE	Projecting flat rim, collar or rib.
FLAT GRINDING	A pair of stones set as close together as possible to produce the maximum amount of flour.
FLAUNCH, FLANCH	[Hammer, Hythe] Circular or shaped sheet of metal mounted on the water-wheel shaft, and onto which the arms are bolted.
FLAWING	The process of checking the flatness of the millstone grinding surface. Syn. STAFFING.
FLEME, FLEUME, FLUME	See HEAD-RACE.
FLIGHTS	The wooden blades of a conveyor.
FLOATING MILL	A mill working as a floating raft, anchored to the bank, where the wheel is driven by the water current.
FLOATS	The projecting wooden or metal blades of some water-wheels. They can be straight or curved; open or closed (L-shaped, or with sole-boards). If shrouded they are called buckets, and not floats. Syn. PADDLES, RUNGS (Arch.).
FLOOD-CILL	See SPILLWAY.
FLOOD-GATE	A sluice to divert water from the wheel to the over-flow or bypass channel. Syn. ESCAPE HATCH, FLOOD-GATE, FLUSH.
FLOOR COLLAR	A wooden collar fixed to the floor around the edge of a hole where a shaft, etc. passes through the floor.
FLOP JACK	An automatic device for lifting a small quantity of water.
FLOUR	Wheatmeal that has been dressed to remove bran, pollards, etc. There were many types of flour, whose names varied through time; generally, the derivatives have increased in modern times – especially in roller-mills. See FINEST, GREYS, MIDDLINGS, SECONDS, SHARPS.
FLOUR MACHINE	A general term for machines that separate ground material into various fractions. See BOLTER, CENTRIFUGAL, PLANSIFTER, REEL, WIRE MACHINE.
FLOUR REEL	See REEL.
FLUME	See HEAD-RACE.
FLUSH	See FLOOD-GATE.
FLY	(1) The fan that automatically turns a windmill into the wind. Syn. FANTAIL.
	(2) (Arch.) An old term for the crown wheel.
	(3) The triangular shaped area of 'land' adjacent to the rim on the dressed face of a millstone; there is one in each 'harp'.
FOLDING WEDGES	Iron wedges which are inserted into cavities around the rims of millstones to facilitate lifting them. Syn. CLAMS, LEWIS BOLTS.
FOOTSTEP BEARING	The bearing at the bottom of the mill-stone spindle. It is housed in the bridging box. Syn. FOOT BRASS, STEP BEARING, STEP BRASS, STEP BEARING, TOE BRASS.
FORKED LEVER	A term for a method of disengagement of gears where the stone nut is raised by a pivoted lever which lifts the gear via an iron rod or fork. Syn. LEVER AND FORK.
FOUNTAIN MIXER	A machine for mixing additives into animal foodstuffs.
FOUR-BEAT DAMSEL	See DAMSEL.
FOUR O'CLOCK WATER-WHEEL	One where the water is applied to the wheel at what would be the 4 o'clock position, if the side of the wheel was seen as a clock face.
FRENCH BURR-STONE	See BURR-STONE.
FRICTION DRIVE	[Ashbourne, Hythe] An intermittent driving arrangement involving two wooden friction-faced wheels. Usually, they are bevelled, and made up of numerous wooden segments, sometimes faced [Hammer]. One friction wheel is made, by levers, to bear against the other, so that the unit effectively forms a clutch. Syn. FRICTION CLUTCH.
FULLING	The process of cleansing cloth of grease and oil (scouring) and, in the case of short wools, to promote felting and shrinkage (milling). Originally done by trampling or walking, but later by water-powered mallets, called fulling mills, beating the cloth in water with a detergent. Syn. TUCKING.

FUNNEL BINS	See SELF-CLEARING BINS.
FURROWING	Cutting furrows in the face of the millstone; part of the dressing process. Syn. DRIFTING.
FURROWING STRIPS	Templates or strips used to mark out the furrows on the face of a millstone.
FURROWS	The main grooves or channels cut on the grinding face of a millstone.
GABLE	(1) Triangular upper part of the wall at the end of a ridged roof.
	(2) Triangular frame with a plumb-bob, which was superseded by the spirit level.
GAMBREL ROOF	(1) A roof of two sections, the upper of low pitch and the lower of steep pitch, the junction occurring at a side purlin or aisle-plate.
	(2) American name for MANSARD ROOF. See MANSARD ROOF.
GARNER	Storehouse for corn, etc.
GARNER FLOOR	See BIN-FLOOR.
GATE	(1) The damper or slide controlling the flow of grain from the hopper to the stones. See SPATTLE.
	(2) A loose term for a sluice.
GEAR	A wooden or cast-iron wheel with projecting teeth; if the wheel carries morticed wooden teeth, it is called a cog-wheel. See BEVEL GEAR, FACE-GEAR, SPUR-GEAR.
GEARED RING	See RING-GEAR.
GETTING UP	The wearing away of the burrs in the eye of a French stone.
GIMBAL, GYMBAL	A mechanical contrivance to allow the top stone to 'float' level while being driven. A gimbal ring was used in association with a mace having trunnions. See also BRIDGE.
GIMBAL BAR	See BRIDGE.
GLEANING	(1) Gathering ears of corn left on the fields by the reapers.
	(2) The trade of grinding the same.
GLUT BOX	A type of bearing at the top of a spindle. The box can be opened, allowing the shaft to be moved, and thus the gear to be disengaged. Often found at the top of quants in overdriven stones.
GLUTEN	Nitrogenous part of flour remaining as a sticky substance after the starch has been washed away.
GOIT	See MILL-RACE.
GORGING	Uneven feeding of grain through the stones.
GOVERNOR	An automatic device to either (a) adjust the gap between the stones or, (b) regulate the flow of water onto the wheel. In watermills the Watt type is invariably encountered – either with spherical weights [Field, Burnt, Groombridge, etc.], or pear-shaped weights [Chegworth, Hythe, etc.]. Syn. CENTRIFUGAL GOVERNOR, REGULATOR (Arch.).
GRADING	The separation of a single product into fractions consisting of different-sized particles.
GRAFT SHAFT	A removable portion of the bearing round the neck of a stone spindle.
GREAT SPUR-WHEEL	The gear which drives the stone nuts. It is usually mounted on the upright shaft, above the wallower.
GREEK MILL	See NORSE MILL.
GREYS	A class of flour containing impurities.
GREY-STONES	See PEAK STONES.
GRIPE	(1) A type of brake. Not found in watermills.
	(2) A term for overdriven stones. See OVERDRIVEN.
GRIPED ARMS	See CLASP-ARMED.
GRIST	(1) Corn which is to be ground.
	(2) Animal feed; grinding oats or beans, etc., for use of livestock.
GROAT MACHINE	A machine for grinding oats.
GROATS	Ground oats; excluding the hulls.

GUDGEON	An iron journal let into the end of a wooden shaft. See CROSS-HEAD GUDGEON, PINTLE.
GUILLOTINE HATCH	See HATCH.
GUSSETS	Triangular webs to strengthen a structure.
HACKLE SCREWS	Set screws in a bridging-box. Used for centring the millstone spindle. Syn. PINCHING SCREWS.
HACKLE PLATE	This plate, together with a leather washer, keeps dirt from entering the neck bearing of a millstone spindle.
HALF-BRASS	The curved bearing brass supporting the underside of a journal; often found on the wheel-shaft.
HALF-HIPPED	[Maplehurst] Small triangular roof that slopes between the ridge of a roof and the top of a gable wall that extends above eaves level.
HALF-HOUSED	See CROSS-HALVED.
HAMMER POND	A mill-pond which served a hammer mill, where water power was used for forging iron.
HAND-HOIST	See SACK HOIST.
HAND MILL	See QUERN.
HAND-ROPE	The rope controlling the sack hoist drive.
HARP	The triangular areas on the grinding face of a millstone that carry a group of parallel furrows. Most millstones are dressed with either 8, 10, or 11 harps. Syn. QUARTERS.
HARP STRINGS	See STITCHING.
HATCH	A movable wooden gate in a sluice or penstock. Syn. GUILLOTINE HATCH, SLIDING HATCH.
HEAD GOIT	See HEAD-RACE.
HEAD-RACE	A channel carrying water to the water-wheel. Syn. FLEME, FLEUME, FLUME, HEAD GOIT, LADE, LEAT, MILL FLUME. See also MILL-RACE.
HEAD SILL	See SILL.
HEFT	See THRIFT.
HELVE	(1) See THRIFT. (2) The wooden beam carrying the iron head of a trip hammer.
HIGH BREAST	Type of water-wheel where the water is applied to the wheel above the level of the wheel-shaft. See BREAST-WHEEL.
HIGH MILLING	The process of breaking down grain gradually by passing it between the stones in various stages. The distance between the stones is progressively reduced from its initial large gap.
HIPPED GABLE	A triangular area of roof that extends from the eaves of a gable wall up to the ridge of the roof.
HOG CORN	Corn for grist milling, i.e. animal feed.
HOG FEED	Animal feed that has been ground.
HOIST	See SACK HOIST.
HOOD-WAY	The wooden casing which encloses the upper half of a wheel; examples occur in drainage mills.
HOOP	An iron ring surrounding a millstone, or the end of a wooden shaft or hub. All burr-stones have hoops, often more than one.
HORSE	The frame or cradle, usually of wood but sometimes of metal [Chegworth], for supporting the hopper above the millstones. Syn. CRADLE.
HORSE LOAD	A ton – 2240 lbs.
HUB	See NAVE.
HULLS	The outer covering of seeds, especially peas and beans, etc.
HUNTING COG	An additional cog introduced into a gear to avoid exact ratios between the two engaged gears. This prevents the same cogs meeting repeatedly. The same result may be obtained by omitting one cog.

HURSTING	The wooden frame supporting the millstones, and enclosing the main gears. Syn. HURST, HURST FRAME, HUSK (Arch.).
HUSK	(1) The dry outer skin of seeds, such as is found around wheat and barley. (2) Archaic term for hursting.
HUSK CUPBOARD	Container for oat husks winnowed out by a groat machine.
HUTCH	Corn bin in the loft. Syn. BIN, CORN BIN, STORAGE BIN.
HYDRAULIC RAM	A self-acting device which utilises the ram effect of water down an inclined pipe to deliver smaller amounts to a much greater height.
INERTIA GOVERNOR	One where the two weights are suspended from the ends of projecting rods; as the spindle revolves, the weights lift a rod which passes through eyes at the end of each pendulum rod, and thus lift the central collar. Syn. LAG GOVERNOR.
INTERMEDIATE GEARING	A train of gears inserted into the driving system.
JACK	The wooden bar or trammel fitted over the top of the millstone spindle, and used in 'brigging the spindle'. As the spindle slowly rotates, a quill at the end of the bar is checked against the bedstone grinding face to get the spindle aligned. Syn. JACK SHAFT, JACK STICK, TRACER BAR.
JACKING RING	A circular iron ring which is used for lifting a stone nut out of gear. The ring is pushed up by rods passing through the bridge-trees. Syn. JACK RING AND SCREW, RING AND SCREW, SCREW AND RING.
JACKING THE STONES	The process of using the jack. See JACK.
JIGGER	See SACK JOGGER.
JOCKEY	Small pulley, usually for tensioning a belt.
JOG SCRY/JOGGER/ JOGGLING SCREEN	An inclined oscillating sieve carrying several layers of wire mesh of different gauges to extract any middlings or pollards adhering to the bran, or gound oats, etc. Syn. BRAN JUMPER, JUMPER, PLANSIFTER, VIBRATING MACHINE.
JOURNEYMAN MILLWRIGHT	A qualified millwright hiring out his services daily, and moving from mill to mill.
JUMPER	See JOG-SCRY.
KEST	A toll cupboard.
KEY	An iron wedge, sometimes rebated into machined slots or grooves, called KEY-WAYS, for holding wheels, gears, etc., onto the shafts. Syn. REED (long key).
KIBBLER	A machine having two grooved steel plates to break up grain. Used for maize; thus 'kibbled'.
KNEES	[Chegworth, Field] Wooden braces or supports that usually are curved, and which are up in the corners between the wall-posts and the undersides of the floor beams.
LADE	See HEAD-RACE.
LANDS	The flat surfaces of the grinding faces of the stones, which are picked or finely grooved.
LANDSIDE BEARING	The wheel-shaft bearing on the outer side or landside of the water-wheel.
LANTERN WHEEL	An old type of gear consisting of a ring of staves or bars set between two wooden discs. Syn. LANTERN GEAR, LANTERN PINION, LANTERN WHEEL.
LAUNDER	See TROUGH.
LAY-SHAFT	Horizontal shaft for driving gears or belts.
LAZY-BACK-CATCH	See PAWL.
LEAD	See DRAFT.
LEAT	See HEAD-RACE.
LEFT-HAND STONES	A pair of stones which have had to be dressed unconventionally because the runner stone revolves anti-clockwise, or against the sun – called WIDDERSHINS.

LEVER AND FORK	See FORKED LEVER.
LEWIS BOLT	See FOLDING WEDGES.
LIFT TENTER	A lever for 'tentering' the millstones by hand.
LIGGER	See BEDSTONE.
LIGHTENING GEAR	The steelyard and links connecting the bridge-tree to the governors.
LIGHTER BAR	See BRIDGE-TREE.
LIGNUM VITAE	The wood of a West Indian tree – Guaiacum, the heartwood of which is dark green in colour, and is very hard and heavy. Very suitable for cogs that have to run in wet conditions.
LINESHAFT	See LAY-SHAFT.
LOCUM	See LUCAM
LOW BREAST	Type of water-wheel where the water is applied to the wheel below the level of the wheel-shaft. See BREAST-WHEEL.
LOW MILLING	Where the maximum grinding effect is achieved in a single pass through the stones with them set close together.
LOWER MILLSTONE	See BEDSTONE.
LUBRICATION	The oiling or greasing of bearings and cogs. Tallow is good between woods; olive oil and sperm oil is preferred for use between metals; hogs, lard for use between iron and wood cogs. For wheel-shaft journals on wood, water is good, provided that there is provision for its entry between the surfaces – otherwise a mixture of black lead and lard was used.
LUCAM, LUCOMB, LOCUM, LUCARNE	(1) The small weatherproof cabin projecting from the mill, and housing the external sack hoist. (2) A garret window, or window in the roof of a house. From the French *lucarne*.
LYER	(Arch.) The lower millstone. See BEDSTONE.
MACARONI	Wheaten paste, mainly gluten, formed into long tubes, and used as food.
MACE	See RYND.
MAINSHAFT	See VERTICAL SHAFT.
MALT MILL	(1) A machine that crushes malt between rollers. (2) Millstones used for grinding malt.
MANSARD ROOF	A roof of two sections, the upper of low pitch and the lower of steep pitch, the whole supported by a framed truss above the tie beam. Named after the French architect, François Mansard (1596–1666), this particular construction was introduced in the eighteenth century. Roofs of similar outward appearance can be much earlier (see Gambrel Roof), but the trussed construction allows more flexibility. The object is to create more head-room for storage or living accommodation.
MANYHEIGHT	A stepped pivot, used with a crowbar, for raising a runner stone.
MEAL	Ground pulse or grain; the product of the stones.
MEAL BIN	A bin used for the storage of meal. Syn. TROW.
MEAL FLOOR	The floor of the mill where the meal bins are situated. This is usually the floor immediately below the stone floor.
MEAL SPOUT	The wooden chute and spout through which the meal drops, from the stones, into a sack or bin.
MEZZANINE	A low storey between two higher ones; an intermediate floor, stage or platform.
MIDDLINGS	An intermediate or coarse product from the wire machine. Used for coarse household bread or animal feed. Syn. CANAILLE (Arch.) SHARPS, SUPERS, THIRDS, TOPPINGS.
MILL BILL	Tempered chisel for dressing millstones. Syn. BILL, BIT, MILL-BIT.
MILL DAM	See BAY.
MILL EYE	The hole and chute where the meal leaves the skirting of the stones.

MILL FLUME	See HEAD-RACE.
MILL HOLME	See WATER MEADOW.
MILL PICK	Tempered, pointed metal pick used with a hammer for dressing millstones. Syn. PICK. PRITCHELL.
MILL PIVOT	See STONE SPINDLE.
MILL-RACE	A major water-channel either going to, or coming from, a mill. Syn. GOIT, RACE. See HEAD GOIT, HEAD-RACE, TAIL GOIT, TAIL-RACE.
MILL RYND	See RYND.
MILL SPINDLE	See STONE SPINDLE.
MILL STAFF	See WOOD PROOF.
MILL TAIL	See TAIL-RACE.
MILLER'S THUMB	(1) A reference to the broadening and flattening of the miller's thumb through constantly feeling the quality and temperature of the meal as it came from the stones by rubbing it between his index finger and thumb. (2) A small river fish so called because of its fancied resemblance to the thumb of a miller.
MILLER'S WILLOW	The wooden spring that holds the shoe against the revolving damsel. See RABBET.
MILLING SOKE	Ancient manorial custom whereby the tenants were obliged to use the lord's mill, and pay toll or multure for the grinding operation. Syn. SOKE.
MILLSTONES	Millstones work in pairs. With horizontal stones there is a lower, stationary stone (see BEDSTONE) and an upper, moving stone (see RUNNER). Vertical millstones also have one moving and one stationary stone (see VERTICAL MILLSTONES.) Horizontal stones are either underdriven or overdriven, and may be made from many different materials: see BLUE STONES, BURR-STONES, COMPOSITION STONES, PEAK STONES.
MILLSTONE CRANE	[Maplehurst] An iron crane, pivoted at floor and ceiling level, with caliper arms that insert into rim sockets of the runner stone, for lifting it. Syn. CRANE.
MILLSTONE DRESSER	A journeyman, specialising in the dressing of millstones. Syn. STONE DRESSER.
MILLSTONE FLOOR	The floor on which the millstones are situated in the mill.
MILLSTONE GRIT	See PEAK STONES.
MILLWRIGHT	A builder and repairer of wind, water or other mills.
MITRE WHEELS	Equal-sized wheels with bevel teeth of 45°, and set on shafts that are at right angles to each other.
MIXER	A machine for mixing the component parts of animal foodstuffs.
MORTICE	A slot prepared in an item for it to receive the tenon or projection on a piece of wood, e.g. an iron wheel morticed to receive wooden cogs; wooden arms morticed into a shaft.
MULTIPLYING GEAR	Set of pulley blocks or sheaves for a rope tackle.
MULTURE	See TOLL.
NAFF	See NAVE.
NAILBOURNE	A stream that flows only in the winter. Syn. WINTERBOURNE.
NAVE	The central piece, hub or boss of a wheel. Syn. HUB, NAFF.
NECK BOX	The bush in the eye of the bedstone. Syn. EYE TIN (Arch.).
NETHER STONE	See BEDSTONE.
NIP	The gap between the millstones.
NORSE MILL	A more primitive water-powered mill having a vertical shaft carrying at its lower end a morticed hub fitted with impellers against which a stream of water is directed. The top of the shaft carries and drives the upper mill-stone. Syn. GREEK MILL.

OAT DUST	Fine by-product of milling oat kernels; the coarser elements are called scree dust.
OAT ROLLER	A machine with steel rollers for crushing oats. Syn. OAT CRUSHER.
OAT SCREENINGS	The rejected fraction produced when cleaning oats, before they are ground, e.g. broken grains, weeds, straw, chaff, etc.
OATMEAL SEEDS	The husks of small oats and some kernel.
OFFALS	The inferior by-products of flour milling, including middlings, pollards, bran; used for animal food, except for some finer middlings.
OIL ENGINE	An internal combustion engine in which sprayed or evaporated oil is ignited.
OIL RING	In bearings having an oil reservoir, the oil is fed to the top of the journal by an oil ring, which is supported and turned by the journal.
OPEN STONES	A stone that has an open, rather than a close or fine grain. Such stones usually require a very prominent dressing.
OVERDRIVEN	Millstones which are driven from above, rather than from below. Windmill stones are nearly always overdriven; in watermills they are found only rarely. [Chilham, Hythe]. Syn. OVERDRIFT.
OVERHUNG	A wheel or pulley, etc., which is mounted on the end of a shaft, but which does not have a bearing between it and the end of the shaft.
OVERSHOT	A wheel where the water is applied at the highest point, so that the top of the wheel moves in the same direction as the water in the trough.
OVERSPILL	See SPILLWAY.
PADDLE	(1) See FLOATS. (2) The brush or blade attached to the runner stone for sweeping the meal into the chute from the annular gap between the stones and that vat. Syn. SWEEP, SWEEPER, TAG.
PAINT STAFF	See WOOD PROOF
PASTRY	An old term for a bolter, probably because it dressed pastry flour. See BOLTER.
PATENT FLOUR	See FINEST.
PATTERNS	The wooden shapes or patterns used in foundry work to produce cast-iron objects such as gears, pulleys, etc.
PAWL	A pivoted iron catch which automatically locks a gear under load and stops it reversing; it allows gear rotation in one direction only, until thrown out of gear. Syn. CLICK, LAZY-BACK-CATCH.
PEAK STONES	Millstones made of coarse sandstone, called Millstone Grit; hewn in one piece, softer and less durable than burr-stones, and used mainly for grinding barley and oats. Syn. DERBY PEAK, GREY STONES. See also MILLSTONES.
PEARL BARLEY	Polished barley. Syn. POT BARLEY.
PECK LOAF	A loaf weighing $17\frac{1}{2}$ lbs. (A peck of flour is 14 lbs.).
PELTON WHEEL	An impulse turbine, developed in 1870, in which a high-pressure jet of water is directed against a series of curved cups on the rim of a rotating wheel.
PENSTOCK	(1) The gate or sluice controlling the water entering the wheel. Syn. CLEWER, CLOUGH, CLOW, SHUT, SHUTTLE, SLUICE. (2) The trough carrying the water onto the wheel. See TROUGH. Syn. PEN-TROUGH. (3) The pipe or pipes delivering water to a large turbine installation.
PENTROUGH	See TROUGH, PENSTOCK.
PICK	See MILL PICK.
PIG STONES	See BARLEY STONES.
PIN-GEAR	(Arch.) An early, crude type of gear where the teeth consist of projecting rods or pins of wood; used in conjunction with a lantern gear. A pin-gear may be a face- or spur-gear.
PINCHING SCREWS	See HACKLE SCREWS.
PINION	A small, solid, wooden or iron gear. See GEAR.
PINTLE	A small-diameter journal projecting from a wooden shaft, or the top of a post. See GUDGEON.

PINTLE AND POT	A thrust bearing.
PITCH	The distance between cogs or teeth on the imaginary circle which passes through their main point of contact when engaged with another gear.
PITCH-BACK	[Hayle] A type of water-wheel where the water is applied at or near the top, and is deflected down and backwards by a plate; a very high breast-wheel. The bottom of the wheel moves in the same direction as the tail-water.
PIT-GEAR	The gear mounted on the water-wheel shaft. Its bottom half usually turns in a pit. Syn. PIT-WHEEL.
PIVOT	(Arch.) An old term for the stone spindle. See STONE SPINDLE.
PLANKED SOLID	A wooden cog-wheel or pulley where either (1) the side(s) are boarded in inside the rim, or (2) where the cants are so deep as to extend from the rim to the hub.
PLANSIFTER	A wheat-cleaning machine which utilises the sieving principle. It is also used for grading and flour dressing, and this latter is probably its major function.
PLATE MILL	A machine for grinding cattle food; popular with farmers.
PLUMMER BLOCK	The block in which a bearing is mounted.
POLLARDS	A lower grade product of flour dressing, between coarse middlings and bran. Syn. THIRDS.
PONCELOT WHEEL	An improved undershot wheel, introduced in the early nineteenth century, in which the water flows down into curved buckets designed to minimise shock and disturbance as the water enters and leaves them.
POND BAY	See BAY.
POPPET	The frame supporting rope pulleys used for hoisting.
POST AND TRUSS	Box-frame style of building using vertical elements (posts) and horizontal elements (trusses).
POT BARLEY	Polished barley. See PEARL BARLEY.
PRITCHELL	See MILL PICK.
PROVER	See STAFF PROVER and WOOD PROOF.
PULSE	Edible seeds of leguminous plants such as peas, beans, lentils, etc.
PURIFIER	A machine to remove the flour from middlings. See EFFECTIVE PURIFIER.
QUADRANT RING-GEAR	Part of a ring-gear. See RING-GEAR.
QUANT	(1) The square, tapered, lower end of the millstone spindle which carries a stone nut. (2) The spindle driving the runner stone in an over-driven mill. Syn. CROTCH, CROTCH POLE, CROTCH SPINDLE, QUILL.
QUANT BEARING	The glut box or bearing at the top of the quant.
QUARTERN LOAF	A 4 lb. loaf.
QUARTERS	The harps on the grinding face of a millstone.
QUERN	Hand-mill for grinding corn, either reciprocating or rotary.
QUILL	See QUANT.
QUOINS	External angle of a building; stone or brick forming the angles in doorways, windows, etc.
RABBET	See MILLER'S WILLOW.
RACE	See MILL-RACE.
RACK AND PINIONS	Cast-iron rack with teeth (driven) engaged by a pinion (driver). Used to raise and lower gates, etc.
RADDLE, REDDLE	Red oxide mixture used on the paint staff when checking for high spots on millstones during the dressing operation. Syn. TIVER.
RADIAL ARMS	See COMPASS ARMS.
RAP	A block of hardwood, bone, flint, etc., fixed to the shoe to take the knock of the damsel (or quant in an overdriven stone).
REED	A long key engaging in a splined shaft. See KEY.
REEL	(1) The frame carrying the silk sleeve in a bolter. (2) An inclined, rotary separator for cleaning grain and also for dressing flour from meal. The grain or meal enters the upper end of a rotating cylinder covered

in silk cloths of different degrees of weave. The impurities overtail through the open end. Syn. FLOUR REEL, SEPARATOR, SILK REEL.

REGULATOR
(Arch.) Old term for a governor. See GOVERNOR.

RELIEVED FACES
Recesses on the faces of an iron shaft, e.g. wheel-shaft. [Swanton].

RHYND, RIND
See RYND.

RIGGER
(1)   Spindle on which two chains wind up to disengage a stone nut.
(2)   A pulley driving a belt.

RIGHT-HAND STONE
A millstone which is dressed in such a way as to suit its clockwise rotation, when viewed from above.

RING AND SCREW
See JACKING RING.

RING-GEAR
A toothed cast-iron ring (usually in sections), bolted onto the arms of a water-wheel [Swanton], or gear [Ashbourne]. Syn. GEARED RING.

RIVER MILL
A mill, where the wheel is undershot, and positioned directly in the river, and not served by a head- or tail-race.

ROLLER BEARING
A bearing utilising rollers, usually mounted in a circular cage or case, to take the weight of a shaft.

ROLLER MILL
(1)   Machine with grooved steel rollers for grinding grain. Syn. BREAK ROLLS.
(2)   A factory equipped with roller mills.

ROPE DRIVE
Transmission of power by rope-driven grooved pulleys. The ropes are either of hemp, cotton, manilla (lubricated with plumbago and tallow), or wire – introduced in about 1880.

ROTARY SIFTER
See BRUSH SIFTER.

ROUNDS
Staves or spindles in a lantern gear, etc.

RUBBING BURR
A piece of French burr used to rub down high spots when stone dressing.

RUBBING STRAKES
[Ashbourne, Hythe] Wooden strakes fixed to stone/brick walls, usually on the meal floor, and against which full sacks were leant to prevent them from becoming damp.

RUNG
(Arch.) Old term for float or paddle. See FLOATS.

RUNNER
(1)   The rotating part of a water turbine.
(2)   The upper, moving, millstone. Syn. TOP STONE, UPPER STONE.

RUNNING BALANCE
Balance of a millstone whilst in motion.

RUNNING WET
A term, usually applied to the pit-wheel, where a gear either is running in water or is being sprayed with water.

RUNWAY
The bed of the water-wheel pit.

RUSSIAN TALLOW
See TALLOW.

RYND, RHYND, RIND, RHIND, RINE
(1)   The iron mace or mill rynd, which supports and drives the gimbals, bridge or bar of the millstone. Syn. MACE.
(2)   The iron bar, curved or flat, or sometimes winged (Arch.), which carries and turns the runner stone. Syn. for both (1) and (2) MILL RYND.

S-CLAMPS
Iron S-shaped clamps, used in conjunction with a tie-rod passing through a building, for strengthening purposes. The clamps may be of other shapes. See also WALL PLATE.

SACK
280 lbs.

SACK BOLLARD
See BOLLARD.

SACK BOY
Piece of wood with three hooks to keep an unattended sack open under the meal spout, etc. Syn. BOY.

SACK HOIST
The hoist for lifting and lowering sacks of grain, flour, etc., either by hand, water or electric power. The hoist may be external (with a lucam), or internal. Syn. CHAIN HOIST, HAND HOIST, TEAGLE, TIGGLE.

SACK JOGGER
A machine or device for shaking or vibrating a sack while it is being filled. Syn. JIGGER.

SAFETY FLANGES
[Wandle] A coupling with flanges that extend over the bolts to keep them out of harm's way.

SALLE
Room, or area, in a paper-mill where the paper was sorted into various qualities, and counted into the desired quantities.

SCALPER	A machine with a rotating wire reel for removing dirt and small seeds from wheat.
SCANTLING	The cross-section of a piece of timber.
SCARFED JOINT	A timber joint where the pieces overlap without any increase in thickness.
SCOOP WHEEL	A driven-wheel with scoops or floats around it. Used for drainage or irrigation purposes. See MARSH MILL.
SCOTCH WEDGE	Wooden block for raising a millstone.
SCOURING	Removal of grease and oil from cloth. See FULLING.
SCRATCHDIAL	[Maplehurst] A sundial, scratched into wood or stone.
SCRATCHING	See STITCHING.
SCREE DUST	By-product from milling oat kernels; slightly coarser than oat dust.
SCREENER	A machine similar to a dresser, but equipped with only one grade of wire gauze, which brushes dust from grain. Used after, or in place of, a separator.
SCREW AND RING	See JACKING RING.
SCREW CONVEYOR	See CONVEYOR.
SCRIBE	A curved flexible steel marker. Used when fitting new cogs.
SCRIER, SCRY	See JOG-SCRY.
SECONDS	The second-best grade of flour. Syn. STANDARD WHEATEN, WHOLEMEAL FLOUR.
SEED CLEANER	See BRUSH MACHINE.
SELF-CLEARING BINS	Bins which have bottoms sloping towards the outlet. Syn. FUNNEL BINS.
SEMOLINA	Hard particles of wheat left after bolting flour, and having the texture of coarse sand.
SEPARATOR	See REEL (2), CENTRIFUGE.
SHAKER	See JOG-SCRY.
SHARPS	A superior grade of offal, sometimes used for coarse household bread, but usually for pig and cattle food. Syn. COARSE MIDDLINGS, SUPERS, THIRDS, TOPPINGS.
SHEAVE	[Groombridge] An iron wheel, in a wooden block. Used for guiding and supporting. Syn. SHEAVE WHEEL. See also BLOCK.
SHIELD	See SHROUD (1).
SHOE	The small wooden trough which feeds grain into the eye of the millstone. Syn. FEED SHOE, SLIPPER.
SHORTS	See MIDDLINGS.
SHROUD	(1) The vertical rim or flange enclosing the buckets of an overshot or breast wheel. Syn. SHIELD. (2) A flange or rim enclosing the ends of teeth, e.g. a shrouded pinion.
SHUDES	Oat husks or hulls.
SHUTTLE, SHUT	See PENSTOCK.
SICKLE DRESS	A style of millstone dressing where the furrows curve in from the perimeter to the eye.
SIEVING	Coarse separation, e.g. removal of strings, labels and stones, etc.
SIFTER	See BRUSH SIFTER.
SILK	See BOLTING CLOTH.
SILK MACHINE	See BOLTER.
SILK REEL	See REEL.
SILL	Top of wall of weir or dam. Syn. HEAD SILL.
SINGLE-PIECE	A wheel, for example, cast as a single unit; not cast in parts and subsequently bolted together.
SIZE HOUSE	Room or building, in a paper mill, where the sizing operation was performed.
SIZING	Treatment of paper, or papermaking fibres, with chemicals to reduce the absorbency of the paper.
SKEW BEVEL GEAR	A gear for taking a tangential drive off a bevel gear.
SKIRT, SKIRTING BOARD	See VAT.
SLEEVE	(1) A hollow casting between the bore of a gear, or wheel, and its shaft. (2) The cloth tube used as a flexible chute for meal.
SLIDING HATCH	Invented by John Rennie in 1783. It is a curved iron gate, operated by rack and

pinion, which moves against a fixed curved plate with inclined slots. This allows the utilisation of the maximum head available.

SLIP COGS	Cogs that slip out of place, for disengaging the gears.
SLIPPER	See SHOE.
SLUB	The ooze at the bottom of a pond or waterway.
SLUICE	A water-control gate. A general term that includes the penstock, or any gate on the pond, bypass, etc. See PENSTOCK.
SMUT	A disease of corn which produces grains filled with black powder.
SMUTTER	[Chilham] A machine for removing smuts from grain by throwing them in such a way as to break the diseased grain open. This, being lighter, is then removed on an air jet. It also removes light grains and dust, etc. Syn. SMUTTER MILL.
SOKE	See MILLING SOKE.
SOLE	(1) The inner face of the periphery or felloes; the bottom boards or plate below the buckets on a water-wheel. Syn. BACKING, SOLE-BOARD, SOLE-PLATE. (2) The bed plate of a machine. Syn. SOLE-PLATE.
SPATTLE	The slide or gate controlling the flow of the grain from the hopper to the shoe. Syn. DAMPER, GATE.
SPILLWAY	A cill, over which excess water spills. Syn. FLOOD-CILL, OVERSPILL, TUMBLING BAY.
SPLAY	(1) A bevelled edge of a window or door surround. (2) A bevelled face on the external corner of a building.
SPLINED SHAFT	A metal shaft having machined grooves along its surface, and parallel to its axis; the bore of a pulley or gear would have corresponding ribs to slide onto the splined shaft.
SPLIT WHEEL	Cast-iron wheel made in sections and subsequently bolted together; usually made in halves.
SPOKE ARM WHEELS	See COMPASS ARMS.
SPOUT	Wooden chute or spout for delivering grain or meal.
SPOUT MAN	Person that looked after the spouts and sacks of meal, etc.
SPRATTLE BEAM	(1) The wooden beam or iron casting [Hope] supporting the footstep bearing of the main vertical shaft. (2) The wooden beam supporting a sprattle or glut box. See SPRATTLE BOX.
SPRATTLE BOX	The top bearing of a vertical shaft. Term usually associated with windmills.
SPROCKET WHEEL	Wheel with a toothed rim, designed to carry a chain; each tooth engages a link.
SPUR-COGS/GEARS	Gears whose teeth protrude radially. Syn. CONTRATE. See also GEAR.
STAFF	See WOOD PROOF.
STAFF PROOF/PROVER	A steel straight edge against which the wood proof or staff is itself proved. Used in dressing the stones, Syn. PROVER, STEEL PROOF.
STAFFING	Process of checking the flatness of the millstone's surfaces. Syn. FLAWING.
STAGNUM	(Arch.) Old term for a mill-pond or dam.
STANDING BALANCE	The balance of the runner stone when at rest.
STARTER BOX	A device for helping set in motion very large water-wheels.
STARTS	[White] The projections, usually wooden, from the rim of a water-wheel. They support the floats.
STAUFFER	A small metal grease reservoir, with a screw cap, for lubricating bearings; usually, it is screwed into a cavity on top of the bearing cover.
STAVES	The rods, usually iron, serving as teeth in a lantern gear.
STAY BOLT	A long metal rod, usually in tension, for strengthening (1) a large wheel, etc., or (2) a building. Syn. TIE ROD, WALL TIE.
STEAMAGE	A quaint term for a toll.
STEEL GROUND	Material that has been ground with steel rollers or plates; the product of a roller mill.
STEEL PROOF	See STAFF PROOF.
STEELYARD	Steel bar, sometimes cranked [Wandle], linking the bridge-tree with the governors.
STEP BEARING	See FOOTSTEP BEARING.

STEP BRASS	See FOOTSTEP BEARING.
STITCHING	(1) The stitches or fine grooves cut on the grinding surface of a millstone. Syn. DRILLS. FEATHERING.
	(2) The process of cutting stitches. Syn. CRACKING, FEATHERING, SCRATCHING.
STIVES	The husks, etc., removed from corn by a winnower.
STOCK	See THRIFT.
STONE CASES	See VAT.
STONE DRESSER	See MILLSTONE DRESSER.
STONE DRESSING	See MILLSTONE DRESSING.
STONE FLOOR	The floor of the mill on which the millstones are situated.
STONE FURNITURE	The vat, horse, shoe and hopper.
STONE NUTS	The pinions, mounted and keyed onto the stone spindle, and which are driven by the great spur-wheel.
STONE PIVOT	See STONE SPINDLE.
STONE SHAFT	See STONE SPINDLE.
STONE SPINDLE	The vertical shaft or spindle which carries and drives the runner stone. Syn. MILL PIVOT, MILL SPINDLE, STONE PIVOT, STONE SHAFT.
STONE STAFF	See WOOD PROOF.
STRAIGHT DRESSING	A style of dressing millstone faces where there is a large number of main furrows tangential to the eye. Syn. UNION DRESSING.
STRAP	See DOG IRON.
STRICKLE	A wooden bar used to strike off level a measure of wheat in a bowl, etc.
STRIKE OF WHEAT	Toll taken in a bowl, etc., and levelled off with a strickle.
STRIKER	See FAST AND LOOSE PULLEY.
STUDDING	The vertical timbers, or studs, on which lathes, weatherboards, or planks are attached on external or internal division walls.
STUFF CHESTS	Large circular tanks, often tile-lined, and fitted with an agitator. Used to contain the fibre/water mixture (called stuff or stock) immediately prior to the paper-making operation.
SUPERS	See MIDDLINGS.
SUSPENDED ROTARY SIFTER	See BRUSH SIFTER.
SWALLOW	The relief or depression of the grinding surface round the eye of the stone. Syn. BOSOM, WAIST.
SWEEP	See PADDLE (2).
SWING POT BEARING	A bearing that has a trunnion at right angles to the axis of the bearing, i.e. self-aligning.
TACKLE	Combination of two blocks, suspended by ropes or chains, one of which is attached to the load, for lifting.
TAG	See PADDLE (2).
TAIL GOIT	See TAIL-RACE.
TAIL-RACE	The water-course flowing away from the wheel. Syn. MILL TAIL, TAIL GOIT.
TAILINGS	A term for the products that pass through the middle of a rotary dressing or grading machine, and which 'tail-out' over the end of the machine.
TAIL-WATER	See BACKWATER.
TALLOW	Product of melting the harder and less fusible kinds of fat, especially animal types.
TEAGLE	See SACK HOIST.
TEME, TENSE	Sieve used for bolting meal by hand.
TENTERING	Adjusting the gap between the stones, using the brayer, bridge-tree, etc. – called TENTERING GEAR.
THIRDS	See MIDDLINGS.
THONE	Wet or damp; term applied to stones, grain, etc.
THREE-ARM ARCH	A cast-iron arch with an additional curved leg on one side.
THREE-BEAT DAMSEL	See DAMSEL.

THREE-CONE PULLEY	A stepped pulley having three different diameters adjacent to each other. Arranged from small to large diameters.
THREE-QUARTER DRESSING	A style of dressing the grinding face of a millstone; in each harp there are three furrows leading to the perimeter.
THRIFT	The wooden handle of a mill bill. Syn. HEFT, HELVE, STOCK.
THROUGHS	Products which pass through the gauze of a dresser or bolter.
TIDE MILL	A mill, usually coastal, where the wheel is driven from a pond, which is filled by the tide. Operational only at certain states of the tide.
TIE ROD	See STAY BOLT
TIGGLE	See SACK HOIST.
TILT HAMMER	A forge hammer where the pivoted beam (helve) is tripped by a rotating cam mounted on the wheel-shaft. Syn. TRIP HAMMER.
TITHE	Tax of one-tenth of the annual proceeds of the land and personal industry. Taken for the support of the church and clergy. Originally payable in kind.
TIVER	See RADDLE.
TOE BEARING	See FOOTSTEP BEARING.
TOE BRASS	See FOOTSTEP BEARING.
TOLL	Payment in kind for grinding corn, pulses, etc., or dressing meal; usually taken as part of the input, or its products – especially the offals. Syn. MULTURE.
TOLL CUPBOARD	Storage place for the collected tolls. Syn. KEST.
TOP STONE	See RUNNER.
TOPPINGS	Middlings. See FLOUR.
TRACER BAR	See JACK.
TRASH GRILLE/GRID	See DÉBRIS GRILLE.
TREE-NAIL	Pin or dowel, made of hardwood (holly, oak, etc.), used for fixing together beams, planks, etc. Syn. TRUNNEL.
TRESTLE GRINDSTONE	Belt-driven machine for sharpening mill bits, etc. Usually half-cased, and standing on trestle legs.
TRIEUR	A machine for riddling corn of foreign matter; rye, barley, oats, cockles, etc.
TRIP HAMMER	Term used for a tilt hammer or for the falling stocks or hammers in a fulling mill. See TILT HAMMER.
TROUGH	The fabricated channel delivering water to the wheel. It can be made of timber [Hammer], brick [Dunster's, Hythe], tongue-and-grooved stone slabs [Mill Hall], concrete [Hope], or a combination of these materials. Syn. FALLTROUGH, LAUNDER, PENTROUGH.
TROW	See MEAL BIN.
TRUING	See BRIGGING.
TRUNDLE	An old type of gear having pegs instead of cogs. Used in conjunction with the lantern wheel. Syn. COW-POP GEAR, TRUNDLE WHEEL.
TRUNNEL	See TREE-NAIL.
TRUNNIONS	Each of any similar pair of opposite pins or pivots on which anything is supported.
TUCKING MILL	See FULLING.
TUFA	(1) Textured cellular rock of volcanic origin. (2) calc-tufa – deposit of calcium carbonate found in cavities and springs in limestone regions. Used by the Romans and Normans for building. [Chegworth].
TUMBLING BAY	See SPILLWAY.
TUMBLING IN	Sloping surface of brickwork used to effect the transition from one shape to another.
TUN	See VAT.
TURBINE	A term originally given to any vertical-shaft water-powered wheel, but now applied to many water-powered machines, generally of much higher speed and efficiency than water-wheels. They can be of the reaction (filled with water), impulse (partially filled), or transition type.
TWIBILL	An old term for a tool for cutting out mortices.

TWIST PEG	A socketed peg around which the crook string is wound.
TWO-QUARTER DRESSING	A style of dressing the grinding face of the stone; in each harp there are two furrows leading to the rim. Syn. TWO-FURROW DRESSING.
UNDERDRIFT	A term applied when the final drive to the millstones is from below. See OVERDRIVEN also. Syn. UNDERDRIVEN.
UNDERSHOT	A type of water-wheel, such as that found at river mills, which has radial floats or paddles working in a more or less level water-course.
UNION DRESSING	See STRAIGHT DRESSING.
UNIVERSAL JOINT	A coupling that includes yokes and a cross-type trunnion, allowing a direct drive to change its direction.
UNVENTILATED BUCKET	A bucket whose long, lower edge is flush with the inner face or sole plate of the wheel. See also VENTILATED BUCKET.
UPPER STONE	See RUNNER STONE.
UPRIGHT SHAFT	See VERTICAL SHAFT.
V-PULLEY	A pulley wheel with one or more V-section profiles on its rim to carry ropes.
VAT	(i) The casing, usually wooden, enclosing the mill-stones. It is usually round or octagonal. Syn. CASE, CASING, SKIRT, SKIRTING BOARDS, STONE CASES, TIN, TUN. (ii) The open-topped container of papermaking stock at which a vatman stands when he makes sheets of hand-made paper.
VENTILATED BUCKET	Bucket which has a narrow space between each one on the inside or sole of the wheel. This is to facilitate the release of entrained air, and hence to provide quicker emptying and filling.
VERTICAL MILL-STONES/STONE MILL	A pulley-driven machine that superseded the old horizontal stones. Supplied complete with its own feeding hopper and mechanism, tentering facility, bearings and casing enclosing the vertical stones; one driven and one stationary.
VERTICAL SHAFT	The main vertical driving shaft of a mill. Usually made of wood (oak, elm or pine), often faceted. Syn. MAIN SHAFT, UPRIGHT SHAFT.
VIBRATING MACHINE	See JOG-SCRY.
VITRUVIAN MILL	Named after the Roman who first described a watermill with a vertical wheel and a horizontal shaft.
WAIST	See SWALLOW.
WALL BOX	A cast-iron bearing box inbuilt in a wall.
WALL PLATE	(1) Wooden fillet in a wall, onto which partitions could be fixed. (2) Beam laid in, or on, a wall. (3) A cast-iron plate, usually circular, used with a stay bolt for strengthening a building.
WALL TIE	See STAY BOLT.
WALLOWER/WALLER	The first driven wheel in a watermill. It is mounted on the bottom of the vertical shaft, and is driven by the pit-gear. Syn. WALLOW WHEEL.
WARBLER	See BELL ALARM.
WASTE	See BYPASS.
WATER MEADOW	A field liable to flooding; considered to be very fertile ground. Syn. MILL HOLME.
WEATHER SHIELD	The plate or shield inserted into a barrel vault, where the wheel-shaft passes into the mill, to reduce the ingress of water.
WEB	A strengthening member in a casting, e.g. a solid web pulley.
WEIR	(1) Dam across a river or stream to raise the water level upstream; sometimes to divert water to a mill. (2) Enclosure of stakes, etc., set to trap fish.
WHEATMEAL	Meal as it comes from the stones – not dressed. Syn. WHOLEMEAL.
WHEAT-STONES	French burr-stones. See BURR-STONES.
WHEEL HOUSE	The enclosure or room for a water-wheel; especially an addition on the side of an existing building.

WHEEL-PIT	The emplacement or pit in which a water-wheel runs.
WHEEL-SHAFT	The wooden or iron shaft turned by the water-wheel, and on which it is fixed.
WHOLEMEAL	See WHEATMEAL.
WHOLEMEAL BREAD	Bread made from wheatmeal – including the bran.
WIDDERSHINS	(1) An old term meaning rotation against the sun, i.e. anti-clockwise. (2) Dressing millstones for anti-clockwise rotation. See also LEFT-HAND STONES.
WINCH BARREL	See BOLLARD.
WINTERBOURNE	See NAILBOURNE.
WINDLASS	See SACK BOLLARD.
WINNOWER	A machine which has a fan for blowing dust, etc., from grain. Syn. CORN CLEANER AND WINNOWER.
WIRE MACHINE	A machine for dressing meal, to extract flour and other products, using a cylindrical, rotating wire sieve. The wire cylinder was inclined over a series of hoppers, and the whole was enclosed in a box-like structure. Syn. DRESSER.
WOOD PROOF	The wooden staff or straight edge, usually of red deal, oak, mahogany, or walnut, used to check the level of the grinding surface during dressing. Syn. MILL STAFF, PAINT STAFF, PROOF, STAFF, STONE STAFF.
WOOD RIGGER	An old term for a pulley.
WORM GEARING	Two gears, usually of iron, where the teeth of one element form a helix wound round the shaft. This drives the second element – a spur-gear. The mechanical ratio is usually very high.
Y-WHEEL	A pulley wheel, usually of iron, which has an indented Y-section rim for gripping the chain. Used with a hand-powered endless chain. Syn. CHAIN PURCHASE WHEEL.
YOKE AND CHAIN	A method of stone nut disengagement where the nut is lifted by two chains attached to a pivoted bar with a yoke at one end.
YOKE ARM	Bar with a fork or yoke at the end.

GENERAL INDEX

Abbey Mill, 90
Addington, 13
  Mill, 13
Alexander, Mr. and Mrs., 23
All Souls College, Oxford, 148
Allnut's Mill, (see Lower Tovil Mill)
Amos, Mr., 73
Anderida, Forest of, 2
Argentina, 152
Arnold, family, 27
  W. and Sons, 27
  W.P.G., 25
  William, 2
Arnolds (Branbridges) Limited, 25
Ashbourne Mill, 13–20
Ashford, 29, 59, 77, 78, 156
  Corn Exchange, 150
  Mill, 165
  Railway Works, 169
Asswan Dam, 115

Barham Mill, 163
Barnards Smutter, 99
Barron Vertical Grinder, 156
Bartley Farm, 27
Basted, 20, 138
  Mill, 20–1
  Paper Mill, 21
Bateman's, 110
  Mill, (see Park Mill)
Bates, Tom, 22
Bayton Mill, 21–2
Bearsted, 54
Bedgebury, 157
Bell Farm, 157
Benenden, 128
Beult, River, 25, 33
Biddenden, 66
Biggleston's, Messrs., 164
Billingsgate Market, 155
Black Mill, 164
Blacksmith's Hill, 157

Blakes Hydram, 122
Boby, Robert, Ltd., 80
Bockingford Mill, 22–3, 74
Boughton Malherbe, 23
Bourne, River, 21, 25, 138
Bow Road, 134
Bowley Mill, 23–4
Boxley, 116
Branbridge Mill, 25–7
Brandbridges, 25
Brattles Mill, 134
Bridge Mill, 142
Brook, 156
Broomfield, 89
Brown, Stuart, 81
Buckland Mill, 143
Budapest, 43
Burdge, Mr., 72
Burnt Mill, 27–33
Burwash, 110
Bury St. Edmunds, 80

Canterbury, 1, 35, 78, 150
Chapel Farm, 21
Charing, 23, 27, 59
  Heath, 173
Chart Mill, 33–5
  Sutton, 33
Chartham, 35
  Mill, 35
Chatham, 116
Chegworth, 11, 172
  Mill, 38–44, 90, 172–8
Chelmsford, 115
Child, Mr., 156
Chilham, 35–7, 44
  Mill, 44–52, 164
Christian's Mill, 53
Christiansen, Mrs. Gay, 128
Christy Brothers and Middleton, 115
Church Mills, 53
Clarke and Dunham, 84

Clementson, Gordon, 157–63
Coldharbour Mill, 172
Coles Finch, William, *Watermills and Windmills*, 11,
 140
Comark Lane, London, 18
Comb, The, 54
Coombe & Co., 18
Corbet, Mr., 119
Cowes, 142
Cranbrook, 14, 72, 109, 172
Crisbrook, 143, 148
Crompton & Co., 115
Croydon, 17.

Dann, family, 172
Darent, River, 77
Darenth, 54
 Mill, 54–5
Denne & Sons Ltd., 78
Denne's Mill, 164
Ditton, 103
Dover, 41, 143
 Road, 58
Dunster's Mill, 55–8

East Farleigh, 64
East Malling, 95, 103
East Malling Stream, 103
East Mill, 170
East Stour, River, 120
Easton, water-rams, 22
Egerton, 27
 Mill, 157
Evegate Mill, 156
Exeter, 143
Eyhorne Mill, 58
 Street, 58

Fairbourne, 173
Faversham, 164, 168
Feltons Grist Mill, 99
Fennemor & Son, 14
Field Mill, 59–61
Floodgate Wood, 65
Ford, Henry, 123
 Mill, 61–2
 Place, 61
Frant, 27
French Mill, 49
Frittenden, 95, 100
Fulling Mill House, 53

Ganz & Co., 43
Gardner, William, 97
Gilkes, Gilbert & Co. Ltd., 115

Gloucester, 97
Godalming, 163
Goldwell Ltd., 103
Goodsall, R.H., *The Kentish Stour*, 46
Goudhurst, 55, 75, 157
 Hill, 158
 Mill (Hope Mill), 100
Great Ivy Mill, 148
Great Stour, River, 21, 23, 77
Green, Jack Barcham, 142, 148–9
 Simon Barcham, 149
Groombridge, 61, 159
 Mill, 61–4
Grove Mill, 58
Gurney's Mill, 64–5

Hainaker Windmill, 163
Hall, F., 67, 71–2
Halls of Dartford, 123
Hammer Mill, 65–72
 Stream, 65
Hammond & Co., 17
Hancock, Philip, 123, 149–57
Hanover Mill, 150–7, 169
Harrietsham, 173, 176
Hartfield, 107
Hartridge Manor Farm, 72
 Mill, 72–3
Hawkhurst, 116
Hawkridge Mill, see Paley Mill
Hawley Mill, 73
Hayle Mill, 73–4, 141–9
Hellingley, 172
Hicks, Mr., 157
Hill, J., 29
Hill & Son, 59, 156
Hippisley, Julian, 157
Hockers Edge, 72
Hoddiford Mill, 156
Hogben, Mr., 155
Hollingbourne, 58, 108–9
 Brook, 108
Holman, Billy, 164
 Brothers, 155–6, 163, 168
Hooker's Mill, 164–5
Hookers of Canterbury, 151
Hope Mill, 75–7, 100, 157–63
 Cottages, 157
Horsmonden Park, 159
Horton Kirby Paper Mill, 77
Hothfield Mill, 77–81
Howes, S., 18
Hughes, 58, 80, 99
Hughes & Son, 41
Hythe, 81, 156
 Mill, 81–9

Ickham, 1
Iden Green, 128
Ipswich, 64
Ivy Mill, 22

Jones, Glyn, 163

Kelly, *Directories of Kent*, 3
Kendal, 115
Kent, 2, 3
Kipling, R. *Something of Myself*, 115
    Rudyard, 110, 115
Kipson Bank Windmill, 163

Lambert, William, 159
Langley, 173, 176
Le Hoggestye, 91
Le Nethertoune Mill, 91
Ledys, 91
Leeds, 91, 108–9, 173
    Castle, 38, 89–91, 108
Leg-o-Mutton, 65, 90–1
Len, River, 38, 54, 108
Lenham, 21
    Heath, 27. 173
Leybourne Stream, 61
Linton, 33
    Road, 64
Little Church Mill, 53
Littlebourne Mill, 164
Liverton Hill, 173
London, 18, 41
Loose, 64, 73, 90, 92
    Stream, 142
    Village Mill, 92
Lovehurst Manor, 93
    Mill, 92–5
Lower Basted Mill, 21
Lower Crisbrook Mill, 142, 146
Lower Milgate Mill, 54
Lower Mill, 95–6, 103
Lower Tovil Mill, (Allnut's Mill), 142, 148

Maidstone, 53, 104, 141
Manchester, 115
Manitoba, 150
Maplehurst Mill, 95–102
Mark Lane, 18
Marsham, Admiral, 22
    Mrs., 22
Martin, C.W., *The History and Description of Leeds
    Castle, Kent*, 89
Mayfield, 104
Medway, River, 8, 25, 140, 142, 146
Mereworth, 103
    Castle, 103

Mill, 103
Mersham, 120, 149, 157
Michelham Mill, 172
Mid-Kent Water Company, 44
Middle Mill, 95, 103
Military Engineering, Royal School of, 116
Mill Hall Mill, 103–4
Mill Street, 53
Moat Mill, 104–7
Mote Park, 116

Neve Brothers, 105
New York State, 18
Newbridge Mill, 107–8
Newcomen Society, 123
Newmill Channel, 13
North America, 4
North Downs, 61
Nye, Wally, 123–4, 165–71

Old Mill (Borough Green), 108
    (Hollingbourne and Leeds), 108–10
Oliver, Frank, 154–5

Paley Mill (Hawkridge Mill), 109–10
Papillon, David, 95
Park Mill (Bateman's Mill), 110–6
    (Hollingbourne), 58
Pledge's Mill, 170–1
Pole Mill, 116
Potter, Harold, 172–8
Priory Stream, 91, 108
Pye Corner, 173

Quarry Wood, 90

Red Wheat, 167
Reeves, Alice, 128
    George, 157, 159, 162
Rolvenden, 13
Roman Watermills, 1, 2
Rose, Mr., 22
    T., 22
Rother, River, 8

Salts Lane, 64, 90
Scotney Estate, 157
Sellindge, 156
Short Bros,. 142
Shrubsole, Mr., 165
Silver Creek, 18
Sissinghurst, 65
Slip Mill, 116–9
South Darenth, 77, 119
    Mill, 119
Southall, 22

Spain, Alf, 141–9
  George, 142
  Grace, 145
Spelmonden Hill, 158
Spring Grove Mill, 81–9
Springfield Mill, 147
  Pond, 90
Staplehurst, 92, 95, 100
Steel, Mr., 92
Still's Mill, 92–5
Stour, River, 35
Straw Mill, 142
Sturry, 134, 164
Surrey, 8
Sussex, 8, 27
Sutton-at-Hone, 73
Sutton Valence, 173, 176
Swanton Lane, 157
  Mill, 120–8, 150–7, 165–70
Sweden, 150

Taylor and Bodley, 143
Teasaucer Hill, 22
Teise, River, 25, 75
Tenderden, 13
Thomas, Mr., 120
Ticehurst, 55
Tilling Stevens, 143
Tremenheere, Mr., 109
Tunbridge Wells, 75
Turner, F. & E.R., 64

Ulcombe, 33, 38, 173
Union Mill, 172
Upper Crisbrook Mill, 74, 143, 146
  Mill, 90

Ureka, 43
Uren, Ted, 171–8
Urry, Dr. William, 163–4
  George, 163–4
  Richard, 163

Wandle Mill, 128–34
  River, 128
Warden Mill, 134–5
Wateringbury, 103, 134
Watermill House, 72
Weald, 2, 33
Weeks & Son, 34
  W., 38, 104
  W. & Son Ltd., 39, 111, 134, 159
Wells, A., 140
West Malling Golf and Country Club, 13
West Wittering, 163
Westwell, 77
White Mill, 134–8
Whites, John Samuel, 142
Whitstable, 159
Wickhambreaux, 164
Wicks, Bakers and Millers, 175
Willcocks, Sir William, 115
Willesborough Windmill, 165
William of Normandy, 2
Wilson, Alan, 22, 90–1
Wilson's Mill, 65
Winfield Mill, 135, 138–9
Wrotham, 61
  Tithe Map, 20
  Water, 61
Wye Mill, 78

Yeoman Wheat, 150, 167